FOREST MEASUREMENTS

THE AMERICAN FORESTRY SERIES

HENRY J. VAUX, *Consulting Editor*

Allen and Sharpe · An Introduction to American Forestry
Avery · Forest Measurements
Baker · Principles of Silviculture
Boyce · Forest Pathology
Brockman · Recreational Use of Wild Lands
Brown, Panshin, and Forsaith · Textbook of Wood Technology
   Volume II—The Physical, Mechanical, and Chemical Properties
    of the Commercial Woods of the United States
Bruce and Schumacher · Forest Mensuration
Chapman and Meyer · Forest Mensuration
Chapman and Meyer · Forest Valuation
Dana · Forest and Range Policy
Davis · Forest Fire: Control and Use
Davis · Forest Management: Regulation and Evaluation
Duerr · Fundamentals of Forestry Economics
Graham and Knight · Principles of Forest Entomology
Guise · The Management of Farm Woodlands
Harlow and Harrar · Textbook of Dendrology
Hunt and Garratt · Wood Preservation
Panshin and de Zeeuw · Textbook of Wood Technology
   Volume I—Structure, Identification, Uses, and Properties of the
    Commercial Woods of the United States
Panshin, Harrar, Bethel, and Baker Forest Products
Shirley · Forestry and Its Career Opportunities
Stoddart and Smith · Range Management
Trippensee · Wildlife Management
   Volume I—Upland Game and General Principles
   Volume II—Fur Bearers, Waterfowl, and Fish
Wackerman, Hagenstein, and Michell · Harvesting Timber Crops

WALTER MULFORD WAS CONSULTING EDITOR OF THIS SERIES FROM ITS IN-
CEPTION IN 1931 UNTIL JANUARY 1, 1952.

New techniques in forest inventory:
(A) transporting field crews into
roadless areas via helicopter, (B)
locating sample plots on aerial
photographs with a stereoscope,
(C) using a wedge prism for point-
sample timber cruising, and
(D) recording the tree tally on
port-a-punch machine-sort cards

*Courtesy of Department of Natural
Resources, state of Washington.*

FOREST MEASUREMENTS

T. EUGENE AVERY, Ph.D.
Professor and Head, Department of Forestry
University of Illinois

McGRAW-HILL BOOK COMPANY

New York, St. Louis, San Francisco

Toronto, London, Sydney

FOREST MEASUREMENTS

Library of Congress Catalog Card Number 67-11563
02500

1234567890   MP   7432106987

To Marjorie Lee and Mark Douglas

In acknowledgment of the inspiration they have provided

PREFACE

As envisioned by many, the subject of forest mensuration encompasses timber inventories, game censuses, public opinion surveys, biometrics, computer programming, and operations analysis. If this be the case, it is equally true that most universities offer separate courses in these fields and that no single textbook can be expected to suffice for all. This particular volume is devoted to applied forest measurement techniques. An attempt has been made to present subject matter in a simple and concise fashion that is easily grasped by the neophyte forester. If this has been accomplished, there will be little to inhibit the eloquent instructor who wishes to add his own favorite embellishments.

This is a book for undergraduate courses in forest inventory. It is presumed that the reader will have previously studied college algebra, trigonometry, and plane surveying. A prior knowledge of basic statistics and sampling methods will be helpful, although the more elementary concepts are briefed here. Material covered in Chap. 2 on forest surveying has been included for persons with an inadequate background of this subject. At the instructor's discretion, it may be omitted without loss of continuity.

Certain subjects traditionally discussed in mensuration textbooks have been purposely left out of this treatise. Among these are alignment charts and their application in constructing standard volume tables. Today standard volume tables are usually derived by multiple regression techniques, and it is felt that this subject is adequately covered by authoritative statistical references. Furthermore, few foresters have occasion to construct such tables during their entire careers.

On the other hand, this volume includes several techniques not generally covered in previous mensuration textbooks. Among these are weight scaling of pulpwood and sawlogs, applications of point-sample timber cruising, use of aerial photographs in forest inventory and mapping, and adaptation of machine-sort cards for attaining greater efficiency in field tallies and data compilation. The investigator interested in greater subject matter detail should find special assistance in the references that follow each chapter. These have been carefully chosen from recent publications to provide up-to-date coverage of new forest inventory developments.

It is virtually impossible to acknowledge all persons who have contributed to the compilation of this volume. Many reviewers, for example, remain anonymous to the author; still, their indispensable assistance is gratefully recognized. Known reviewers who read various portions of the manuscript are Mr. Frank Freese, U.S. Forest Products Laboratory; Prof. Albert C. Worrell, Yale University; Prof. Kenneth D. Ware, Iowa State University; Prof. James P. Barrett, University of New Hampshire; and Prof. Jerome L. Clutter, University of Georgia.

Many of the line drawings were prepared by Prof. Dennis M. Richter, Wisconsin State University at Whitewater. Special information on continuous forest inventory was supplied by Mr. Wendell C. Snowden, Iowa State University; Mr. Harold J. Belcher, Rayonier Incorporated; and Mr. J. C. Mottayaw, Container Corporation of America. Appreciation is also expressed to Messrs. H. J. Hovind and C. E. Rieck of the Wisconsin Conservation Department for permission to reproduce several tables and illustrations on point-sample timber cruising.

Certain tables in the Appendix also warrant special acknowledgements. The table of square root conversions appears by courtesy of SCM Corporation, New York, and the table of random numbers is reproduced by permission from "Statistical Methods" by George W. Snedecor, 5th ed., c. 1956 by The Iowa State University Press. I am indebted to the literary executor of the late Sir Ronald A. Fisher, F.R.S., Cambridge, to Dr. Frank Yates, F.R.S., Rothamsted, and to

Messrs. Oliver & Boyd Ltd., Edinburgh, for permission to reprint Appendix Table 6 (The Distribution of t) from their book, "Statistical Tables for Biological, Agricultural, and Medical Research."

To successfully complete a task of this nature, an author must have time, encouragement, and a pleasant working environment. For providing all these necessities, I owe special thanks to a friend and former colleague, Dean Allyn M. Herrick of the School of Forestry, University of Georgia.

T. Eugene Avery

CONTENTS

Chapter 3
CORD MEASURE, WEIGHT SCALING, AND CUBIC VOLUMES

Chapter 4
LOG RULES AND SCALING PRACTICES

Lumber Tally Versus Log Scale

Derivation of Log Rules

Board-foot Log Scaling

Weight Scaling of Sawlogs

Chapter 5
MEASURING STANDING TREES

Tree Diameters

Tree Heights

Tree Form Expressions

Chapter 6
VOLUMES OF STANDING TREES

Simple Graphical Techniques

Types of Tree Volume Tables

Standard Volume Tables

Local Volume Tables

Cumulative Tally Sheets

Elementary Computations

Common Sampling Designs

Chapter 9
TIMBER CRUISING WITH SAMPLE STRIPS OR PLOTS

Introduction

Special Considerations in Cruising

Strip System of Cruising

Line-plot System of Cruising

Chapter   10
POINT-SAMPLE TIMBER CRUISING

Chapter 11
USES OF AERIAL PHOTOGRAPHS

Introduction to Photo Interpretation

Basic Measurements

Species Identification and Type Mapping

Photo Estimates of Stand Volume

Photo Stratifications for Ground Cruising

Chapter 12
SITE, STOCKING, DENSITY, AND TREE GROWTH

Evaluation of Site Quality

**Chapter 13
STAND GROWTH AND PREDICTION**

Chapter 14
CONTINUOUS FOREST INVENTORY AND DATA PROCESSING

Continuous Forest Inventory

Machine-sort Cards for Data Processing

The U.S. Forest Survey

Functions of Electronic Computers

CHAPTER 1
INTRODUCTION

1-1 Forest inventory defined. In essence, forest inventory, mensuration, and enumeration are terms that describe the application of mathematical procedures to forestry problems. Foresters primarily responsible for assessing standing timber have been traditionally known as cruisers. Their counterparts in research work, often engaged in studies of tree growth and yield, were referred to as mensurationists. Today, the cruiser has been largely replaced by the forest inventory specialist, a practitioner in the design and execution of forest surveys. He may be additionally adept in interpreting aerial photographs or in writing computer programs for electronic data processing machines. Meanwhile, the mensurationist has evolved into a "biometrician," or numbers mechanic *par excellence*. His exacting task is now one of developing or adapting mathematical and statistical procedures for the solution of new and complex problems confronting the woodland manager, land economist, and research specialist.

This book is largely concerned with the forest inventory specialist. Although a "how-to-do-it" approach is employed, there are still many inventory problems for which no satisfactory solutions exist. Furthermore, there is room for considerable improvement in currently employed techniques and instruments. During recent years, new ideas have been responsible for such practices as weight scaling of pulpwood, point-sample timber cruising, and adaptation of data processing equipment to mensurational problems. To a large degree, however, we are still measuring timber volumes, tree form, growth, cull factors, and mortality just as foresters did five decades ago. The continued need for inventory personnel with imagination and inventiveness is clearly apparent.

1-2 Justification for measurements. Organizations that depend on wood as a raw material often have large capital investments in land and standing timber. Periodic inventories of these lands are required for tax records, for justification of various forest management expenditures, and for determining the amount and quality of wood available for utilization. Some inventories are concerned with plantation survival counts, some with wood stockpiles and land appraisal, and still others with studies of tree growth or site evaluation.

Forest inventories and measurement of cut-wood products are justified primarily as conveniences in making purchases and sales, or as aids in formulating timber management plans. When log scaling is relied upon as a basis for a business transaction, it is recognized that the estimate of board-foot volume is less accurate than that obtained from a tally of sawed lumber. However, it is equally obvious that each truckload of logs cannot be individually tagged, sawed, and tallied when scores of such transactions are involved daily. Furthermore, payments to some wood suppliers might be delayed for weeks until their logs had been processed. The convenience and continued application of such activities as log scaling are thus established.

1-3 Measurement cost considerations. In all inventory undertakings, cost factors assume an importance equal to or greater than the statistical accuracy required. The forester must continually seek out more efficient methods for counting, measuring, and appraisal. Timber stands are not grown simply to be inventoried, and the measurement of trees or logs adds no real value to the material scaled. Thus forest inventory is termed a service function rather than a control function. Measuring techniques must be subordinate to the productive phases of an operation, for the operation itself cannot be modified just to accommodate an inventory requirement. As an example, the loading of log trucks in the forest cannot be delayed because certain logs at the skid landing have not yet been scaled. Instead, the logs must be scaled during some phase of the operation where a logical time interval is normally available.

It is an obvious though commonly overlooked fact that the amount expended for a given inventory task must be geared to the value of the material being measured. The nearer one approaches the finished product, the greater can be the allowable cost of measurement. Therefore, more can be spent per unit for scaling quality veneer logs than for cruising standing timber; similarly, the value of finished lumber justifies greater inventory costs than does log scaling. In any event, measurement costs should rarely exceed 5 per cent of the value of the item inventoried. The forester who becomes "cost conscious" early in his professional career has an attribute that will be highly respected by his employer.

1-4 English versus metric systems. In spite of its obvious complexities and disadvantages, the English system persists as the primary basis for measurements in the United States. The more logical metric system, devised and adopted in France around 1790, has gained limited acceptance in scientific research, but foresters are still surveying by feet and acres rather than meters and hectares. Bills requiring universal adoption of the metric system have been introduced several times in the Congress of the United States, but none have yet been enacted into law.

Admittedly, an abrupt changeover to the metric system would result in considerable confusion for an extended period of time. For example, the conversion of real estate records alone would require years of revising deeds and property descriptions; highway markers and automobile speedometers would require changes from miles to kilometers, and so on. The myriad of problems that would be generated seems to assure that adoption of the metric system in this country will proceed gradually, if at all.[1]

Origins of many of the English units of measure are rather obscure; nevertheless, it is interesting to speculate on how some of these accepted "standards" were formulated. The appraisal that follows is condensed from a 1954 article that appeared in a popular domestic magazine.[2]

It is said that King Henry I (about 800 years ago) decreed that a yard should be the distance between the tip of his royal nose and the tip of his extended fingers. Our *foot,* of course, is based on the length of the human extremity. However, it has varied as an official measurement from 11 to 14 inches in various countries. Persia and other Middle East nations made it 12.6 inches. The *inch,* along with the ounce, came from the Latin *uncia,* meaning one-twelfth.

King Henry took care of the yard, but before that we had the *rod, pole,* and *perch.* The rod of 16½ feet was commonly used in rural American speech

---

[1] Shortly after this chapter was written, Great Britain announced plans to convert to the metric system over a 10-year period. The United States Senate subsequently initiated a study of the metric system and the feasibility of adopting it in the United States.

[2] Reprinted by permission of *True Magazine,* Fawcett Publications, Inc., Greenwich, Conn.

in expressing distance. *Pole,* the same length, is understandable, as is *perch,* a roosting pole in a chicken coop. *Mile* came from the Latin *milia passuum,* meaning 1,000 paces. Romans called that 1,620 yards as against our 1,760 yards.

Our word *acre* comes from the Anglo-Saxon *aecer,* which meant pasture land, and it originated as a rough measure by herdsmen and owners of livestock. After many centuries, it arrived at the present 43,560 square feet. A *furlong,* now used mostly in horse racing to mean an eighth of a mile, had an agricultural origin. It started out as a furrow across an ordinary English field.

Several other measurements came from the human body. A *digit* in England was the width of a finger, taken as 0.75 inch. A *hand* was always available for short measurements. Today, a *hand* is four inches and is used only for horses' heights. A *fathom,* now 6 feet, was once 5 feet or 5½ feet. It was the stretch of a man's two arms; undoubtedly it came from lifting a lead line while sounding depths in harbours.

The *vara* is an old measure of length used in Spain and Portugal, measuring 32.91 inches and 43.31 inches, respectively. Something must have happened to the Spanish vara stick when it was brought to the Americas, as it ranges from 31.5 inches in Colombia to 33.63 in Uruguay. In Texas under Spanish rule, the vara was set at 33.33 inches, which it remains today. In California, it is forgotten and now Mexico no longer uses it. As the word *vara* comes from an old Latin word meaning forked pole, this may explain the differences.

Although the English system appears to be grounded in concepts of human anatomy, the metric system was formulated from geodetic measurements. The fundamental metric unit, the meter, was originally defined as being equal to one ten-millionth of the meridional distance from the equator to the earth's poles. In terms of English units, the meter is approximately 39.37 inches in length or slightly longer than one yard. Following are several common equivalents for converting English to metric units and vice versa:

Converting English Units to Metric System

1 in. or 1,000 mils	= 2.5400 cm
1 ft or 12 in.	= 30.4800 cm
1 yd or 3 ft	= 0.9144 m
1 U.S. statute mile or 5,280 ft	= 1.6093 m
1 acre or 43,560 sq ft	= 0.4047 ha
1 cu ft or 1,728 cu in.	= 0.0283 cu m

Converting Metric Units to English System

1 cm or 10 mm	= 0.3937 in.
1 dm or 10 cm	= 3.9370 in.
1 m or 10 dm	= 39.3700 in.
1 km or 1,000 m	= 0.6214 U.S. statute mile
1 ha or 10,000 sq m	= 2.4710 acres
1 cu m or 1,000,000 cu cm	= 35.3147 cu ft

1-5 Rounding off numbers. To minimize personal bias and assure a degree of consistency in computations, it is desirable to adopt a systematic technique for rounding off numbers. The necessity for such a method arises when a calculated value apparently falls exactly halfway between the units being used, i.e., when the number 5 immediately follows the digit positions to be retained.

As an example, suppose the values of 27.65 and 104.15 are to be rounded off to 1 decimal place. A commonly used rule is to ignore the 5 when the digit preceding it is an even number; thus 27.65 becomes 27.6. Conversely, if the digit preceding the 5 is an odd number its value is raised by one unit. Therefore, in the example here, 104.15 would be recorded as 104.2.

Rounding off should be done after all intermediate calculations have been completed. Intermediate calculations should be carried at least two places beyond that of the final rounded figures.

1-6 Bias, accuracy, and precision. Although most persons have a general idea of the distinction between these three terms, it appears appropriate to define the terms from the statistical viewpoint. *Bias* is a systematic distortion arising from such sources as a flaw in measurement or an incorrect method of sampling. Measurements of 100-ft units with a tape only 99 ft long will be biased; similarly, biases may occur when a timber cruiser consistently underestimates tree heights or ocularly shifts a field plot location to obtain what he regards as a more typical sample.

Accuracy refers to the success of estimating the true value of a quantity, and *precision* refers to the clustering of sample values about their own average. A badly biased estimate may be precise, but it cannot be accurate; thus it is evident that accuracy and precision are not synonymous or interchangeable terms. As an example, a forester might make a series of careful measurements of a single tree with an instrument that is improperly calibrated or out of adjustment. If the measurements cluster about their average value, they will be precise. However, as the instrument is out of adjustment, the measured values may be biased and considerably off the true value; thus the estimate will not be accurate. The failure to attain an accurate result may be due to the presence of bias, the lack of precision, or both.

1-7 Abbreviations and notations. In this book and in other references dealing with forest inventory and mapping, a number of abbreviations are employed for convenience and brevity. Some of the more common ones are as follows:

d, diam   tree diameter or log diameter in inches
dbh, d.b.h.   tree diameter at breast height (4.5 ft above ground)

d.i.b.	diameter inside bark
d.o.b.	diameter outside bark
bd ft	board feet
cu ft	cubic feet
M	thousand
BA, B	basal area
BAF	basal area factor, in square feet per acre (used in point sampling)
ha	hectare
cu m, m^3	cubic meter
GLO	General Land Office of the United States
CFI	continuous forest inventory
USDA	United States Department of Agriculture
USGS	United States Geological Survey

1-8 Preparation of technical reports. As a professional group, for-esters are sometimes inclined to minimize the value of neat, concise, and well-written technical reports. Yet in many instances, such reports may provide the only concrete evidence of work accomplished; thus they may constitute the prime basis for judgment of field proficiency by supervisors.

It goes without saying that one must be more than an accomplished grammarian; no amount of flowing penmanship can compensate for de-ficiencies in fieldwork and data collection. Nevertheless, the importance of producing technically accurate and grammatically correct reports can hardly be overemphasized.

Whenever feasible, all but the most routine reports should be type-written (double-spaced) on white bond paper. Figures and tables are preferably placed on separate pages and numbered consecutively. Line drawings, graphs, and charts should be drawn in black ink and presented on an appropriate drafting medium. Although a single format cannot be expected to meet the requirements for all reports, the following outline may prove useful for student term papers or technical reports on assigned experiments:

TITLE PAGE: Title in centered caps, followed by author's name. Lower part of page should show location of study (e.g., Cripple Creek National Forest) and the date (month and year completed).

TABLE OF CONTENTS: Chapter headings and major subdivisions of chapters should be listed, along with corresponding page numbers.

INTRODUCTION: Statement of the problem, justification and importance of the study, specific objectives, and practical considerations.

REVIEW OF PREVIOUS WORK: A concise, critical review of published literature bearing on the problem, including a statement on the relationship of the present study to previous research.

THE STUDY AREA: Location of the study and a description of the area involved (e.g., physiography, forest types, site conditions, climatic factors, legal description, size of area, ownership, management or silvicultural history).

COLLECTION OF FIELD DATA OR LABORATORY PROCEDURE: For some studies, *Design of the Experiment* may be a more appropriate heading. List all data collected, arrangement of field samples, special instruments or techniques employed, illustration of field forms, size of crews, time or expense involved, and special problems encountered. (See Appendix.)

ANALYSIS OF RESULTS: Compilation of field data, statistical procedures, presentation and discussion of results.

SUMMARY AND CONCLUSIONS: A brief synopsis of the study undertaken, results obtained, and implications of the findings. For some types of reports, a brief summary or abstract may be required at the beginning of the discussion, i.e., preceding the introduction.

LITERATURE CITED: Arranged in standard form according to an acceptable style manual or in conformance with requirements of a specific technical publication. (See references at end of chapter.)

APPENDIX: Copies of field forms and/or original raw data are often included here. Detailed statistical formulas or computations may also be shown. The various sections of the appendix should be designated by alphabetical divisions or by use of Roman numerals.

1-9 Reviews of technical literature. Among principal sources of forest inventory literature are research papers issued by state and federal experiment stations, the *Journal of Forestry, Forest Science,* and the *Forestry Chronicle*. The forester who expects to comprehend and evaluate such articles must adopt a disciplined attitude to the reading of scientific literature. If an abstract precedes the main report, this should be read first, followed by a rapid scanning of the entire article. Then, if the study appears to be of special interest or utility, the article should be carefully reread.

Although an abstract may obviate the necessity of making notes on each article, it is well to look for salient points. After noting the locale of the study and the author's affiliation, the reader should ask himself, What were the real objectives of this study? Next, it may be appropriate to note the laboratory procedure or statistical design employed, along with the number and type of samples measured. Finally, any tables or graphical presentations should be studied to see whether they fully substantiate the author's principal findings or conclusions. Only by taking such an analytical approach can the reader expect to gain any real benefit from reports of specialized research.

PROBLEMS

1-1 Extract the square roots of the following:
(*a*) 24.36, (*b*) 1.089, (*c*) 254.378,
(*d*) 441.00, (*e*) 5,280.00, (*f*) 10,240.856

1-2 Convert these measurements as specified:
(*a*) 51.3 miles to poles
(*b*) 20,000 leagues to fathoms

(c) 125 m to Texas varas

(d) 45 cu m per ha to cubic feet per acre

(e) 327 cu ft per acre to cubic meters per hectare

1-3 How many acres are included within the boundaries of a football (or soccer) field, including end zones? Convert this value to hectares.

1-4 Be able to write equations for:

(a) Determining the radius for a circular plot when the area is known

(b) Determining the length of the hypotenuse of a right triangle

(c) Determining the length of one side of a square plot when the area is known

1-5 Without using instruments or scales, explain how you might determine the height of a tree from its shadow length.

1-6 Round off these values to 2 decimal places:

(a) 121.9554, (b) 108.6653, (c) 0.9954

Round off these values to the nearest whole number:

(d) 31.53, (e) 1.95, (f) 8.50

1-7 Give two examples of possible bias in conducting a public opinion survey.

1-8 Describe two instruments or measuring techniques that you consider to be extremely precise.

1-9 Refer to a recent issue of the *Journal of Forestry* or the *Forestry Chronicle*. What is the preferred style for preparing references to literature citations?

1-10 Prepare a typewritten abstract of not more than 250 words for a published technical article dealing with some phase of forest inventory.

REFERENCES

American Institute of Biological Sciences
1960. Style manual for biological journals. Washington, D.C. 92 pp.

Bergamini, David
1963. Mathematics. Life Science Library, Time, Inc., New York. 200 pp., illus.

Crouch, W. George, and Zetler, Robert L.
1964. A guide to technical writing, 3d ed. The Ronald Press Company, New York. 458 pp., illus.

Larson, E. vH.
1947. Style manual for publications. *U.S. Forest Serv., Northeast. Forest Expt. Sta., Sta. Paper* 6. 26 pp., illus.

Martin, W. H.
1962. Trends and developments in wood measurement. Paper presented at joint meeting of American Pulpwood Association and C.P.P.A. Woodlands Section, Newton Falls, N.Y., June 20–22. 5 pp.

Perrin, Porter G.
1950. Writer's guide and index to English, rev. ed. Scott, Foresman and Company, Chicago. 833 pp., illus.

Rennie, P. J.
1962. Measure for measure. Forest Research Branch, Canada Department of Forestry, Ottawa. 43 pp.

Thornton, Cleo
1962. How to prepare literature citations for U.S.D.A. publications. U.S. Forest Service, Washington, D.C. 22 pp.

CHAPTER **2**

FOREST SURVEYING

DISTANCES AND ANGLES

2-1 Applications of surveying. A knowledge of the elements of land surveying is essential to the inventory forester. Although he may rarely be responsible for original property surveys, he is often called upon to retrace old lines, locate property boundaries, and measure land areas. To adequately perform these tasks, the forester should be adept in pacing, chaining, running compass traverses, and various methods of area estimating. He should also be familiar with the principal systems of land subdivision found in his particular region of the country.

The fundamental unit of horizontal measurement employed by foresters is the surveyors' or Gunter's chain of 66 ft. The chain is divided into 100 equal parts that are known as links; each link is thus 0.66 ft or 7.92 in. in length. Distances on all U.S. Government Land Surveys are measured in chains and links. The simple conversion from chained dimensions to acres is one reason for the continued popularity of this measurement standard. Areas expressed in square chains can be immediately converted to acres by dividing by 10. Thus a tract 1 mile square (80 chains on a side) contains 6,400 square chains or 640 acres.

2-2 Pacing horizontal distances. Pacing is perhaps the most rudimentary of all techniques for determining distances in the field; nonetheless, accurate pacing is an obvious asset to the timber cruiser or land appraiser who must determine distances without the aid of an assistant. With practice and frequent measured checks, an experienced pacer can expect to attain an accuracy of 1 part in 80 when traversing fairly level terrain.

The pace is commonly defined as the average length of two natural steps; i.e., a count is made each time the same foot touches the ground.[1] A natural walking gait is recommended, because this pace can be most easily maintained under difficult terrain conditions. One should never attempt to use an artificial pace based on a fixed step length such as exactly 3 ft. Experienced pacers have demonstrated that the natural step is much more reliable.

In learning to pace, a horizontal distance of 10 to 40 chains should be staked on level or typical terrain. This course should be paced over and over until a consistent gait has been established. The average number of paces required, divided by the measured course distance, gives the number of paces per chain. Most foresters of average height and stride have a natural pace of 12 to 13 paces (double steps) per chain. It is also helpful to compute the exact number of feet per pace, for pacing is often relied upon in locating boundaries of sample plots during a timber cruise.

Uniform pacing is difficult in mountainous terrain, because measurement of horizontal rather than slope distance is the prime objective. Steps are necessarily shortened in walking up and down steep hillsides, and special problems are created when obstructions such as deep stream channels are encountered. Thus some individual technique must be devised to compensate for such difficulties.

The inevitable shortening of the pace on sloping ground can be handled by repeating the count at certain intervals, as 1, *2*, *2*, 3, 4, 5, *6, 6*, and so on. Or, if pace lengths are cut in half, counts may be restricted to every other pace. For obstructions that cannot be traversed at all (such as streams and rivers), the distance to some well-defined point ahead can be ocularly estimated; then a nonpaced detour can be made around the obstacle.

Paced distances should always be field recorded as horizontal distances

[1] Some foresters prefer to count *every* step as a pace. Advantages claimed for this technique are (1) less chance of losing count, (2) fewer problems with fractional paces, and (3) easier adjustments for slope.

in chains or feet—not in terms of actual paces. When accurate mental counts become tedious, a reliable pacing record can be kept by a written tally or by using a hand-tally meter. The importance of regular pacing practice cannot be overstressed; without periodic checks, neither accuracy nor consistency can be expected.

2-3 Chaining horizontal distances. Two men, a head chainman and a rear chainman, are needed for accurate measurement with a steel tape. On level terrain, the chain can be stretched directly on the ground. If 11 chaining pins are used, one is placed at the point of origin, and the head chainman moves ahead with 10 pins and the "zero end" of the chain. If the head chainman carries the compass, he must keep himself and the chain on the correct bearing line at all times; otherwise, it is the rear chainman's duty to keep his partner on a straight and proper course.

A good head chainman paces the length of the tape so that he can anticipate when he has moved to the approximate chaining interval. When the end of the tape approaches the rear chainman, he calls, "Chain!" The head chainman pulls the tape taut until the rear chainman yells, "Stick!" Upon sticking the pin, the head chainman replies, "Stuck!" The rear chainman picks up the first pin, and the procedure is repeated until the desired length has been measured. When the head chainman "sticks" his last pin, 10 chain intervals will have been covered. The rear chainman then passes the 10 pins he has collected to the head chainman for continuing the measurement. A distance of 12 chains and 82 links is recorded as 12.82 chains.

In rough terrain, where the chain is held high off the ground, plumb bobs may be used at each end to aid in proper pin placement and accurate measurement of each interval. On steep slopes, it may be necessary to "break chain," i.e., to use only short sections of the tape for holding a level line. In mountainous country where horizontal distance cannot be chained directly, slope distances can be measured and converted to horizontal measurements as described in the next section. Experienced foresters can expect an accuracy of 1 part in 1,000 to 1 in 2,500 by careful chaining of horizontal distances.

Precautions must be observed in chaining to avoid loops or tangles that will result in a broken or permanently "kinked" tape. The ends of the tape should be equipped with leather thongs, and the loss of chaining pins can be minimized by tying colored plastic flagging to each. Chains should be lightly oiled occasionally to prevent rust and properly coiled or "thrown" when not in use.

2-4 Chaining slope distances. For converting slope measurements to horizontal distances, the forester should be equipped with a 1- or 2-chain trailer tape and an Abney hand level having a topographic arc that is graduated in percentages of 66 ft.

The head chainman proceeds up or down slope until the full length of the tape, excluding the trailer, is reached. The rear chainman then uses the Abney level to determine the slope percentage between his position and that of the head chainman. With the correct slope percentage and distance in mind, a correction is read from specially prepared tables. The rear chainman then makes the chainage adjustment by adding the proper number of links from the trailer tape. When the tape is again stretched taut, the head chainman sets a new chaining pin at the correct horizontal distance between the two points. This procedure is repeated until the entire slope has been traversed, with each measured slope interval corrected to the horizontal by addition of graduations from the trailer end of the tape.

2-5 Nomenclature of the compass. In elemental form, a compass consists of a magnetized needle on a pivot point, enclosed in a circular housing that has been graduated in degrees. Inasmuch as the earth acts as a huge magnet, properly calibrated compass needles in the Northern Hemisphere point to the north magnetic pole. If a sighting base is attached to the compass housing, it is then possible to measure the angle between the line of sight and the position of the needle. Such angles are referred to as magnetic *bearings* or *azimuths.*

Bearings are horizontal angles that are referenced to one of the quadrants of the compass, viz., NE, SE, SW, or NW. Azimuths are comparable angles measured clockwise from due north, thus reading from 0 to 360°.[1] Relationships between bearings and azimuths are illustrated in Fig. 2-1. It will be seen that a bearing of N 60° E corresponds to an azimuth of 60°, while a bearing of S 60° W is the same as an azimuth of 240°. In the United States, the compass needle points to the north magnetic pole rather than toward the north geographical pole (true north). The angle formed between magnetic north and true north is called declination, and allowance must be made for this factor in converting magnetic bearings and azimuths to true angular readings.

2-6 Magnetic declination. In North America, corrections may be required for either *east* or *west* declination, the former when the north magnetic pole is east of true north and the latter when it is west of true north. Isogonic charts illustrating magnetic declination are issued periodically by government agencies (Fig. 2-2). On such maps, points having equal declination are connected by lines known as *isogons.* The line of zero declination (no corrections required) passing through the

[1] Some organizations, notably military agencies, measure azimuth angles clockwise from due south instead of due north.

eastern section of the country is called the *agonic* line. It will be noted that areas east of the agonic line have west declination, while areas west of the agonic line have east declination.

As of 1960 the agonic line was shifting westward at a rate of approximately 1 min per year. In some parts of conterminous United States,

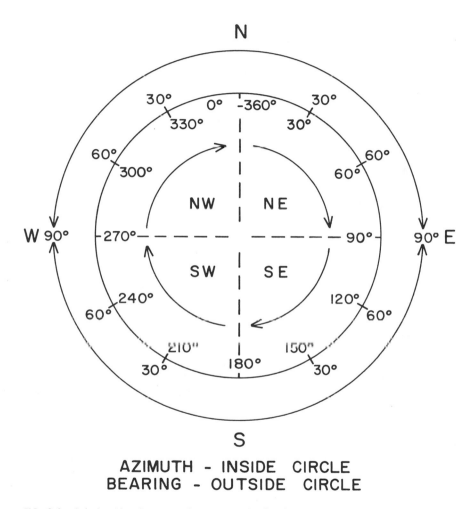

AZIMUTH - INSIDE CIRCLE
BEARING - OUTSIDE CIRCLE

FIG. 2-1   Relationship of compass bearings and azimuths.

however, the change in declination is as high as 4 to 5 min annually. Because the position of the north magnetic pole is constantly shifting, it is important that current declination values be used in correcting magnetic bearings. Where reliable data cannot be obtained from isogonic charts, the amount of declination can be determined by establishing

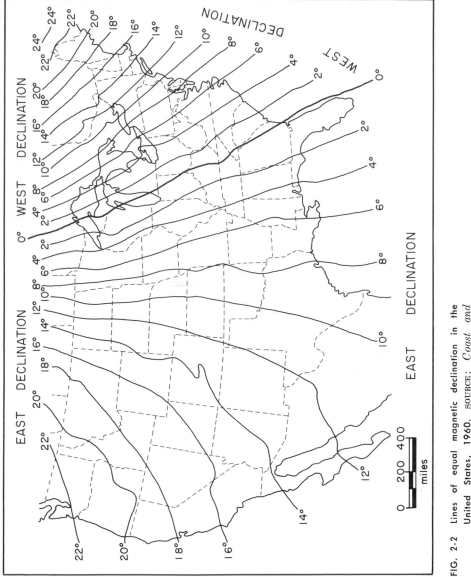

FIG. 2-2 Lines of equal magnetic declination in the United States, 1960. SOURCE: *Coast and Geodetic Survey, U.S. Department of Commerce.*

a true north-south line through observations on the sun or Polaris. The magnetic bearing of this true line provides the declination for that locality. As an alternative to this approach, any existing survey line whose true bearing is known can be substituted.

2-7 Allowance for declination. In establishing or retracing property lines, angles should preferably be recorded as *true* bearings or azimuths. The simplest and most reliable technique for handling declination is to set the allowance directly on the compass itself. Thus the graduated degree circle must be rotated until the north end of the compass needle reads true north when the line of sight points in that direction. For most compasses, this requires that the graduated degree circle be turned counterclockwise for east declination and clockwise for west declination.

When there is no provision for setting the declination directly on the compass, the proper allowance can be made mentally in the field, or magnetic bearings may be recorded and corrected later in the office. For changing magnetic azimuths to true readings, east declinations are added, and west declinations are subtracted. Thus if a magnetic azimuth of 105° is recorded in Colorado where the declination is 15° east, the true azimuth would be 120°.

Changing magnetic bearings to true bearings is slightly more confusing than handling azimuths, because declinations must be added in two quadrants and subtracted in the other two. The proper algebraic signs to be used in making such additions or subtractions are illustrated in Fig. 2-3.

Accordingly, if a magnetic bearing of S 40° E is recorded in a section of Pennsylvania where the declination is 5° west, the true bearing, obtained by addition, would be S 45° E. In those occasional situations where true bearings and azimuths must be converted back to magnetic readings, all algebraic signs in Fig. 2-3 should be reversed.

2-8 Use of the compass. Whether hand or staff compasses are used, care must be exercised to avoid local magnetic attractions such as wire fences, overhead cables, and iron deposits. In running a traverse, "backsights" of 180° should be taken to check all compass bearings. When such backsights fail to agree with foresights and no instrument errors can be detected, it is likely that some form of local attraction is present. Here it may be necessary to shorten or prolong the bearing line in question so that a new turning point outside the attraction area can be used for the compass setup. Compasses having needles immersed in liquid are generally less susceptible to local attractions than nondampened types.

Most good compasses are provided with a means of clamping the needle in a fixed position while the instrument is being transported.

After each bearing is read, the needle should be tightened before moving to a new compass position; adherence to this practice will save considerable wear on the sensitive needle pivot point. To ensure accurate compass readings, novices must be cautious to see that (1) the compass is perfectly level, (2) the sights are properly aligned, (3) the needle swings freely before settling, and (4) all readings are taken from the *north end* of the needle. Hand compass shots should not normally exceed

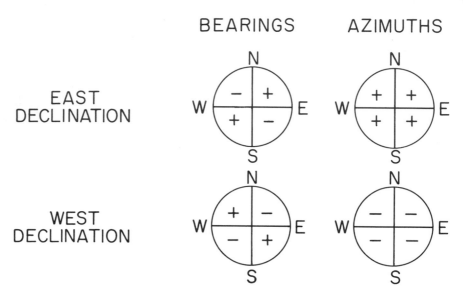

FIG. 2-3   Algebraic signs for changing magnetic bearings and azimuths to true angles.

5 chains, and staff compass sights should be limited to about 10 chains per setup.

AREA DETERMINATION

2-9   A simple closed traverse.   For purposes of this discussion, it is assumed that the primary objectives of a field survey are to locate the approximate boundaries of a tract and determine the area enclosed. Where there are no ownership disputes involved, a simple closed traverse made with staff compass and chain will often suffice for the purposes stated. For most surveys, three men comprise a minimum crew, and a fourth may be used to advantage. The party chief serves as a compassman and noteman, two men chain horizontal distances, and the fourth member handles a range pole at each compass station.

The most reliable property corner available is selected as a starting point; the traverse may be run clockwise or counterclockwise around the tract from this origin. Backsights and front sights should be taken on each line and numbered stakes driven at all compass stations. Immediately upon completion of the traverse, *interior angles* should be computed. If bearings have been properly read and recorded, the sum of all the interior angles should be equal to $(n-2)$ 180°, where n is the number of sides in the traverse.

After interior angles have been checked, the traverse should be plotted at a convenient scale (for example, 10 chains per in.) on standard cross-section paper. If horizontal distances between stations have been correctly chained, the plotted traverse should appear to "close." At this point, the tract area included may be accurately computed by the DMD (double meridian distance) method, or the area can be closely approximated by other techniques. DMD procedures are detailed in all surveying textbooks; hence this approach will not be presented here. Graphical techniques, dot grids, planimeters, and transects are the principal devices used by foresters in estimating areas.

2–10 Graphical area determination. It may be presumed that a closed compass traverse is plotted at a scale of 10 chains per in. on cross-section paper having 100 subdivisions per square inch. All 1-in. squares thus represent 10 acres, and small squares are 0.1 acre. The total acreage can be quickly determined by counting all small squares enclosed. Where less than one-half of a square is inside the tract boundary, it is ignored; squares bisected by an exterior line are alternately counted and disregarded. The method is fast and reasonably accurate when traverses are correctly plotted and when finely subdivided cross-section paper is employed.

2-11 Dot grids. If a piece of clear cellulose acetate were placed over a sheet of cross-section paper and pin holes punched at all grid intersections, the result would be a dot grid. Thus dot grid and graphical methods of area determination are based on the same principle; dots *representing* squares or rectangular areas are merely counted in lieu of the squares themselves. The principal gain enjoyed is that fractional squares along tract boundaries are less troublesome, for the nondimensional dot determines whether or not the square is to be tallied. If an area is mapped at a scale of 10 chains per in. as in the previous example, and a grid having 25 dots per sq in. is used, each dot will represent $^{10}\!\!/_{25}$ or 0.4 acre.

Dot grids are commonly used to approximate areas on aerial photographs as well as maps. If the terrain is essentially level and print scales can be accurately determined, this technique provides a quick and easy method of area estimation (Fig. 2-4). U.S. Department of Agriculture contact prints are most frequently taken at a scale of 25.25 chains per in. (63.77 acres per sq in.). Grids with 64 dots per sq in. can be used on these photographs, with each dot representing 0.996 acre. In regions of rough topography where photographic scales fluctuate widely, area measurements should be made on maps of controlled scale rather than directly on contact prints. Additional applications of aerial photographs are given in Chap. 11.

FIG. 2-4 Dot grid positioned over part of an aerial photograph. Photo scale is 660 ft per in., or 10 acres per sq in. As there are 36 dots per sq in., each dot has a conversion value of approximately 0.28 acre.

The preferred number of dots to be counted per square inch depends on the map scale employed, size of area involved, and precision desired. Grids commonly used by foresters may have from 4 to more than 100 dots per sq in. For tracts of less than 1,000 acres, it is generally desirable to use a dot sampling intensity that will result in a conversion of about 1 to 4 dots per acre. For those who are suspicious of such rules of thumb, a statistical procedure for determining dot sampling intensity is presented in Chap. 8.

2-12 Planimeters. By comparison with other methods briefed here, polar planimeters are relatively expensive instruments. In use, the pointer of the instrument is run around the boundaries of an area in a *clockwise* direction; usually the perimeter is traced two or three times for an average reading. From the vernier scale, the area in *square inches* or *square centimeters* is read directly and converted to the desired area units on the basis of map or photographic scale. Prolonged use of the instrument is somewhat tedious, and a steady hand is essential for accurately tracing irregular tract boundaries.

2-13 Transects. The transect method is basically a technique for proportioning a known area among various types of land classifications, such as forests, cultivated fields, and urban uses. An engineer's scale is aligned on a photograph or map so as to cross topography and drainage at right angles. The length of each type along the scale is recorded to the nearest 0.1 in. Proportions are developed by relating the total measure of a given classification to the total linear distance. For example, if 10 equally spaced, parallel lines 15 in. long are established on a given map, the total transect length is 150 in. If forest land is intercepted for a total measure of 30 in., this particular classification would be assigned an acreage equivalent to $^{30}/_{150}$ or 20 per cent of the total area.

The transect method is simple and requires no special equipment when lines are established with an engineer's scale. A more sophisticated approach to the use of transects requires the use of a modified map measurer, or *transect area-meter.* This special device is equipped with a scanning wheel that is rolled over each transect line, and transect lengths are recorded on a clock-type dial. Limited tests of the transect area-meter indicate that it is faster than using dot grids and comparable in accuracy to the polar planimeter (Aldred, 1964). Common area conversions for the English and metric systems are given in Table 2-1.

TABLE 2-1 Conversions for Several Units of Area Measurement

Square feet	Square chains	Acres	Square miles	Square meters	Hectares	Square kilo-meters
4,356	1	0.1	0.000156	404.687	0.040469	0.000405
43,560	10	1	0.0015625	4,046.87	0.404687	0.004047
27,878,400	6,400	640	1	2,589,998	258.9998	2.589998
107,638.7	24.7104	2.47104	0.003861	10,000	1	0.01
10,763,867	2,471.04	247.104	0.386101	1,000,000	100	1

2-14 Use of available maps. Topographic quadrangle maps have been prepared for sizable areas of the United States by various governmental agencies. Foresters concerned with land surveying often find such maps useful in retracing ownership lines, planning forest inventories, and preparing timber type maps. Current indexes showing map coverage available in each of the 50 states may be obtained free by writing to:

> Map Information Office
> U.S. Department of the Interior
> Geological Survey
> Washington, D.C. 20250

When available, topographic quadrangle sheets at a scale of 1:24,000 (2,000 ft per in.) usually provide the greatest amount of detail of interest to the forester; such maps can be purchased at nominal cost. For areas west of the Mississippi River, including all of Louisiana and Minnesota, maps are available from:

> U.S. Geological Survey
> Distribution Section
> Federal Center
> Denver, Colorado 80225

For areas east of the Mississippi River, including Puerto Rico and the Virgin Islands, orders should be placed at this address:

> U.S. Geological Survey
> Distribution Section
> Washington, D.C. 20250

Maps of Hawaii may be ordered at either address. Mail orders must be accompanied by payment in advance. Other sources of topographic quadrangle maps are the Tennessee Valley Authority, Maps and Surveys Branch, Chattanooga, Tennessee; the Mississippi River Commission, U.S. Army Corps of Engineers, Vicksburg, Mississippi; and the U.S. Coast and Geodetic Survey, Department of Commerce, Washington, D.C.

COLONIAL LAND SUBDIVISION

2-15 Metes and bounds surveys. A sizable segment of the United States, notably in the original 13 colonies, was subdivided and passed into private ownerships prior to the inauguration of a system for disposal of public lands in 1785. Many of these early land holdings were marked off and described by "metes and bounds," a procedure sometimes facetiously referred to as leaps and bounds.

The term *mete* implies an act of metering, measuring, or assigning by measure, and *bounds* refers to property boundaries or the limiting extent of an ownership. In some instances, older metes and bounds surveys may consist entirely of descriptions rather than actual measurements, e.g., "starting at a pine tree blazed on the east side, thence along a hedgerow to a granite boulder on the bank of the Wampum River, thence along the river to the intersection of Cherokee Creek . . . , etc." Fortunately, most metes and bounds descriptions are today referenced by bearings, distances, and permanent monuments. Even so, parcels of land are shaped in unusual and seemingly haphazard patterns, and a multitude of legal complexities can be encountered in attempting to establish the location of a disputed boundary along an old stone fence that disintegrated 50 years ago. Descriptions of metes and bounds surveys can ordinarily be obtained from plat books at various county court houses.

THE U.S. PUBLIC LAND SURVEY

2-16 History. Most of the United States west of the Mississippi River and north of the Ohio River, plus Alabama, Mississippi, and portions of Florida have been subdivided in accordance with the U.S. Public Land Survey (Fig. 2-5). The first law governing public land surveys was enacted by Congress in 1785. That part of the Northwest Territory which later became the state of Ohio was the experimental area for the development of the rectangular system. The original intent was to establish *townships* exactly 6 miles square, followed by subdivision into 36 sections of exactly 1 mile square each. At first, no allowance was made for curvature of the earth, and numerous problems resulted. However, survey rules were revised by later acts of Congress, and the present system evolved as a culmination of these changes.

Adoption of a rectangular system marked the transition from metes and bounds surveys that prevailed in most of the colonial states to a logical and rational method for describing the public lands. Surveyors responsible for the earliest public land surveys were faced with such obstacles as crude instruments, unfavorable or dangerous field conditions, and changing survey rules. Consequently, survey lines and corners in the field were not always located with the desired precision. To eliminate litigation and costly resurveys, the original corners as established on the ground legally stand as the true corners, regardless of irregularities or inconsistencies.

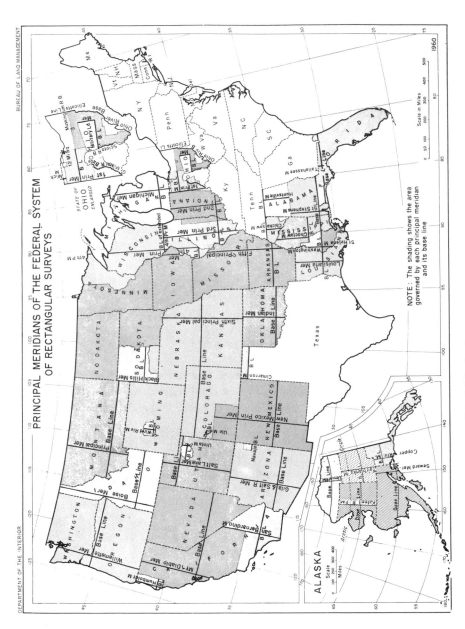

FIG. 2-5   States subdivided under the U.S. Public Land Survey.

2-17 The method of subdivision. The origin of a system begins with an *initial point,* usually established by astronomical observation. Passing through and extending outward from the initial point is a true north-south line known as a *principal meridian* and a true east-west *base line* that corresponds to a parallel of latitude. These two lines constitute the main axes of a system, and there are more than 30 such systems in existence (Fig. 2-5). Each principal meridian is referenced by a name or number, and the meridian is marked on the ground as a straight line. The base line is curved, being coincident with a geographic parallel. Starting at the initial point, the area to be surveyed is first divided into *tracts* approximately **24** miles square, followed by subdivision into **16** *townships* approximately **6** miles square and then into **36** sections approximately 1 mile square. An idealized system is shown in Fig. 2-6.

2-18 The 24-mile tracts. At intervals of **24** miles north and south of the base line, *standard parallels* are extended east and west of the principal meridian. These parallels are numbered north and south from the base line, as "first standard parallel north," and so on. At **24**-mile intervals along the base line and along all standard parallels, *guide meridians* are run on *true north* bearings; these lines thus correspond to geographic meridians of longitude. Each guide meridian starts from a standard corner on the base line or on a standard parallel and ends at a closing corner on the next standard parallel to the north. Standard parallels are never crossed by guide meridians. Guide meridians are numbered east and west from the principal meridian, as "first guide meridian east," and so forth.

The tracts are **24** miles wide at their southern boundaries, but because guide meridians converge, they are less than **24** miles wide at their northern boundaries. As a result, there are two sets of corners along each standard parallel. *Standard corners* refer to guide meridians north of the parallel, while *closing corners* are those less than **24** miles apart which were established by the guide meridians from the south closing on that parallel. Convergence of meridians is proportional to the distance from the principal meridian; the offset of the second guide meridian is double that of the first, and that of the third guide meridian is three times as great. Of course, actual offsets on the ground may differ from theoretical distances because of inaccuracies in surveying.

2-19 Townships. The 24-mile tracts are divided into **16** townships, each roughly **6** miles square, by north-south *range lines* and east-west *township lines.* Range lines are established as true meridians at 6-mile intervals along each standard parallel and are run due north to the next standard parallel. Township lines are parallels of latitude that join township corners at intervals of 6 miles on the principal meridian, guide

THE UNITED STATES PUBLIC LAND SURVEY

TOWNSHIP GRID

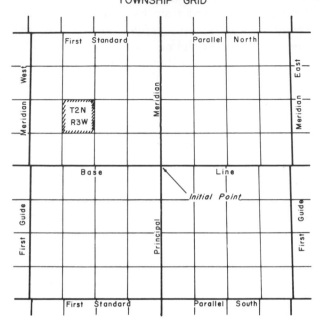

T2N   R3W

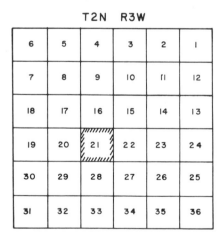

SECTION 21

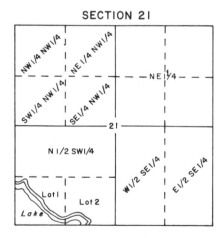

FIG. 2-6   Idealized subdivision of townships and sections.

meridians, and range lines. Since range lines converge northward just as guide meridians do, the width of a township decreases from south to north, the shape is trapezoidal rather than square, and the area is always less than the theoretical 36 square miles.

The survey of townships within the 24-mile tract begins with the southwest township and continues northward until the entire west range is completed; then it moves to the next range eastward and again proceeds from south to north. Townships are numbered consecutively northward and southward from the base line and eastward and westward of the principal meridian. As illustrated in Fig. 2-6, T2N, R3W denotes a township that is 6 miles north of the base line and 12 miles west of the principal meridian.

2-20   Establishment of sections and lots.   Beginning in the southeast corner of a township, sections of approximately 640 acres are formed by running lines 1 mile apart parallel to eastern range lines and 1 mile apart parallel to southern township lines. By starting in the southeastern part of the township, irregularities are thrown into the northern and western tiers of sections in each township. Survey lines are first run around section 36, then 25, 24, 13, 12, and 1. The township subdivision thus starts at the eastern boundary and proceeds from south to north, establishing one tier of sections at a time. Sections are numbered as in Fig. 2-6.

Survey corners actually established on the ground include section corners and quarter corners, the latter being set at intervals of 40 chains for subdividing the sections into 160-acre tracts. These quarter sections may later be further divided into 40-acre parcels known as "forties." A complete land description begins with the smallest land parcel and covers each division in order on a size basis; the specific principal meridian involved is also part of the description. Thus the forty comprising the most northwesterly portion of section 21 (Fig. 2-6) would be described as NW¼ NW¼ S.21, T2N, R3W, 5th P. M. To derive the approximate number of acres in a subdivision, the area of the section is multiplied by the product of the fractions in the legal description. From the previous example, ¼ × ¼ × 640 = 40 acres.

Accumulation of irregularities in northern and western tiers of sections often results in parcels of land that have an area considerably less than the 40 or 160 acres intended. Such subdivisions may be individually numbered as *lots*. Also, navigable streams and large bodies of water encountered on survey lines are meandered by running traverses along their edges. *Meander corners* set during such surveys may result in the recognition of additional irregularly shaped *lots* that commonly range

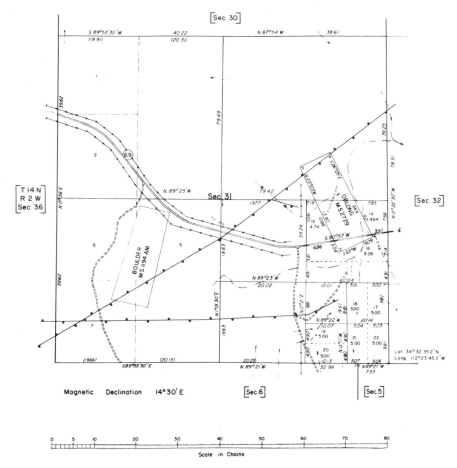

FIG. 2-7 A completed General Land Office plat sheet for Sec. 31, T.14N., R.1W., Gila and Salt River Meridian, Arizona. Surveyed in 1964–1965. *Courtesy of U.S. Department of the Interior.*

from 20 to 60 acres in size. A typical pattern of land parcels resulting from the subdivision of an Arizona section is illustrated in Fig. 2-7.

2-21 Survey field notes. Complete sets of field notes describing public land surveys can be obtained from the U.S. General Land Office in Washington, D.C., and from most state capitals. Field notes are public records, and only a nominal charge is made for copying them. They include bearings and distances of all survey lines, descriptions of corners, monuments and bearings objects, and notes on topography, soil quality, and forest cover types.

Field notes are essential for locating lost or obliterated survey corners from bearings objects or "witness trees." On original surveys, such objects were identified and located by recording a bearing and distance *from the corner to the object*. As a result, lost corners may be reestablished by reversing all bearings and chaining the specified distances from witnesses or bearings objects. Specific procedures for relocating original survey lines and corners are detailed in the U.S. Department of Interior's "Manual of Instructions for the Survey of the Public Lands of the United States."

2-22 Marking land survey lines. In forested regions where land has been subdivided in accordance with the U.S. Public Land Survey, specific rules are sometimes formulated for marking trees so that different classes of land lines can be easily identified. Trees along township, range, and section lines may be marked with three bark blazes, preferably placed vertically on the tree stem near eye level. Quarter-section lines are referenced by two blazes, and finer subdivisions such as forty lines are indicated by a single blaze.

To avoid injury to trees, bark blazes 4 to 6 in. in diameter should be made with a drawknife and then painted with an appropriate color. When feasible, it is desirable to have blazing techniques and paint colors standardized in a given forest region, especially where numerous ownerships are represented. The following marking paint colors have been recommended by the Wisconsin-Michigan Section of the Society of American Foresters:

Type of marking	Paint color
Property boundaries	Blue
Sale boundaries	Red
Cut trees	Yellow or orange
Leave trees	Light green
Research and inventory plots	White
Trails	Aluminum

PROBLEMS

2-1 Establish a pacing course and determine your (*a*) number of paces per chain, (*b*) number of paces required to measure the radii of $\frac{1}{10}$, $\frac{1}{5}$, and $\frac{1}{4}$-acre circular plots, and (*c*) number of feet per pace.

2-2 Why are divisions of a surveyor's chain called *links?* What is meant by the markings 1P, 2P, 3P, and 4P found on a surveyor's chain?

2-3 Change these magnetic bearings to true bearings, utilizing the declination specified for your locality: (*a*) N 15° E, (*b*) S 88° E, (*c*) S 10° W,

(d) N 61° W. Express these bearings as azimuths, and then convert them to backsights.

2-4 Orient a staff compass with true north. Why are the positions of east and west reversed on the face of the compass?

2-5 What should be the sum of the interior angles for closed traverses having (a) three sides, (b) eight sides, (c) 17 sides?

2-6 Plot a closed traverse on cross-section paper at a scale of 20 chains per in. Determine the area by the graphical method and then by use of transects.

2-7 Assume you have a dot grid with 36 dots per sq in. What acreage will be represented by each dot at map scales of (a) 660 ft per in., (b) 25 chains per in., (c) 4 in. per mile?

2-8 Measure a given map area by means of the graphical method, dot grid, transects, and planimeter. Which technique is faster? Which do you feel is most precise?

2-9 On standard USGS topographic quadrangles, how are contours and bench marks designated? What technique is used to denote woodland cover? What map symbols are used for (a) railroads, (b) power transmission lines, (c) churches, (d) schools, (e) airfields?

2-10 On original GLO surveys of nonforested areas, how were section corners monumented in the absence of witness trees? Why was Texas excluded from the U.S. Public Land Survey?

2-11 Refer to the Arizona GLO plat in Fig. 2-7. Can you provide an explanation for the unusual patterns of land subdivision labeled "Oblong" and "Boulder"? How far north and west of the initial point of the system is the center of section 31?

2-12 Referring again to Fig. 2-7, give the complete legal description for the most southeasterly subdivision of section 31.

2-13 Visit the nearest property records repository in your locality. Prepare a facsimile of either (a) a plat and description of a metes and bounds survey or (b) a sample page of field notes from a GLO plat book. If feasible, supplement this data with a recent aerial photograph of the same locality.

REFERENCES

Aldred, A. H.
1964. Evaluation of the transect area-meter method of measuring maps. *Forestry Chron.* **40:**175–183. illus.

Bardsley, Clarence E., and Carlton, Ernest W.
1952. Surveyor's field-note forms, 3d ed. International Textbook Company, Scranton, Pa. 120 pp., illus.

Brown, Curtis M.
1962. Boundary control and legal principles. John Wiley & Sons, Inc.. New York. 275 pp., illus.

Kramer, P. R., and Sturgeon, E. E.
1942. Transect method of estimating forest area from aerial photo index sheets. *J. Forestry* **40:**693–696. illus.

Mason, Earl G., and Richen, Clarence W.
1941. Forest mapping. O.S.C. Cooperative Association, Corvallis, Ore. 168 pp., illus.

Roberts, Edward G.
1963. In lieu of a trailer tape. *J. Forestry* **61**:768.

U.S. Department of the Army
1964. Elements of surveying. Tech. Manual TM 5-232, Government Printing Office, Washington, D.C. 247 pp., illus.

U.S. Department of the Interior
1947. Manual of instructions for the survey of the public lands of the United States. Government Printing Office, Washington, D.C. 613 pp.

U.S. Department of the Interior
1950. Standard field tables and trigonometric formulas. Government Printing Office, Washington, D.C. 245 pp.

CHAPTER 3

CORD MEASURE, WEIGHT SCALING, AND CUBIC VOLUMES

MEASURING STACKED WOOD

3-1 The cord. A standard cord of wood is an imaginary rick that measures $4 \times 4 \times 8$ ft and contains 128 cu ft. Inasmuch as this space includes wood, bark, and sizable voids, the cord is more of an indication of space occupied than actual wood measure. Of course, cordwood is not necessarily cut into 4-ft lengths, and it is rarely stacked in rectangular ricks having 32 sq ft of surface area. Any stacked rick of roundwood may be converted to standard cords by this relationship:

$$\frac{\text{Width (ft)} \times \text{height (ft)} \times \text{stick length (ft)}}{128}$$

When cordwood is cut into lengths shorter than 4 ft (e.g., firewood), a rick having 32 sq ft of surface area may be referred to as a *short*

FIG. 3-1 Stacks of southern pine pulpwood at a large paper mill. Note the wide variation in stick diameters. *U.S. Forest Service photograph.*

cord. If a similar rick is made up of bolts longer than 4 ft, it may be termed a *long cord* or *unit.* In the United States, pulpwood is commonly cut into lengths of 5, 5.25, and 8.33 ft. When these stick lengths are multiplied by a cord surface area of 32 sq ft, the resulting units occupy 160, 168, and 266.6 cu ft of space, respectively. The *cunit,* a measure sometimes used in Canada, refers to 100 cu ft of *solid wood* rather than to stacked volume. Typical specifications for pulpwood purchased in the United States are as follows:

1   Bolts must be at least 4 in. in diameter inside bark at the small end and cut to the specified length.
2   Bolts must not exceed [18 to 24] inches in diameter outside bark at the large end.
3   Wood must be sound and straight.
4   Ends must be cut square and limbs trimmed flush.
5   No burned or rotten wood will be accepted.

6 All nails and other metals must be removed from bolts.

7 Mixed loads of pines and hardwoods are not acceptable.

3-2 The pen. When pulpwood cutters were paid on a piecework basis, the "pen" was commonly used in the South as an approximate measure of wood volume. A pen is a hollow crib of cordwood six feet high, formed by criss-crossed layers of two sticks each. When sticks were cut 5 ft long, it was presumed that 5 or 6 pens were roughly equivalent to 1 standard cd. The fallacy of any single conversion factor is shown by comparing a pen made up of 4-in. wood with another where sticks average 8 in. in diameter. The former will require twice as many sticks per pen but will contain only about one-half the cubic contents of the latter. Today, the pen is rarely used as a basis for wood measure.

3-3 Solid contents of stacked wood. Purchasers of cordwood and pulpwood are primarily interested in the amount of solid wood volume contained in various ricks rather than in the total space occupied. The

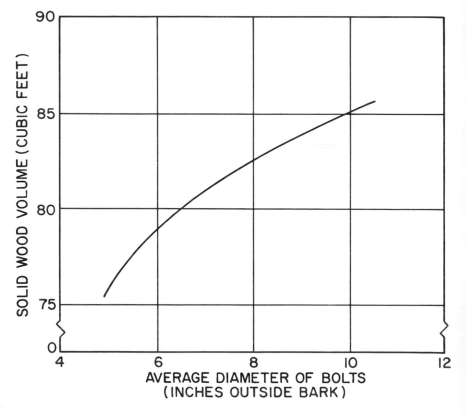

FIG. 3-2 Influence of average bolt diameter on solid wood volumes of stacked cordwood. *From Taras,* 1956.

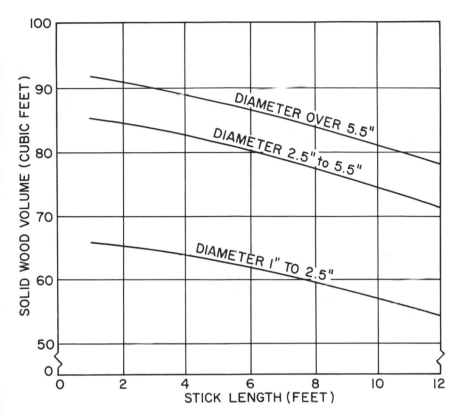

FIG. 3-3   Influence of length of stick on solid wood volume of a cord for conifers. *From Taras,* 1956.

tabulation that follows provides a rough approximation of the volume of wood and bark for ricks with 32 sq ft of surface area and varying bolt lengths:

Size of rick, ft	Space occupied, cu ft	Solid wood and bark, cu ft
4 × 8 × 4	128	90
4 × 8 × 5	160	113
4 × 8 × 5.25	168	119
4 × 8 × 6	192	136
4 × 8 × 8.33	266.6	181

It should be borne in mind that the foregoing values are merely estimates that can vary greatly in individual situations. The species, method

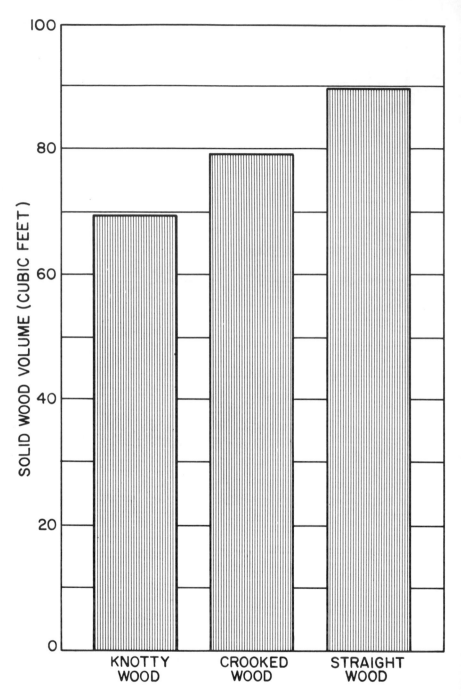

FIG. 3-4   Effect of stick quality on solid wood volume
of 5-ft cordwood. *From Taras,* 1956.

of piling, diameter and length of sticks, straightness, and freedom from knots can exert a significant influence on these average values, as illustrated in Figs. 3-1 to 3-4. Thus the cord method of measurement has been used in the past primarily because of simplicity and convenience rather than because of its accuracy.

When cubic-foot conversions are desired for solid wood alone, the volume of bark present must also be considered in establishing pulpwood values. For many coniferous species, bark may comprise 10 to 30 per cent of the total stick volume; in the Lake states, for example, the average is about 14 per cent. Depending on bark volume and other factors outlined, the solid wood content of a stacked cord may range from about 60 to 95 cu ft. A value of 79 has been widely used in the Lake states, and U.S. Forest Service studies in the South produced averages of 72 cu ft per cd for southern pines and 79 for pulping hardwoods. Mills purchasing pulpwood have traditionally developed their own

FIG. 3-5 Determining the cubic volume of pulpwood by water immersion. The glass-sight gauge is calibrated for direct readings in cubic feet. *Courtesy of Kimberly-Clark Corporation, Woodlands Division, Norway, Michigan.*

cubic-foot conversions based on the size and quality of wood being purchased; there is no single value that can be considered wholly reliable in any given forest region.

3-4 An ideal measure. The perfect unit of measurement would be one that is absolute, unambiguous, accurate, simple, and inexpensive to apply (Ker, 1962). If only peeled or debarked wood was purchased, and sticks could be individually measured, the cubic foot might be a logical unit for adoption. However, since low-value pulpwood bolts cannot be economically handled as separate items, this technique could be accurate but certainly not simple or inexpensive. The *xylometer* or water-immersion method has also been considered for determining cubic volumes, but few equipment models have progressed beyond the experimental stage. By this technique, volume of wood is derived through application of Archimedes' principle; i.e., the measured volume of water displaced is equivalent to the cubic volume of wood immersed (Fig. 3-5).

MEASURING WOOD BY WEIGHT

3-5 The appeal of weight scaling. The use of weight as a measure for purchasing wood is not a new idea; mine timbers and pine stumps utilized in the wood naval stores industry have been purchased on a weight basis for many years. The rather sudden appeal of weight scaling in the pulpwood industry may be largely attributed to changes in the locale of measurement and purchases. Whereas wood was formerly scaled in the forest, measurements are now made at concentration yards or at the mill. Since 1955, a large segment of the pulp and paper industry has adopted weight scaling in lieu of linear measurements for stacked pulpwood (Fig. 3-6).

Weight/price equivalents are usually based on studies of freshly cut wood. It is thus implicit that mills favor green wood with a high moisture content or that purchasers are prepared to assume the cost of carrying large wood inventories for seasoning purposes. As green wood is preferred in most instances, there is some incentive for the producer to deliver his wood immediately after cutting. While there are indications that many species lose very little moisture during the first 4 to 8 weeks in storage, the widespread belief that pulpwood seasons and loses weight rapidly works in favor of mills who desire freshly cut material. From the mill inventory viewpoint, the greener the wood delivered, the longer it can be stored on the yard without deterioration—an important consideration in warm and humid regions.

3-6 Variations in weight. Most mills now utilizing weight scaling have developed their own local conversions by making paired weighings and

FIG. 3-6. **Weight scaling of pine pulpwood.** *Courtesy of Union Bag–Camp Paper Corporation.*

cordwood measurements of thousands of purchases. Weight equivalents may vary by species, mill localities, and points of wood origin. The influence of former measures in cords is reflected in the newer weight units; instead of wood being purchased by the ton or hundredweight, prices arc usually based on average weights per standard cord.

The principal factors contributing to weight variations for a given species are wood volume, moisture content, and density, or weight per cubic foot. Variations in wood volume, or the actual amount of solid wood in a cord, are caused by differences in bolt diameter, length, quality, and bark thickness. Moisture content varies within species for heartwood versus sapwood. Wood density is affected by per cent of summerwood, growth rate, and position in the tree, i.e., density tends to decrease from the lower to the top portion of the stem.

3-7 Wood density and weight ratios. From a knowledge of moisture content and specific gravity (based on ovendry weight and green volume), the weight per cubic foot of any species may be computed by this relationship:

$$\text{Density} = \text{specific gravity} \times 62.4 \left(1 + \frac{\%\ \text{moisture content}}{100}\right)$$

The utility of this formula is illustrated by this example: assume that a weight/cord equivalent is required for loblolly pine, a species having a specific gravity of 0.46, moisture content of 110 per cent, solid wood volume per cord of 72 cu ft, and an estimated bark weight of 700 lb per cd. Substituting in the formula, we have:

$$\text{Density} = 0.46 \times 62.4 \left(1 + \frac{110}{100}\right) = 60.3 \text{ lb per cu ft}$$

As there are 72 cu ft of wood per cord, the weight of solid wood per cord is 72×60.3 or 4,342 lb. By adding the bark weight of 700 lb, the total weight is found to be 5,042 lb per cd. Weight equivalents in Table 3-1 were derived by this procedure.

TABLE 3-1 Computation of Pulpwood Weights for Southern Pines*

Species	Specific gravity	Moisture content, %	Density, lb per cu ft	Solid volume per cord, cu ft	Weight of solid wood, lb	Estimated bark weight, lb	Total weight of wood & bark, lb
Loblolly pine	0.46	110	60.3	72	4,342	700	5,042
Longleaf pine	0.53	105	67.8	72	4,882	650	5,532
Shortleaf pine	0.44	120	60.4	72	4,349	500	4,849
Slash pine	0.52	120	71.4	72	5,141	500	5,641

* From Taras, 1956.

The foregoing technique of computing weight/cord ratios is valid only when both specific gravity and moisture content are accurately determined, because small variations in these factors can result in large weight changes. For each 0.02 change in specific gravity at a level of 100 per cent moisture content, the weight of wood will change about 2.5 lb per cu ft. At the same level, a moisture content difference of 5 per cent can cause a weight change of 1 to 2 lb per cu ft. In a cord having 72 cu ft of solid wood, the 0.02 change in specific gravity alone could mean a loss or gain of 180 lb of wood, while the stated moisture difference might involve 72 to more than 100 lb (Taras, 1956).

Table 3-2 was derived by solving the wood-density formula for a wide range of specific gravities and wood moisture contents. It may therefore be applied in developing approximate weight factors for a variety of tree species. The reader should remember, however, that most mills develop their price ratios by actual scaling of delivered wood rather than by this theoretical approach.

3-8 Advantages of weight scaling. Contrary to popular belief, it has not yet been proven that weight scaling is greatly superior to measuring

TABLE 3-2 Weight in Pounds Per Cubic Foot of Green Wood at Various Values of Specific Gravity and Moisture Content

Moisture content of wood %	Weight in pounds per cubic foot when the specific gravity* is—										
	0.30	0.34	0.38	0.42	0.46	0.50	0.54	0.58	0.62	0.66	0.70
30	24.3	27.6	30.8	34.1	37.3	40.6	43.8	47.0	50.3	53.5	56.8
40	26.2	29.7	33.2	36.7	40.2	43.7	47.2	50.7	54.2	57.7	61.2
50	28.1	31.8	35.6	39.3	43.1	46.8	50.5	54.3	58.0	61.8	65.5
60	30.0	33.9	37.9	41.9	45.9	49.9	53.9	57.9	61.9	65.9	69.9
70	31.8	36.1	40.3	44.6	48.8	53.0	57.3	61.5	65.8	70.0	74.3
80	33.7	38.2	42.7	47.2	51.7	56.2	60.7	65.1	69.6	74.1	78.6
90	35.6	40.3	45.1	49.8	54.5	59.3	64.0	68.8	73.5	78.2	83.0
100	37.4	42.4	47.4	52.4	57.4	62.4	67.4	72.4	77.4	82.4	87.4
110	39.3	44.6	49.8	55.0	60.3	65.5	70.8	76.0	81.2	86.5	91.7
120	41.2	46.7	52.2	57.7	63.1	68.6	74.1	79.6	85.1	90.6	96.1
130	43.1	48.8	54.5	60.3	66.0	71.8	77.5	83.2	89.0	94.7	100.5
140	44.9	50.9	56.9	62.9	68.9	74.9	80.9	86.9	92.9	98.8	104.8
150	46.8	53.0	59.3	65.5	71.8	78.0	84.2	90.5	96.7	103.0	109.2

* Based on weight when ovendry, and volume when green.
SOURCE: "Wood Handbook," USDA, 1955.

stacked ricks from the standpoint of predicting the actual amount of solid wood in a cord. Nevertheless, the technique has continued to gain in popularity for these reasons:

1 It encourages delivery of green wood to the mill.
2 The method is fast, requires no special handling, and saves time for both buyer and seller. A greater volume of wood can be measured in a shorter time period and with fewer personnel.
3 Weight scaling is more objective than cordwood scaling, and positive records of all transactions are provided by automatically stamped weight tickets.
4 Incentive is provided for better piling of wood on trucks; this tends to increase the volume handled by the pulpwood supplier.
5 Woodyard inventories are more easily maintained because of greater uniformity in record keeping.

CUBIC VOLUMES OF LOGS

3-9 **Logs, bolts, and scaling units.** When trees are cut into lengths of 8 ft or more, the sections are referred to as *logs*. By contrast, shorter pieces are called sticks or *bolts*. The process of measuring volumes of individual logs is termed *scaling*. Logs may be scaled in terms of cubic feet, cubic meters, board feet, weight, and other units. The cubic foot is an amount of wood equivalent to a solid cube that measures

$12 \times 12 \times 12$ inches and contains 1,728 cubic inches. The cubic meter, used in countries that have adopted the metric system, contains 35.3 cubic feet. In terms of lumber, the board foot is an imaginary plank one inch thick and twelve inches square; i.e., it contains 144 cubic inches of wood. The present discussion is concerned with log scales expressed in cubic volumes; board-foot volumes and weight scaling of sawlogs are described in Chap. 4.

3-10 Basal area. Although tree cross sections rarely form true circles, they are normally presumed to be circular for purposes of computing cross-sectional areas, i.e., *basal areas* (BA). In measuring cubic-foot contents of logs, it is desirable to derive basal areas in square feet rather than in square inches; cubic volumes are then derived by multiplying average basal area times log length in feet. As diameters instead of radii of logs are measured, BA in square inches may be derived by this expression:

$$\text{Basal area (BA) in square inches} = \frac{\pi D^2}{4}$$

where D is the log diameter in inches.

For this relationship, it is then necessary to divide the result by 144 to convert the basal area to square feet. This is most easily accomplished in one step by reducing the formula as follows:

$$\text{BA} = \frac{\pi D^2}{4(144)} = \frac{3.1416\,D^2}{576} = 0.005454\,D^2$$

By this simple conversion, basal areas are derived in square feet when diameters are measured in inches. Basal area tables for a wide range of diameters are included in the Appendix.

3-11 Log volumes and geometric solids. If logs were perfectly cylindrical, cubic volumes would be derived by merely multiplying cross-sectional area or basal area times log length. However, as logs taper from one end to another, only short sections of perhaps a few inches can logically be treated as cylinders. Still, there are several common geometric solids from which truncated sections can be extracted to approximate log forms. Volumes of these solids of revolution are computed as follows:

Name of solid	Volume computation
Paraboloid	BA/2 $\times$ length
Conoid	BA/3 $\times$ length
Neiloid	BA/4 $\times$ length

As a rule, trees approximate the shape of truncated neiloids while the effects of butt swell are apparent. Logs from middle sections of tree stems are similar to truncated conoids, while upper logs approach the form of paraboloids. From the foregoing, it can be generalized that tree shape resembles (1) a neiloid when taper tends to decrease, (2) a conoid when taper is relatively constant, and (3) a paraboloid when taper tends to increase.

Cubic volumes for all solids of revolution are computed from the product of their *average* cross-sectional area and length. Thus in computing log volumes, the principal problem encountered is that of accurately determining the elusive average cross section. Three common formulas applied to this end are

Huber's: Cubic volume $= B_{1/2}(L)$

Smalian's: Cubic volume $= \dfrac{(B + b)}{2} L$

Newton's: Cubic volume $= \dfrac{(B + 4B_{1/2} + b)}{6} L$

where $B_{1/2} =$ cross-sectional area at log midpoint
$B =$ cross-sectional area at large end of log
$b =$ cross-sectional area at small end of log
$L =$ log length

Areas and volumes are computed inside bark and may be expressed in either English or metric units. Huber's formula assumes that the average cross-sectional area is found at the midpoint of the log; unfortunately, this is not always true. The formula is regarded as intermediate in accuracy, but its use is limited because (1) bark measurements or empirical bark deductions are required to obtain mid-diameters inside bark and (2) the midpoints of logs in piles or ricks are often inaccessible and cannot be measured.

Smalian's formula, though requiring measurements at both ends of the log, is the easiest and least expensive to apply. It also happens to be the least accurate of the three methods, especially for butt logs having flared ends. Excessive butt swell must be allowed for by ocularly projecting a normal taper line throughout the log, or by cutting flared logs into short lengths to minimize the effect of unusual taper. Otherwise, log volumes may be overestimated by application of an average cross-sectional area that is too large. Because it has neither of the disadvantages cited for Huber's formula, Smalian's method of volume computation holds the greatest promise of the three for production log scaling.

Newton's formula necessitates the measurement of logs at the midpoint and at both ends. Although it is more accurate than the other two methods, the expense incurred in application limits its use to research, experimental techniques, and checks against other cubic volume determinations. It will be noted that for perfect cylinders, all three formulas provide identical results.

Where reliable instruments are available for measuring upper-stem diameters of standing trees, log volumes may be determined by "height accumulation," a concept of tree measurement developed by Grosenbaugh (1954). In essence, this technique consists of selecting tree diameters above dbh in diminishing arithmetic progression; then tree height to each such diameter is estimated, recorded, and accumulated. In contrast to usual tree measurement procedures, outside bark diameter at uniform intervals is treated as the independent variable, and heights are recorded at irregular intervals. This technique permits individual trees to be broken down into various product uses and recombined with similar sections from other trees.

3–12 Commercial scaling by the cubic foot. For species having a limited degree of natural taper, logs may be simply scaled as cylinders based on small-end diameters or cross sections. Such an approach has an obvious time and cost advantage over Smalian's method which requires measuring both ends of the log; furthermore, volume outside the scaling cylinder may be safely ignored for short log sections. Disregarding taper would be quite logical for items such as rotary cut veneer logs, because little or no commercial veneer is produced until these logs have been reduced to cylindrical form.

Where log lengths are variable, taper cannot be completely disregarded. An allowance for volume outside the scaling cylinder may be made by applying a *fixed rate of taper* to all logs of a given species-group. For example, a taper rate of $\frac{1}{2}$ in. per 4 ft of length might be established for a certain species. The volume of a 16-ft log with a small-end diam of 20 in. would be computed by 4-ft sections as follows:

Diameter, in.	Basal area, sq ft	Length, ft		Volume, cu ft
20.0	2.1817	× 4	=	8.7268
20.5	2.2921	× 4	=	9.1684
21.0	2.4053	× 4	=	9.6212
21.5	2.5212	× 4	=	10.0848
				37.6012 or 38

This computational procedure would not be followed by the scaler himself, of course. Instead, he would read the appropriate value from a special table showing volumes for many combinations of log diameters and lengths. Such tables are called *log rules*.

Over the past 40 years, there have been numerous attempts to promote the cubic foot as the national log-scaling unit in the United States. However, the obvious advantages of a clearly defined measure which is independent of utilization standards, manufacturing efficiencies, and final product form have thus far failed to impress the principal buyers and sellers of sawlogs. The continued application of ambiguous board-foot scaling methods is an unfortunate triumph of custom and tradition over logic and rational thinking. It now appears that future possibilities of weight scaling sawlogs may provide the first significant breakthrough toward some cubic standard of measurement.

Canada has also experienced difficulties in selling the idea of cubic scaling practices to wood purchasers and forest industries. Smalian's formula was adopted in 1948 by the British Columbia government as the official cubic standard of log measurement for the province. Most forest industries, however, have continued to use board-foot scales. Thus scalers of government timber in British Columbia are often required to measure large quantities of logs in both cubic and board feet (Ker, 1962).

3-13 Hoppus measure. Except for Canada, many countries influenced by British standards measure the "quarter girth" of logs and compute volumes in terms of units known as *Hoppus feet*. As implied by the term, quarter girth refers to log circumference divided by 4. The measurement of girth G in inches is taken at the middle of the log, length L is tallied in feet, and Hoppus cubic-foot content is computed by this relationship:

$$\text{Hoppus cubic feet} = \left(\frac{G}{4}\right)^2 \frac{L}{144}$$

Volumes derived in Hoppus feet are 78.5 per cent of the cubic contents of a cylinder or of that obtained by using Huber's formula. One difference is that quarter-girth measurements are taken outside bark, while values for Huber's formula are normally based on measures inside bark. In a few countries using the metric system, logs may be scaled by the preceding method in terms of Hoppus cubic meters.

3-14 Inscribed square timbers. It is sometimes necessary to determine quickly the dimensions of square timbers that can be cut from logs of various scaling diameters. Such information may be useful in measuring hewed products such as railroad ties or timbers when the outer portions of logs are wasted or ignored. The problem is basically one of fitting the largest possible square inside a circle of a specified size. A formula that will provide the length of the *side* S of an inscribed square from log diameter D is

$$\text{Side } S = \sqrt{\frac{D^2}{2}}$$

Cubic volumes of inscribed square timbers may be determined by merely squaring the length of the side and multiplying by log length. When the side is measured in inches and length is expressed in feet, the product must be divided by 144 for conversion to cubic feet.

PROBLEMS

3-1 Determine the gross volume of pulpwood (in standard cords) on a railroad car or truck in your locality. Make notes on stick quality, length, range of diameters, and method of piling. Compute the total *value* of the wood at locale of measurement by application of current pulpwood prices in your vicinity.

3-2 Using gross pulpwood volume from question 1, how much *solid wood* is contained in the load, assuming an average of 75 cu ft per cd? What is the *value* of solid wood per cubic foot?

3-3 Use the procedure outlined in Sec. 3-7 to compute the theoretical weight per stacked cord for two pulping species utilized in your region. Summarize data as shown in Table 3-1. Then use current pulpwood prices per cord to determine average wood value per 1,000 lb for each species.

3-4 From your instructor or a logging operation, obtain dimensions of three merchantable logs cut from the same tree. Determine cubic volumes of each by Huber's, Smalian's, and Newton's formulas. Tabulate results and explain reasons for differences noted.

3-5 Compile a cubic volume log rule based on Huber's formula. Tabulate volumes for log diameters of 10 to 40 in. and lengths of 8, 10, 12, 14, 16, 18, and 20 ft.

3-6 Compile a cubic volume log rule based on scaling logs as cylinders measured at the small end. Assume a fixed taper rate, such as ½ in. per 4 ft of length. Tabulate volumes for log diameters of 8 to 40 in. and lengths of 8, 12, 16, 20, 24, 28, and 32 ft.

3-7 Prepare a written report of 1,000 to 2,500 words on either (*a*) advantages of cubic measure for log scaling or (*b*) reasons why the concept of cubic measure is unacceptable to log purchasers and wood industries.

3-8 Review at least two forest inventory textbooks that are used in the United Kingdom. Prepare a brief written report for classroom presentation on some phase of log scaling or tree measurement that differs from practices in the United States.

REFERENCES

Anonymous
1953. Weights of various woods grown in the United States. *U.S. Dept. Agr., Forest Serv., Forest Prod. Lab. Tech. Note* 218. 8 pp.

Anonymous
1955. Wood handbook. *U.S. Dept. Agr., Forest Serv., Forest Prod. Lab. Agr. Handbook* 72. 528 pp., illus.

Davey, Reginald
1942. Measurement of trees. Forest Press, Nutley, Sussex, England. 236 pp., illus.

Enghardt, Hans, and Derr, H. J.
1963. Height accumulation for rapid estimates of cubic volume. *J. Forestry* 61:134–137. illus.

Graves, H. S.
1907. Forest mensuration. John Wiley & Sons, Inc., New York. 458 pp., illus.

Grosenbaugh, L. R.
1954. New tree-measurement concepts: height accumulation, giant tree, taper, and shape. *U.S. Forest Serv., Southern Forest Expt. Sta. Occasional Paper* 134. 32 pp.

Hardy, Steven S., and Weiland, George W.
1964. Weight as a basis for the purchase of pulpwood in Maine. *Univ. of Maine Agr. Expt. Sta. Tech. Bull.* 14. 63 pp., illus.

Jerram, M. R. K.
1939. Elementary forest mensuration. Thomas Murby and Co., London. 124 pp., illus.

Ker, J. W.
1962. The theory and practice of estimating the cubic content of logs. *Forestry Chron.* 38:168–172.

MacKinney, A. L., and Chaiken, L. E.
1939 (rev. 1949). Volume, yield and growth of loblolly pine in the Mid-Atlantic Coastal Region. *U.S. Dept. Agr., Forest Serv., Southeast. Forest Expt. Sta. Tech. Note* 33. 58 pp., illus.

Miller, R. H.
1941. Measuring green southern yellow pine pulpwood by weight or by cord. *Paper Trade J.* 113 (July 17).

Taras, Michael A.
1956. Buying pulpwood by weight as compared with volume measure. *U.S. Forest Serv., Southeast. Forest Expt. Sta., Sta. Paper* 74. 11 pp., illus.

Zon, Raphael
1903. Factors influencing the volume of solid wood in the cord. *Forestry Quart.* 1:125–133.

CHAPTER 4

LOG RULES AND SCALING PRACTICES

LUMBER TALLY VERSUS LOG SCALE

4-1 The board-foot anomaly. Although the board foot is a useful and fairly definitive standard for the measure of sawed lumber, it is an ambiguous and inconsistent unit for log scaling. During the past century, at least 100 board-foot log rules have been devised, and several have been widely adopted. However, none of these rules can accurately predict the mill output of boards, except when near-cylindrical logs are sawed according to rigid assumptions on which the rules are based. Although the scaler might employ any of several rules that indicate different log volumes, there is only one correct measure of the boards produced. Thus the terms *board-feet log scale* and *board feet of lumber* are rarely, if ever, synonymous.

The formula commonly used for determining the board-foot content of sawed lumber is

$$\text{Bd ft} = \frac{\text{thickness (in.)} \times \text{width (in.)} \times \text{length (ft)}}{12}$$

Accordingly, a 1 in. $\times$ 12 in. $\times$ 12-ft plank contains 12 bd ft, and a 2 in. $\times$ 8 in. $\times$ 24-ft plank includes 32 bd ft. This method of computation is not entirely correct even for sawed lumber because of accepted dimensional differences between rough green boards versus finished (seasoned and planed) lumber. A green "two-by-four" may be originally cut to the nominal size of 2×4 in., but it can be acceptable in finished form and sold as a two-by-four if it measures only $1\frac{5}{8} \times 3\frac{9}{16}$ in. The purchaser of 1,000 bd ft of finished lumber is therefore likely to receive considerably less than the volume implied by rigid adherence to the formula cited.

The board foot may be considered a logical unit for measuring *manufactured products*, but there is little rationale for transferring this unit back to a raw material as variable as an average log. Pulpwood is not measured by predicted paper output or expected yards of rayon, and crops such as cotton are not scaled in terms of bolts of cloth or thread yields. The lumber industry appears to be the sole American enterprise that requires measurement of its raw material in terms of a manufactured product. There is little to defend board-foot log rules other than past use and resistance to change, for they result in nebulous units that bear little resemblance to consistent measures of volume. As emphasized in Chap. 3, cubic volume or weight scaling is a fairer and more logical method of measuring logs and other roundwood materials.

4-2   General features of board-foot log rules.   To be considered equitable to both buyer and seller, a log rule must be *consistent;* i.e., volumes should be directly correlated with log sizes over the entire range of dimensions encountered. Few log rules currently in use can meet this simple requirement. Most of the differences between board-foot log scale and the sawed lumber tally can be attributed to the inflexible assumptions that necessarily underlie such rules:

1   Logs are considered to be cylinders, and volumes are derived from the small ends of logs. Volume outside the scaling cylinder, resulting from log taper, is generally ignored. In a few instances, a fixed rate of taper is presumed to somewhat compensate for this volume loss.

2   It is assumed that all logs will be sawed into boards of a certain thickness (usually 1 in.) with a saw of a specified thickness or "kerf."

3   A fixed procedure for sawing the log and allowing for slabs is postulated.

4   There is a tacit implication that all sawmills operate at a uniform level of efficiency which provides equal lumber yields from similar logs. The fact

that some mills may be able to cut and market shorter or narrower boards than others is disregarded.

As a corollary to the foregoing, the terms *minimum board width* and *maximum scaling length* are worthy of definition. Minimum board width refers to the narrowest board for which volume would be computed by a given log rule. For most rules, the minimum board width is not smaller than 4 in. or larger than 8 in. Maximum scaling length indicates the longest tree section that may be scaled as a single log. Such a limitation is essential where log rules include no taper allowance; otherwise an entire tree might be scaled from the top end as a 6-in. log. Local scaling practices usually limit the maximum scaling length to 16 ft, though 32 ft may be acceptable in a few regions.

Log rules have been constructed from empirical rules of thumb, sawmill lumber tallies, ratios of board feet to cubic feet, diagrams, mathematical formulas, and by combinations of these techniques. The three most commonly used log rules in the United States are the Scribner, Doyle, and International ¼-in. All three are included in the Appendix.

DERIVATION OF LOG RULES

4-3 Mill-tally log rules. Any sawmill may construct its own empirical log rule by keeping careful lumber tallies of boards cut from various-sized logs. Such rules may provide excellent indicators of log volume at the particular sawmills where they are compiled. However, as they represent only one example of manufacturing efficiency and utilization practice, they are rarely reliable for general use in other localities. The utility of mill-tally log rules is generally limited to mills performing "custom sawing," i.e., the production and sale of boards from logs supplied by customers.

4-4 Board foot-cubic foot ratios. From a purely theoretical viewpoint, 1 cu ft of solid wood contains 12 bd ft of lumber. This mathematical conversion, however, presumes that the cubic foot is rectangular in shape and that twelve 1-in. boards can somehow be extracted without loss of saw kerf. When 1-in. boards must be sawed from round logs, with attendant losses in squaring the log and allowing for kerf, the conversion factor is more likely to range between 4 and 8 bd ft per cu ft. Adding to the difficulty of adopting a uniform conversion is the fact that the board foot-cubic foot ratio changes with log diameter, method of slabbing the log, saw thickness, and sizes of boards produced.

Other factors being constant, the board foot-cubic foot ratio increases with log diameter, because a smaller percentage of cubic volume is wasted in squaring up larger logs. Board foot-cubic foot relationships of 5:1 or 6:1 are sometimes recommended for rough conversions, but there is no single factor that is worthy of complete endorsement. Although the cubic foot alone might constitute an ideal scaling unit, its conversion to the less reliable board foot is unrealistic at best. (See Sec. 4-9.)

4-5 Scribner log rule. Developed by J. M. Scribner around 1846, this rule was derived from diagrams of 1-in. boards drawn to scale within cylinders of various sizes. A saw kerf of ¼ in. is presumed. The exact minimum board width allowed is not definitely known, although it appears to have been 4 in. for at least some log diameters. No taper allowance was included, so the rule ignores all volume outside scaling cylinders projected from small ends of logs. Therefore, this rule will normally underscale logs unless the maximum scaling length is held to about 16 ft. When volumes of 16-ft logs are desired, the rule-of-thumb formula $0.8 \, (D-1)^2 - D/2$ provides a close approximation of the Scribner log rule (Grosenbaugh, 1952).

In general, the Scribner rule is considered to be intermediate in accuracy, although it does not provide board-foot volumes that are entirely consistent with changing log diameters. A slight modification of the rule is the Scribner Decimal C log rule. Here, the original Scribner volumes are rounded off to the nearest 10 bd ft, and the last zero is dropped. This innovation is presumably an aid to the scaler who must record and total volumes for large numbers of logs. The Scribner Decimal C is the official rule of the U.S. Forest Service in Western United States. For eastern national forests, the International ¼-in. rule is generally used.

Those interested in constructing their own diagram log rules may do so by carefully drafting a series of circles representing the desired range of log diameters. It is then necessary to decide upon the minimum acceptable board width and the saw kerf to be employed. End views of boards are drawn to scale within each circle, preferably by using a "four-sided" arrangement of boards. In this way, logs may require only three turns or rotations on the mill carriage to attain the pattern of boards diagramed. When all diagrams have been completed, the number of board feet in each log may be computed by the formula

$$\text{Bd ft} = \frac{\text{total number of sq in. of diagram boards}}{12} \times \text{log length (ft)}$$

4-6 Doyle log rule. This rule, devised by Edward Doyle about 1825, is based on a mathematical formula

$$\text{Bd ft} = \left(\frac{D-4}{4}\right)^2 L$$

where D is the log diameter in inches and L is the log length in feet.

For 16-ft logs, the formula may be reduced to merely $(D-4)^2$. Despite the fact that the formula is algebraically incorrect, use of the rule has persisted in Southern and Eastern United States. It was originally intended that the rule provide for a slabbing allowance of 4 in. and a saw kerf of $\frac{5}{16}$ in. or 25 per cent. The 4-in. slab deduction is more than twice the amount ordinarily needed, and the kerf deduction is actually only about 4.5 per cent. The net result is a highly inaccurate and inconsistent log rule that greatly underscales small logs because of the excessive slab deduction. Conversely, large logs are overscaled, for the insufficient kerf deduction is no longer absorbed by the heavy slab deduction.

The biggest fault of the Doyle rule lies in its inconsistency rather than its basic inaccuracy. The fact that volumes increase erratically with changing log diameters prohibits uniform adjustments in log prices to compensate for the abortive scale values. The rule can thus be considered a fair basis for transactions only when both buyers and sellers of logs are fully aware of its deficiencies. To provide a slight concession to the seller of small logs, some purchasers may either allow the inclusion of one bark thickness in measuring log diameters, or record a scale equal to the log length when Doyle values are less than that amount. However, such local rules of thumb do little to alleviate the inherent inequalities of this anomalous rule.

In a few localities, the more erratic attributes of the Doyle and Scribner log rules are combined to form a diabolical yardstick called the *Doyle-Scribner* log rule. Doyle volumes are employed to underscale logs to about 24 to 28 in.; then the rule changes over to Scribner values to maintain the lowest possible board-foot values. If log prices are adjusted accordingly, the rule may be used without argument. All too often, however, it is the occasional seller of logs who may be unfamiliar with local scaling practices, and the buyer gains an undue advantage in the transaction.

4-7   International log rule.   This rule, based on a reasonably accurate mathematical formula, is the only one in common use that makes an allowance for log taper. Devised in 1906 by Judson Clark, the International rule includes a fixed taper allowance of $\frac{1}{2}$ in. per 4 ft of log length. Thus scale values for a 16-ft log are derived by totaling board-foot volumes of four 4-ft cylinders, each $\frac{1}{2}$ in. larger in diameter than the previous one. In addition to the allowance for taper, the rule also provides rational deductions for slabbing and saw kerf. The original International $\frac{1}{8}$-in. rule assumed a $\frac{1}{8}$-in. saw kerf, plus $\frac{1}{16}$ in. allowance for board shrinkage, giving a total deduction of $\frac{3}{16}$ in. The International $\frac{1}{4}$-in. rule, devised from the original, provides for a $\frac{1}{4}$-in. saw kerf plus $\frac{1}{16}$ in. for shrinkage or a total kerf deduction of $\frac{5}{16}$ in.

Slabs are deducted in the form of an imaginary plank 2.12 in. thick and having a width equal to log diameter. It is assumed that all logs are cut into boards 1 in. thick.

Construction of the International $\frac{1}{8}$-in. rule begins with the simple basal area formula

$$\text{BA} = \frac{\pi D^2}{4} = 0.7854\, D^2$$

When log diameter D is substituted in inches, BA is determined in square inches. Since 1 bd ft has a cross-sectional area of 12 sq in., the number of solid board feet in a cylinder is thus

$$\text{Solid bd ft} = \frac{0.7854\, D^2}{12}\, L \text{ or } 0.06545\, D^2L$$

where L is the log length in feet.

If the full cross-sectional area of a log could be cut into boards without loss of saw kerf, the foregoing formula would constitute a mathematically correct method of computing board-foot contents. As this is not the case, deductions must be made for kerf (sawing out the boards) and for slabs (squaring the log). The percentage p of log volume lost in saw kerf is derived by

$$p = \frac{k}{t + k}$$

where k is the saw kerf in inches and t is the board thickness in inches.

For the International $\frac{1}{8}$-in. rule ($\frac{3}{16}$-in. total deduction for kerf and board shrinkage), the kerf percentage for sawing 1-in. boards is

$$p = \frac{\frac{3}{16}}{1 + \frac{3}{16}} = \frac{3}{19} = 0.158 \text{ or about 15.8 per cent}$$

With a fixed maximum scaling length of 4 ft, the International $\frac{1}{8}$-in. rule now becomes

$$\text{Bd ft} = (1 - p)0.06545\, D^2L \text{ or } (1 - 0.158)0.06545\, D^2(4)$$
and
$$\text{Bd ft} = (0.842)0.06545\ \text{D}^2(4) = 0.22\, D^2$$

The expression $0.22\, D^2$ includes the correct saw kerf allowance, but no deduction has been made for loss of log volume due to slabbing. Whereas kerf deductions are related to total log volume, slab allowances are closely associated with log diameter or circumference. Thus a correct slab deduction can be made by (1) decreasing log diameter or (2) extracting a plank with a width equal to log diameter. For the International rule, the latter method is used by removal of an imaginary plank 2.12 in. thick. The board-foot volume of the plank is computed for a 4-ft log section by

$$\text{Deduction for slabs and edgings} = \frac{2.12\ D}{12} \times 4 = 0.71\ D$$

When this final deduction is appended to the previously derived portion of the formula, the complete International ⅛-in. rule for a 4-ft log section is

$$\text{Bd ft} = 0.22\ D^2 - 0.71\ D$$

Some years after the International ⅛-in. rule was published, it was modified to make it applicable for sawmills employing a ¼-in. kerf (total kerf and shrinkage allowance of ⁵⁄₁₆ in.). Instead of all scale values being recomputed by the process described here, the ⅛-in. rule was reduced by the converting factor of 0.905. Thus, for 4-ft sections, the formula for the ¼-in. rule may be expressed as 0.905 (0.22 D^2 − 0.71 D). For 16-ft log lengths, a simpler formula, 0.8 $(D - 1)^2$, will provide approximate volumes for the International ¼-in. rule (Grosenbaugh, 1952).

If the slab deduction for a formula log rule were made by reducing log diameter rather than by the International "plank method," a mathematically sound rule might be expressed as

$$\text{Bd ft} = (1 - p)0.06545\ (D - s)^2 L$$

where p = proportion of log volume lost as kerf
D = log diameter, in.
s = slab deduction, in.
L = log length, ft

As no log taper allowance is automatically included in the rule, this factor must be controlled by placing limitations on the maximum scaling length.

Of the three principal log rules described here, the International is undoubtedly the most consistent, and it becomes quite accurate for mills producing mainly 1-in. boards with a ¼-in. saw thickness. The International ¼-in. rule has been officially adopted by several states and is widely used on the U.S. Forest Survey. In spite of its relative virtues, however, it has never gained the favor accorded such rules as the Scribner and even the Doyle for scaling work. Unrealistic as it may seem, many foresters are required to derive forest inventory data with the International rule and then handle log sales based on Scribner or Doyle volumes. As outlined in subsequent sections, conversions from one log rule to another are erratic and troublesome at best.

4-8 Overrun and underrun. Comparisons of log rule values by various scaling diameters are presented in Table 4-1. The contrast in board-foot volumes for logs of identical sizes is even more strikingly illustrated by Fig. 4-1, where the International rule is used as a standard of comparison. For logs 10 in. in diameter, the Doyle value comprises less than 60 per cent of International scale, and the Scribner volume amounts

TABLE 4-1 Comparison of Board-foot Log Rules for 16-ft Logs

Log diameter, in.	Log rule				
	International ¼-in., bd ft	Scribner, bd ft	Scribner Decimal C, bd ft	Doyle, bd ft	Doyle— Scribner, bd ft
8	40	32	30	16	16
12	95	79	80	64	64
16	180	159	160	144	144
20	290	280	280	256	256
24	425	404	400	400	400
28	585	582	580	576	582
32	770	736	740	784	736
36	980	923	920	1,024	923
40	1,220	1,204	1,200	1,296	1,204

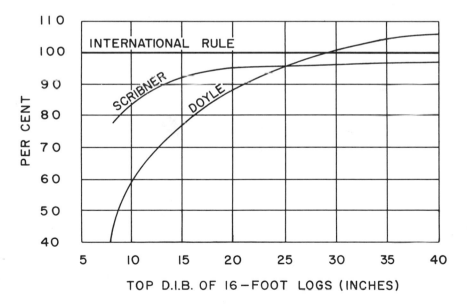

FIG. 4-1 Relationships between three log rules for 16-ft logs. The International ¼-in. rule is used as the standard of comparison. *Adapted from Schnur and Lane,* 1948.

to less than 85 per cent. For 25- to 30-in. logs, all three log rules show a reasonable agreement. Beyond this point, the Scribner rule underscales logs, and the Doyle rule gives values much too large. The trends graphically shown here explain the reason for the devious combination log rule that utilizes Doyle volumes to about 24 in. and then abruptly switches to the Scribner scale.

The preceding comparison is not intended to convey the impression that the International log rule is faultless; nevertheless, it is a consistent rule that often closely approximates sawmill tallies. There is always some disparity between log scale and lumber yield. If the lumber output is greater, the excess difference is called *overrun*. When log scale values are larger than sawed output, an *underrun* occurs. Overrun and underrun are expressed as a per cent of log scale by this relationship:

$$\text{Per cent of overrun or underrun} = \frac{\text{mill tally} - \text{log scale}}{\text{log scale}} \times 100$$

When log sizes and sawmilling practices are equal, the amount of overrun or underrun is primarily dependent on the log rule used for scaling. This fact can be verified at any mill by checking a random selection of logs as shown in Table 4-2. Here, scale values and lumber

TABLE 4-2 Scale and Overrun Comparison of Doyle and International ¼-in. Log Rules*

Log no.	Scaling diameter, in.	Log length, ft	Doyle scale, bd ft	International scale, bd ft	Lumber tally, bd ft
1	13	10	50	70	83
2	11	14	43	70	70
3	16	12	108	130	127
4	11	16	49	80	107
5	11	16	49	80	70
6	15	12	91	115	112
7	18	12	147	170	174
8	11	12	37	55	55
9	10	12	27	45	45
10	13	12	61	85	82
11	10	14	32	55	55
12	16	12	108	130	124
13	11	12	37	55	65
14	19	12	169	190	190
15	12	12	48	70	87
Totals, bd ft			1,056	1,400	1,446
Overrun, per cent			+36.9	+3.3	

* Based on data collected by the author at a circular sawmill in southeast Arkansas, 1955.

tallies were recorded for 15 logs at a hardwood mill in Arkansas. All logs were cut into 1-in. boards with a saw kerf loss of ¼ in. Overrun averaged 3.3 per cent for the International ¼-in. rule and nearly 37 per cent for the Doyle rule. Discrepancies of this magnitude are acceptable only when prices paid for logs are adjusted according to the scaling rule locally applied.

4-9 Board-foot volume conversions. In spite of the difficulties of equating various log rules and volume units such as board feet versus cords, conversions are occasionally desirable. Graphs similar to Fig. 4-1 may be used to change board-foot scales from one log rule to another, or individuals may develop their own factors that reflect local sizes of logs handled. In western Oregon, Washington, and Alaska, for example, the U.S. Forest Service considers that 1,000 bd ft scaled by the Scribner Decimal C rule is roughly equal to 1,400 bd ft by the International ¼-in. rule.

In most regions of the United States, factors have been developed for converting stacked cordwood to board feet and vice versa. A sample tabulation of such factors for the Lake states is shown in Table 4-3.

TABLE 4-3 Number of Rough Cords Per Thousand Board Feet, Lake States*

Bolt top d.i.b., in.	Cords per MBF			No. of 8-ft bolts per cord
	Doyle	Scribner Decimal C	International ¼-in.	
6	11.1	4.4	2.2	45
7	6.7	3.0	3.0	33
8	5.0	4.0	2.7	25
9	4.2	2.5	2.5	20
10	3.5	2.1	2.1	16
11	3.2	2.5	2.2	13
12	2.8	2.3	2.0	11
13	2.5	2.0	1.8	10
14	2.5	2.1	1.9	8
15	2.4	2.0	1.9	7

* Adapted from Ralston, 1956. Conversions assume an average of 79 cu ft of solid wood per standard cord.

Although it is theoretically possible to convert cordwood of any size to board-foot units, results are questionable unless bolts are large enough to have been scaled as *bona fide* logs.

BOARD-FOOT LOG SCALING

4-10 Scaling straight, sound logs. The scaling of a straight and sound log is simply a matter of determining its length and average d.i.b. at the small end. Lengths may be estimated or measured with a tape. Diameters are commonly determined with a *scale stick*, i.e., a rule grad-

FIG. 4-2 Use of a scale stick for estimating board-foot contents of logs. *U.S. Forest Service photograph.*

uated in inches and imprinted with log rule volumes for varying lengths (Fig. 4-2). The "average" log diameter to be scaled is ocularly selected in most cases. However, on unusually elliptical logs the two extreme diameters may be measured for computing an average value.

Depending on local scaling practices, the minimum scaling diameter is ordinarily set at 6 to 8 in. Smaller logs are given zero scale or *culled*, i.e., disregarded and eliminated from the scale record. When log diameters fall exactly halfway between scale-stick graduations (such as 12.5 in.), it is customary to drop back to the lower value—12 in. in this instance. Scaling diameters definitely above the halfway mark are raised to the next largest graduation; thus a 12.6-in. log would be scaled as 13 in.

Log lengths are usually taken at 2-ft intervals, although 1-ft intervals may be allowed for certain species. All logs should have a trim allowance of 2 to 6 in. When logs are cut "scant" (without sufficient trim allowance) or in odd lengths, the scale is ordinarily based on the next shortest acceptable length. When long logs or tree-length sections are being scaled, the locally adopted maximum scaling length should be observed to avoid loss of volume due to excessive taper.

4-11 Log defects. If a log is straight and free from defects, the gross scale (as read from the scale stick) is also the *net* or *sound* scale. From the standpoint of log scaling, defects include only those imperfections that will result in losses of wood *volume* in sawing the log. By contrast, those imperfections affecting log *quality* or *grade* only are not regarded as scaling defects. Thus scale deductions are made for such items as rot, wormholes, ring shake, checks, splits, and crook but not for sound knots, coarse grain, light sap stain, or small pitch pockets.

Making scale deductions for log defects is basically a matter of determining (1) the type and extent of the defect and (2) computing the board-foot volume that will be lost as a result. When the defect volume is subtracted from gross log scale, the usable volume remaining is the net or sound scale. Although certain guides or rules can be developed to somewhat standardize deduction techniques, the extent of many interior log defects can be learned only by working with experienced scalers and seeing defective logs sawed into boards on the mill carriage.

A point worthy of mention is that no deductions are made for defects outside the scaling cylinder or for those that penetrate 1 in. or less into the scaling cylinder. Defects outside the scaling cylinder are disregarded because this volume is ordinarily excluded from the original log scale (except for the International rule). Defects that penetrate the scaling cylinder 1 in. or less may be ignored because this portion of the log is normally lost in slabbing anyhow. If, for example, an exterior defect penetrates 3 in. into the cylinder of a log scaled by the Scribner rule, only the last 2 in. of penetration would be considered in making a scale deduction.

The principal forms of quantitative log defects encountered are:

1   Interior defects, such as heartrot or decay, hollow logs, and ring shake (mechanical separation of annual rings)

2   Exterior or peripheral defects, such as sap rot, seasoning checks, wormholes, catface, and fire or lightning scars

3   Crook defects, such as excessive sweep, crook, and forked or "crotched" logs

4   Operating defects, such as breakage, splits, and end brooming

4-12 Board-foot deduction methods. Defect deductions can be accomplished by at least three approaches, viz., by reducing log diameters, by reducing log lengths, or by diagraming defects for mathematical computations. Exterior or peripheral defects (checks, sap rot) are best handled by diameter reductions. Butt rot and many crook defects are accommodated by reducing log lengths. For internal and partially hidden defects, the diagram-formula method is suitable. By this method, interior defects are enclosed by an imaginary solid and the board-foot contents computed for subtraction from gross log scale. Deductions are made as 1-in. boards, and that part of the defective section that would normally be lost as saw kerf is not deductible. For the Scribner and other cylinder log rules assuming 1-in. boards and a $\frac{1}{4}$-in. kerf, the standard deduction formula is

$$\text{Bd ft loss} = \frac{w \times t \times l}{15}$$

where w = width of defect enclosure, in.

       t = thickness of defect enclosure, in.

       l = length of defect enclosure, ft

One inch is usually added to both the width and thickness of the defect in calculating the deduction. For defects that run from one end of a log to the other, measurements are taken at the larger defect exposure. It will be recognized that this is the basic board-foot formula for lumber (Sec. 4-1), except that the denominator has been changed from 12 to 15. This reduction to 80 per cent of the solid board-foot content effectively removes the 20 per cent deduction due to a $\frac{1}{4}$-in. saw kerf, because this portion would be lost anyway. For the International $\frac{1}{4}$-in. rule, where the kerf-shrinkage allowance is actually $\frac{5}{16}$ in., a denominator of 16 rather than 15 has been suggested for the formula. Several common log defects are illustrated in Fig. 4-3. In three instances, the standard deduction formula has been used for determining net log scales.

All nine logs illustrated have scaling diameters of 24 in. and lengths of 16 ft; gross scale by the Scribner Decimal C log rule is 40 (400 bd ft). For purposes of illustration here, it is assumed that log and

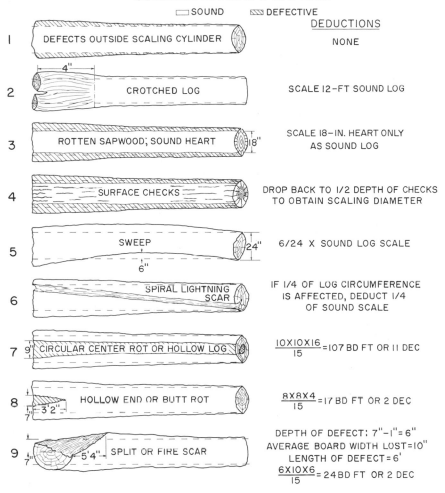

SCRIBNER DECIMAL C LOG RULE

☐ SOUND   ▨ DEFECTIVE

DEDUCTIONS

1 DEFECTS OUTSIDE SCALING CYLINDER — NONE

2 CROTCHED LOG — SCALE 12-FT SOUND LOG

3 ROTTEN SAPWOOD; SOUND HEART — SCALE 18-IN. HEART ONLY AS SOUND LOG

4 SURFACE CHECKS — DROP BACK TO 1/2 DEPTH OF CHECKS TO OBTAIN SCALING DIAMETER

5 SWEEP — 6/24 X SOUND LOG SCALE

6 SPIRAL LIGHTNING SCAR — IF 1/4 OF LOG CIRCUMFERENCE IS AFFECTED, DEDUCT 1/4 OF SOUND SCALE

7 CIRCULAR CENTER ROT OR HOLLOW LOG — $\frac{10 \times 10 \times 16}{15} = 107$ BD FT OR 11 DEC

8 HOLLOW END OR BUTT ROT — $\frac{8 \times 8 \times 4}{15} = 17$ BD FT OR 2 DEC

9 SPLIT OR FIRE SCAR — DEPTH OF DEFECT: $7'' - 1'' = 6''$; AVERAGE BOARD WIDTH LOST $= 10''$; LENGTH OF DEFECT $= 6'$; $\frac{6 \times 10 \times 6}{15} = 24$ BD FT OR 2 DEC

FIG. 4-3 Typical log defects and methods of computing deductions by the Scribner Decimal C log rule.

board lengths are acceptable only in 2-ft multiples, with a minimum length of 8 ft. Minimum board width is 4 in. Where deductions have been computed, they are rounded off to the nearest 10 bd ft and converted to decimal scale. In most cases, deductions are made in accordance with the National Forest Log Scaling Handbook (USDA, 1964).

LOG 1: As all defective material is outside the scaling cylinder, no deduction is necessary.

LOG 2: The 4-ft crotched portion is deemed unusable; thus the length is reduced, and the scale for a sound 12-ft log is recorded.

LOG 3: Because of rotten sapwood, only the heartwood portion of this log is scaled. The deduction is automatically made in scaling by diameter reduction.

LOG 4: For surface or sun checks that penetrate along the radii of the log, it is common practice to drop back to one-half the depth of the checks to obtain the sealing diameter. If the checks here were 4 in. deep on all sides, the scaling diameter would be $24 - (2 + 2) = 20$ in. The reason for not scaling entirely inside the checks is that the loss due to checks is not usually as great in the interior of a log as it is at the ends.

LOG 5: Sweep results in a deduction only when it causes a deviation that exceeds the top taper. For the log illustrated, a sweep of 6 in. was established by projecting the scaling cylinder straight through the log. As losses due to sweep are related to log size, the deduction may be approximated by expressing the sweep measurement as a per cent of scaling diameter. In this example, the deduction is $\%_{24} \times 400 = 100$ or 10 decimal scale. Both sweep and crook can be minimized by careful log bucking. When logs are excessively crooked, deductions are made by merely reducing the length as in log 2.

LOG 6: Sector or V-shaped defects bear the same relationship to log volume as the sector bears to a circle. For the spiral lightning scar affecting one-fourth of the log circumference, the deduction is one-fourth of the gross scale. Wormholes and frost cracks may also be handled by this method of deduction.

LOG 7: The standard deduction formula is applied for hollow logs and those with center rot; such defects are usually larger at the butt end of a log, because they tend to follow the configuration of annual rings. In this example, the defect encompasses a 9-in. circle at its larger end. One inch must be added in boxing the defect to allow for sawing around it. The deduction is thus (10 in. $\times$ 10 in. $\times$ 16 ft)/15 or 11 decimal scale.

LOG 8: When logs are hollow or decayed at one end only, considerable judgment and experience is required to determine the depth of the defect. In this example, the defect is 7 in. in diameter and slightly more than 3 ft deep. Again, 1 in. is added to allow for sawing around the defect and the depth of the hollow is increased to 4 ft, because boards are acceptable only in 2-ft multiples. The deduction is thus (8 in. $\times$ 8 in. $\times$ 4 ft)/15 or 2 decimal scale. It should be noted that if the defect had penetrated more than 8 ft into the length of the log, it would have been deducted for the full 16 ft—just as if the log had been hollow. This would be necessary because boards opposite the defect would be less than the minimum acceptable length of 8 ft.

LOG 9: Splits, fire scars, or catfaces may be handled by merely reducing log length or by applying the deduction formula. In the latter case, it is necessary to determine (1) the length of the defect with respect to the projected scaling cylinder, (2) the depth of the defect into the scaling cylinder, and (3) the average board width lost because of the defect. As shown here, the length is 5 ft 4 in. or 6 ft. The depth of 7 in. is reduced by 1 in. because of slabbing loss, and the average board width lost is estimated as 10 in. The deduction is therefore (6 in. $\times$ 10. in. $\times$ 6 ft)/15 or 2 decimal scale.

4-13 Cull per cent deduction methods.
When log defects are computed in terms of board feet as in Sec. 4-12, a different deduction formula is required for each log rule used. A simpler and more logical approach

is to estimate the defect volume as a *per cent* of total log volume, thereby avoiding deduction methods that are tied to the inconsistencies of a particular log rule. When defects are computed as cull per cents, the volume to be deducted can be easily translated into board feet, cubic feet, or other desired units. L. R. Grosenbaugh (1952) has devised five basic cull per cent formulas for handling common log defects.[1] In all cases, d refers to average diameter of the log at the small end in inches, and L is the length in feet.

RULE 1: Proportion lost when defect affects entire section:

$$\text{Cull per cent} = \frac{\text{length of defective section}}{L}$$

RULE 2: Proportion lost when defect affects wedge-shaped sector:

$$\text{Cull per cent} = \frac{\text{length of defective section}}{L} \times \frac{\text{central angle of defect}}{360°}$$

RULE 3: Proportion lost when log sweeps (or when its curved central axis departs more than 2 in. from an imaginary chord connecting the centers of its end-areas; ignore sweep less than 2 in.):

$$\text{Cull per cent} = \frac{\text{maximum departure minus 2 in.}}{d}$$

RULE 4: Proportion lost when log crooks (or when a relatively short section deflects abruptly from straight axis of longer portion of log):

$$\text{Cull per cent} = \frac{\text{length of deflecting section}}{L} \times \frac{\text{Maximum deflection}}{d}$$

RULE 5: Proportion lost when average cross section of interior defect is enclosed in ellipse (or circle) with major and minor diameters measurable in inches:

$$\text{Cull per cent} = \frac{(\text{major})\,(\text{minor})}{(d-1)^2} \times \frac{\text{length of defect}}{L}$$

When rule 5 is applied, defect in peripheral inch of log (slab collar) can be ignored, but the ellipse should enclose a band of sound wood at least $\frac{1}{2}$ in. thick. When it is necessary to use a rectangle instead of an ellipse to enclose the defect, the cull per cent will be five-fourths as much as for an ellipse with the same diameters as the rectangle. An obvious modification when a ring of rot surrounds a sound heart with average diameter H (in inches) is to estimate the sound proportion as $(H-1)^2/(d-1)^2$ and the defective proportion as $1 - [(H-1)^2/(d-1)^2]$.

In the rare case when cubic scale for products other than sawlogs is being used, sweep ordinarily is not considered to cause loss and $(d+1)^2$ is used instead of $(d-1)^2$ as a divisor for interior defect deduction.

[1] In reality, Grosenbaugh's formulas provide cull proportions rather than cull per cents; they may be regarded as per cents if multiplied by 100.

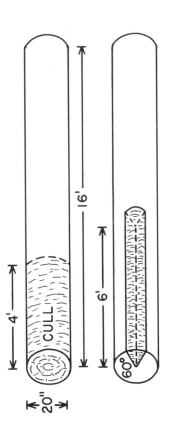

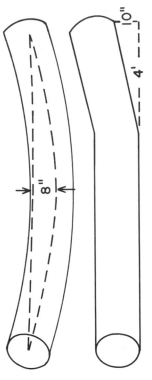

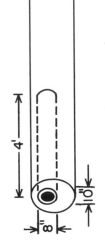

RULE 1: CULL SECTION

$$CULL = \frac{4}{16} = 25\%$$

RULE 2: CULL SECTOR

$$CULL = \left(\frac{6}{16}\right)\left(\frac{60}{360}\right) = 6\frac{1}{4}\%$$

RULE 3: SWEEP

$$CULL = \frac{8-2}{20} = 30\%$$

RULE 4: CROOK

$$CULL = \left(\frac{4}{16}\right)\left(\frac{10}{20}\right) = 12\frac{1}{2}\%$$

RULE 5: INTERIOR DEFECT

$$CULL = \frac{(8)(10)}{(20-1)2}\left(\frac{4}{16}\right) = 5\frac{5}{9}\%$$

FIG. 4-4 Application of cull per cent deductions for log defects. *Adapted from Grosenbaugh,* 1952.

Applications of the preceding formulas are illustrated in Fig. 4-4. Cull per cents are multiplied by gross log volume to derive the defect volume in terms of desired units. These values are then subtracted from gross log volumes to arrive at net or sound scales.

4-14 Merchantable versus cull logs. Logs are considered merchantable (valuable enough for utilization) if they can be profitably converted into a salable product such as lumber. Nonmerchantable logs are referred to as *culls*. If minimum dimensional requirements are met, the distinction between merchantable and cull logs is usually determined by the amount of defect encountered. In many localities, logs are considered merchantable only if they are at least 50 per cent sound. The exact percentage applied, of course, is dependent on log size and species. A high-value, black walnut veneer log might be acceptable if only 30 per cent sound, but a yellow pine log having a comparable defect would probably be culled. Thus merchantability limits vary with locality, kind of log, and changing economic conditions.

4-15 Scaling records. Log scaling data are recorded on specially printed forms or in scale books. A complete scaling record includes the individual log number, species, diameter, length, gross scale, type and amount of defect, and net scale. When few log defects are encountered, the essential tally may occasionally be limited to species, log length, and gross scale. Log diameters are normally needed only for calculating defect deductions.

To conserve writing space and time, the type of defect can be indicated by locally accepted letter codes. Suggested designations are rot, R, sweep, S, wormholes, W, crack, C, catface or fire scar, F, and so on. The completed scaling record should additionally show the location or name of purchaser, scaler's initials, date, and log rule used. When gross scales are in terms of a decimal scale, defect deductions should be computed accordingly.

Standardized scaling records are essential when such tallies are the basis for log sales and purchases. When complete records of log dimensions and defects are required, scalers are more likely to make all measurements carefully. Furthermore, "check scaling" by supervisory personnel is most effective when specific data for each log are clearly noted in scale books.

WEIGHT SCALING OF SAWLOGS

4-16 Advantages and limitations. In general, the advantages of weight scaling pulpwood as cited in Chap. 3 apply equally well to transactions involving sawlogs (Fig. 4-5). The chief difference is that price adjust-

FIG. 4-5   Weighing a truckload of southern pine logs.
U.S. Forest Service photograph.

ments must be made in weight scaling sawlogs to take care of variations in log quality and size. Without such adjustments, crooked or defective logs might command the same price as straight, clear logs, and small-diameter logs (yielding less lumber per ton) could bring as much as larger logs (Page and Bois, 1961).

Circumstances most favorable to weight scaling of sawlogs exist when truckloads are made up of a single species and when there is a relatively narrow range of log diameters present on any given load. It is therefore not surprising that numerous experiments in sawlog weight scaling have been conducted with southern pine logs. Such logs are fairly uniform in size and quality, with few defect deductions being required. On the other hand, mixed hardwood logs of varying quality, degree of soundness, and log size present severe obstacles to effective weight scaling.

Changing from stick scaling to weight scaling raises many questions, the primary one being, What log weight provides an equivalent for 1,000 bd ft of lumber? There is no single or ready answer to this query, of course. Approximations for several species are presented in Table 4-4, but it must be recognized that these values are affected not only by log size and quality but also by such items as moisture content, wood density, and proportion of heartwood versus sapwood. As in measuring pulpwood, volume-weight conversions are preferably based on local measurements by purchasers of logs.

4-17 Volume-weight ratios for sawlogs. Because of the ingrained custom of using board-foot log rules, volume-weight conversions are likely to be initially based on predicted log scales rather than on expected lumber yields. A series of 50 to 100 paired weighings and stick-scaled truckloads will provide a basis for determining the number of pounds or tons per MBF, according to a particular log rule (Fig. 4-6). When log sizes encompass a wide diameter range, the number of logs per load

TABLE 4-4 Average Green Weights of Logs Per Thousand Board Feet of Lumber

Species	Weight, lb	Species	Weight, lb
Ash, white	11,100	Maple, red	11,900
Aspen (Popple)	10,800	Maple, sugar	12,900
Basswood	9,500	Oak, red	14,800
Beech	12,700	Oak, white	14,400
Birch, yellow	13,200	Pine, jack	11,500
Cedar, western red	6,200	Pine, loblolly	12,400
Cherry, black	10,500	Pine, longleaf	11,100
Chestnut	12,600	Pine, Norway (red)	9,700
Cottonwood	10,700	Pine, pitch	12,400
Cypress, southern	11,800	Pine, shortleaf	10,400
Elm, slippery	12,600	Pine, slash	12,200
Elm, white	11,300	Pine, sugar	11,500
Fir, balsam	10,400	Pine, white	9,000
Fir, Douglas	8,700	Pine, yellow (western)	11,300
Gum, black	10,400	Poplar, yellow (tulip)	8,800
Gum, red (sweet)	10,600	Redwood	8,900
Hackberry	11,300	Spruce, black	7,700
Hemlock, eastern	11,200	Sycamore	12,000
Hickory	14,700	Walnut, black	11,900
Locust, black	13,400	Willow, black	11,800

SOURCE: U.S. Forest Service. In most cases, the presumed range of log diameter is 10 to 16 in.

should also be determined. Because diameter is a fair indication of log quality, the log count per ton is useful as a rough grading index or as a basis for premium payments.

Ideally, volume-weight relationships for sawlogs would be derived independently of any board-foot log rule. Mill tallies of green lumber yield per ton can be empirically developed without regard to conventional log scale values (Fig. 4-7). Again, wide variations in log diameters may necessitate changing volume-weight ratios according to average log

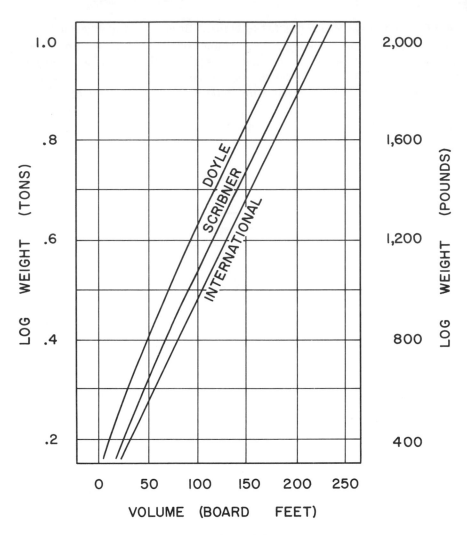

FIG. 4-6   Relation of southern pine sawlog weights to
scaled volume. *Adapted from Siegel and
Row,* 1960.

weight or count per ton. Mills whose average log size is relatively uniform may be able to use a single weight factor per MBF.

As increasing amounts of pulpwood, sawlogs, and other wood products
are sold on a weight basis, the inventory forester will likely develop
methods of cruising and marking timber by the ton rather than in terms
of cords or board feet. An early requirement naturally following this
trend will be the development of local weight tables for standing trees.
Compilation of tree-weight tables is discussed in Chap. 6.

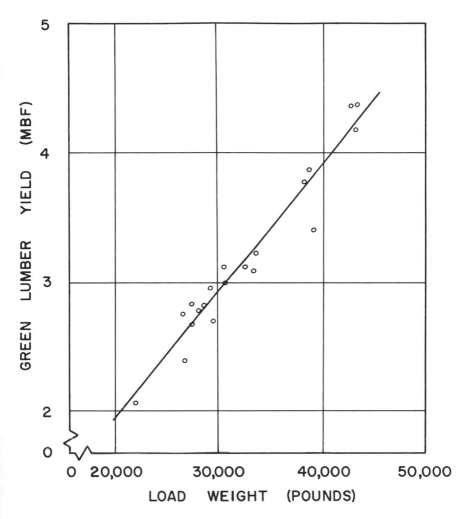

FIG. 4-7 Relation of green-lumber yield to trucked
weights for southern pine sawlogs. *Adapted
from Guttenberg, Fassnacht, and Siegel,*
1960.

PROBLEMS

4-1 Compute the total volume and total value for these items of lumber:
  (*a*) 129 pieces 3 in. × 6 in. × 16 ft @ $128.50 per MBF
  (*b*) 256 pieces 2 in. × 4 in. × 18 ft @ $232.45 per MBF
  (*c*) 346 pieces 2 in. × 8 in. × 20 ft @ $136.00 per MBF
  (*d*) 85 pieces 2 in. × 6 in. × 14 ft @ $65.00 per MBF
  (*e*) 68 pieces 2 in. × 4 in. × 16 ft @ $87.00 per MBF

4-2 Devise a diagram log rule for scaling diameters of 10 through 40 in., by 2-in. classes. Assume a saw kerf of ¼ in., board thickness of 1 in., minimum board width of 6 in., and a uniform log length of 16 ft. Compare diagram volumes with those listed for the Scribner log rule.

4-3 Compute cubic-foot contents for each cylinder diagramed in problem 4-2. Derive board foot-cubic foot ratios for each diameter class. Explain possible reasons for the consistency or variability of these ratios.

4-4 Compile a log rule based on the formula in Sec. 4-7. Assume a ⁵⁄₁₆-in. kerf, and make the slab deduction in the form of a 1-in. collar around the circumference of the log. Using a taper allowance of 1 in. per 10 ft of log length, compute log rule values for diameters of 12 to 40 in. and a log length of 20 ft.

4-5 Visit a sawmill in your own locality, and conduct a simple study of mill overrun based on two different log rules. Tabulate results as shown in Table 4-2.

4-6 The following tabulation of mill overrun or underrun for southern pine logs was compiled by the U.S. Forest Service (Campbell, 1962):

Log d.i.b., in.	Per cent of overrun or underrun			No. of logs
	Doyle	Scribner Decimal C	International ¼-in.	
6	+400	+28	−2	89
7	200	26	−2	102
8	130	23	−3	134
9	90	21	−3	162
10	70	19	−4	155
11	50	17	−4	132
12	42	14	−5	167
13	32	12	−5	119
14	26	10	−6	128
15	20	8	−6	85
16	16	5	−7	74
17	12	3	−8	43
18	8	1	−8	42
19	4	−2	−9	22
20	0	−4	−9	16
21	−2	−6	−10	8
22	−4	−8	−11	8
23	−6	−10	−11	3
24	−8	−13	−12	2
Total				1,491

On a sheet of 8½ × 11-in. cross-section paper, plot per cent of overrun (+) or underrun (−) over log diameter for each of the three log rules. Draw smooth curves (in different colors) for each set of plotted points. Label curves as in Fig. 4-1, and title the graph. Then prepare a brief written report on advantages and disadvantages of the three log rules.

4-7 Select 10 to 20 defective sawlogs for a sample scaling project. Tally by log number, species, diameter, length, gross scale, type and amount of defect, and net scale. Record gross volumes in terms of the Scribner Decimal C log rule. Compute defect deductions by using (a) board-foot deduction methods described in Sec. 4-12 and (b) Grosenbaugh's cull per cent formulas outlined in Sec. 4-13.

4-8 Investigate sawlog weight-scaling practices in your own locality. Determine which species are involved, average green log weights per MBF, and average number of logs per ton. Prepare a written report on your findings.

REFERENCES

Belyea, Harold C., and Sheldon, T. Robert
1938. Some anomalies in the board foot measurement of logs. *J. Forestry* **36**:963–969.

Bower, David R.
1962. Volume-weight relationships for loblolly pine sawlogs. *J. Forestry* **60**:411–412.

———
1961. Are scales better than scale sticks? *Southern Lumberman* **203**:38. illus.

Campbell, Robert A.
1964. Forest Service log grades for southern pine. *U.S. Forest Serv., Southeast. Forest Expt. Sta. Res. Paper SE*-11. 17 pp., illus.

———
1962. Overrun—southern pine logs. *U. S. Forest Serv., Southeast. Forest Expt. Sta. Res. Note* 183. 2 pp.

Chapman, H. H., and Meyer, W. H.
1949. Forest mensuration. McGraw-Hill Book Company, New York. 522 pp., illus.

Dilworth, J. R.
1961. Log scaling and timber cruising. O.S.U. Cooperative Association, Corvallis, Ore. 386 pp., illus.

Grosenbaugh, L. R.
1952. Shortcuts for cruisers and scalers. *U.S. Forest Serv., Southern Forest Expt. Sta. Occasional Paper* 126. 24 pp., illus.

Guttenberg, S., Fassnacht, D., and Siegel, W. C.
1960. Weight-scaling southern pine logs. *U.S. Forest Serv., Southern Forest Expt. Sta. Occasional Paper* 177. 6 pp., illus.

Lange, Keith D.
1962. Selling stumpage by weight in the South: A case study. *J. Forestry* **60**:810–820. illus.

Page, Rufus H., and Bois, Paul J.
1961. Buying and selling southern yellow pine saw logs by weight. *Georgia Forest Res. Council Rept.* 7. 9 pp., illus.

Ralston, R. A.
1956. The break-even point for rough 8-foot bolts merchantable as sawlogs or cordwood. *U.S. Forest Serv., Lake States Forest Expt. Sta. Tech. Note* 469. 2 pp.

Rapraeger, E. F.

1940. The cubic foot as a national log-scaling standard. U.S. Forest Service, Northern Rocky Mountain Forest and Range Experiment Station. 40 pp., illus.

Schnur, G. Luther, and Lane, Richard D.

1948. Log rule comparison: International ¼-inch, Doyle, and Scribner. U.S. Forest Service, Central States Forest Experiment Station. 6 pp., illus.

Siegel, William C., and Row, Clark

1960. Selling sawlogs by the ton. *Forest Farmer* **19**(13):8-9. illus.

U.S. Department of Agriculture

1964. National forest log scaling handbook. U.S. Forest Service, Government Printing Office, Washington, D.C. 193 pp., illus.

CHAPTER 5

MEASURING STANDING TREES

TREE DIAMETERS

5-1 Diameter at breast height. This is the most frequent tree measurement made by foresters. In the United States, dbh is defined as the average stem diameter, outside bark, at a point 4.5 feet above ground. Direct measurements are usually made with a diameter tape, tree caliper, or Biltmore stick. Collectively, instruments employed in determining tree diameters are referred to as *dendrometers*.

With a diameter tape, tree circumference is the variable actually measured (Fig. 5-1). The tape graduations, based on the relationship between the diameter and circumference of a circle, provide for direct readings of tree diameter, usually to the nearest 0.1 in. If a steel diameter tape is level and pulled taut, it is the most *consistent* method of measuring dbh. However, as tree cross sections are rarely circular, taped readings of elliptical trees are likely to be positively biased; thus the tape is

FIG. 5-1 Measurement of tree dbh with a steel diameter tape. *U.S. Forest Service photograph.*

less accurate than caliper measurements when irregular stems are involved.

Wooden or steel tree calipers provide a quick and simple method of directly measuring dbh. For ordinary cruising work, a single caliper measurement will usually suffice. Directional bias can be minimized by measuring all diameters from the tree face closest to a cruise plot center. If stem cross sections are decidedly elliptical, two caliper readings at right angles should be made and the average diameter recorded. When caliper arms are truly parallel and in correct adjustment, the instrument gives reliable measures of dbh to the nearest 0.1 in. Calipers are ideal for trees to about 18 in. in diameter. The diameter tape is often preferred for bigger stems, because large calipers are bulky and awkward to handle in thick underbrush.

A modification of the conventional caliper is the diameter "fork," a two-pronged instrument that can be held in one hand while measuring small trees. One prong of the fork is movable and spring-loaded, resulting in an automatic adjustment to the sides of the stem. Diameters are read from a built-in arc-type scale on the fork.

The Biltmore stick is a straight wooden stick specially graduated for direct readings of dbh. Based on a principle of similar triangles, the stick must be held horizontally against the tree dbh at a predetermined distance from the observer's eye. The cruiser's perspective view is compensated for by the dbh graduations; i.e., the inch units get progressively shorter as tree diameters increase. Thus it is possible to measure a 40-in.-diameter tree with a stick about 25 in. long.

Scale graduations for the Biltmore stick may be computed by this formula:

$$\text{Dbh graduation} = \sqrt{\frac{AD^2}{A + D}}$$

where A is the fixed distance from the eye to the stick in inches and D is any selected tree diameter in inches.

On commercially manufactured Biltmore sticks, diameter graduations are usually based on a fixed distance of 25 in. from the observer's eye to dbh. However, foresters may construct sticks based on a different arm reach by use of the preceding formula (Avery, 1959). Because of the difficulty of maintaining the proper distance from eye to tree, the Biltmore stick must be regarded as a rather crude measuring device. With care, diameters of small trees can be read to the nearest full inch, but accuracy tends to decrease for larger trees, because of the shortened intervals between inch graduations. The Biltmore stick is handy for occasional cruising work, but tree calipers or the diameter tape should be used for reliable measurements of individual trees.

5-2 Diameter at breast height for irregular trees. Whatever the type of dendrometer used, constant care must be exercised to measure trees exactly at dbh—or at a rational deviation from this point when irregular stems are encountered. For trees growing on slopes, for example, it is recommended that dbh be measured 4.5 ft above ground on the *uphill* side of the tree. Figure 5-2 illustrates suggested methods of maintaining consistency in obtaining diameter measurements.

When swellings, bumps, depressions, or branches occur 4.5 ft above ground, tree diameters are usually taken just above the irregularity at a point where it ceases to affect normal stem form. If a tree forks immediately above dbh, it is measured right below the swell resulting from the double stem. Stems that fork below dbh are considered as two separate trees, and diameters are measured (or estimated) approximately 3.5 ft above the fork. Cypress, tupelo gum, and other swell-butted species are measured 1.5 ft above the pronounced swell or "bottleneck," if the swell is more than 3 ft high. Such measurements are usually referred to as *normal diameters* and are abbreviated dn.

When there is heavy snow cover on the ground or when diameters

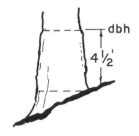
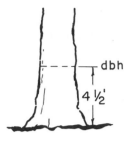
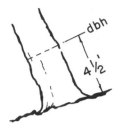

1. TREE ON SLOPE

2. TREE ON LEVEL GROUND

3. LEANING TREE

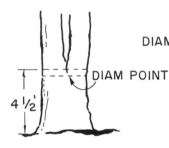
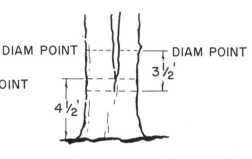

4. TREE FORKING AT OR ABOVE 4 1/2 FEET

5. TREE FORKING BELOW 4 1/2 FEET

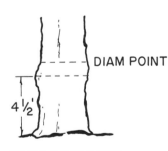
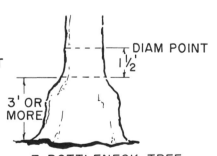

6. TREE DEFORMED AT 4 1/2 FEET

7. BOTTLENECK TREE

FIG. 5-2 Points of dbh measurement for sloping ground or irregular tree stems. *Reprinted from the "Forest Survey Handbook,"* 1964.

are measured under swampy or floodwater conditions, a 4.5-ft pole should be used as a probe to locate true ground level; otherwise, the point of diameter measurement may erroneously be made too high up on the tree stem.

5-3 Diameters inside bark. When tree d.i.b. are desired, two bark thicknesses are measured to the nearest 0.1 in. with a *bark gauge* and subtracted from the outside bark measurement. If d.o.b. are measured with a tape, it is preferable to take the two bark readings 90° apart on the stem—and at exactly the same height as the taped measurement. When d.o.b. are obtained with calipers, the two bark readings should be made where the caliper arms make contact with the tree stem.

If only one bark thickness is measured (and doubled for subtraction from d.o.b.), bias may be avoided by taking the reading on the side of the tree facing a sample plot center or other fixed reference point. When commercially manufactured bark gauges are not available, a fair substitute can be improvised by filing 0.1-in. graduations on the steel bit of a sharpened screwdriver.

5-4 Tree diameter classes. Although tree diameters are commonly measured to the nearest 0.1 in., it is often expedient to group such measurements into diameter classes. If 1-in. classes are used, it is customary to drop back to the lower value when diameters fall exactly halfway between inch graduations—just as in log scaling (Sec. 4-10). Thus the class boundaries or true class limits for 8-in. trees are 7.6 to 8.5 in.; the 9-in. class ranges from 8.6 to 9.5 in., and so on.

The continued application of electronic data processing equipment in forest inventory has made it desirable to modify numerical class limits in some instances. Referring again to the 8-in. tree-diameter class, the span of 7.6 to 8.5 in. requires added sorting time in segregating trees in this group, because two-digit numbers beginning with both "sevens" and "eights" are involved. If, instead, the 8-in. class limits range from 8.000 to 8.999+, the 9-in. class from 9.000 to 9.999+, and so on, machine sorting or retrieval time for a given class may be considerably reduced. Placement of class limits in this fashion also simplifies the field tally and lessens chances for human error in assigning a given tree to its proper dbh class.

When 2-in. tree-diameter classes are used, the 8-in. class boundaries commonly range from 7.000 to 8.999+ in.; the 10-in. class spans from 9.000 to 10.000+, and so on. Contrary to the earlier example, no modifications are needed here to adapt the 2-in. class limits to data processing machines.

5-5 Upper-stem diameters. Out-of-reach diameters are frequently required in studies of tree form, taper, and volume. Although such diameters are most reliably obtained by direct measurement, use of ladders and climbing irons is time consuming, awkward, and often hazardous. As a result, a number of diverse upper-stem dendrometers have been proposed. These include such items as calipers attached to a pole, binoculars with a mil scale in one eyepiece, telescopic stadia devices, and split-

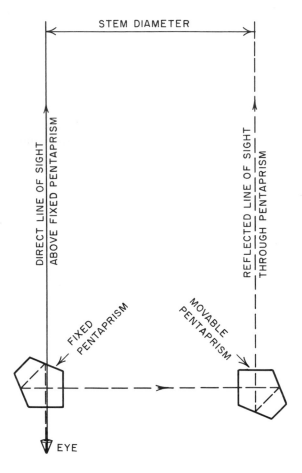

FIG. 5-3 Schematic diagram of the Wheeler pentaprism tree caliper. *Drawing by U.S. Forest Service.*

image rangefinders. A comprehensive investigation of optical dendrometers has been conducted by Grosenbaugh (1963).

Most upper-log dendrometers are limited in usefulness, because they either do not provide sufficient accuracy or they are prohibitively expensive. Some are also quite complex in operation. An ideal upper-stem dendrometer would be simple to use, portable, relatively inexpensive, accurate to the nearest 0.1 in. at tree heights of 50 to 100 ft, and operable independently of distance from point of measurement. Although it may be unrealistic to expect all these attributes in a single instrument, a promising possibility is the pentaprism tree caliper (Wheeler, 1962).

In effect, the pentaprism caliper may be compared to an imaginary giant wooden caliper that can be clamped on a tree stem at any point and from any distance without special calibration. Two pentaprisms, one fixed and the other movable, are mounted so that extended parallel lines of sight may be viewed simultaneously (Fig. 5-3). Prisms are oriented so that the right side of the tree stem is brought into coincidence with the left side which is viewed directly. A scale is provided so that d.o.b. may be read through the fixed (left-hand) prism at the point of coincidence.

Preliminary tests of the Wheeler pentaprism caliper on the U.S. Forest Survey indicate that upper-stem diameters as high as 50 ft above ground may be read to an accuracy of 0.2 to 0.5 in. Greater accuracy may be feasible if an optical-lens system is used to replace the simple sighting tube used on original pilot models of the instrument.

TREE HEIGHTS

5-6 Height measurement principles. Instruments used for measuring tree heights are collectively referred to as *hypsometers*. Many types of height-measuring devices and instruments have been evolved, but only a few have gained wide acceptance by practicing foresters. Thus only two of the more common designs are discussed here. The basic trigonometric principle most frequently embodied in hypsometers is illustrated in Fig. 5-4. The observer locates himself at a fixed horizontal distance from the base of the tree, usually 50, 66, or 100 ft. Tangents of angles to the top and base of the tree are multiplied by horizontal distance to derive the height of each measured section of the stem. The Abney level and several clinometers or *altimeters* operate on this principle, yielding height readings directly in feet or meters at fixed horizontal distances from the tree.

For accurate results, trees must not lean more than 5° from the vertical, and the fixed horizontal distance must be determined by taped measurement or careful pacing. Instruments equal in caliber to the Abney level will provide readings within 2 to 5 per cent of true heights, provided both points of tree measurement are clearly discernible. Leaning trees should be measured at right angles to the direction of lean to minimize height errors. The Abney level and many clinometers yield best results when the observer stands at a distance equal to about one-half the tree height. Few instruments are wholly reliable for reading vertical angles that exceed 45°.

When using an instrument such as the Abney level on gentle terrain, a level line of sight from the observer's eye will usually intercept the tree stem somewhere between stump height and the tree top. As a result, angular readings to the base and the top of the tree will appear on *opposite* sides of the zero point on the graduated instrument scale. In such instances, the two readings must be *added* together to obtain the desired height value.

In mountainous terrain, the observer's hypsometer position may be below the base of the tree or occasionally above the desired upper point

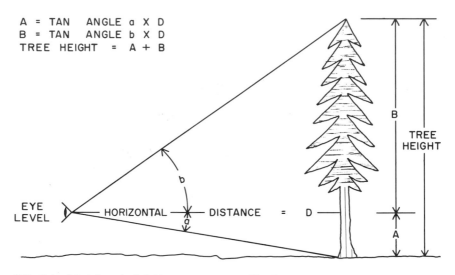

FIG. 5-4   Principle   of   height   measurement   with   the
Abney level.

of measurement. If a level line of sight from the observer fails to intercept the tree stem, both angular readings will then appear on the *same side* of the instrument zero point. Tree height is derived by taking the *difference* between the two readings.

5-7   Merritt hypsometer. This linear scale, usually imprinted on one face of a standard Biltmore stick, is based on a principle of similar triangles. It is normally used for determining merchantable log heights rather than total heights, and graduations are placed at 16-ft log intervals or 8-ft half-log intervals. Like the Biltmore stick, the hypsometer must be positioned at a fixed distance from the eye and the observer must stand a specified slope distance from the tree. In use, the Merritt hypsometer is held vertically with the lower end of the stick on a line of sight to tree-stump height. With the stick held firm, the observer then glances up to note the log height at the desired point on the upper stem. Improvised rules may be calibrated for any desired arm reach and specified distance by this relationship:

$$\frac{\text{Arm reach (in.)}}{\text{Distance from tree (ft)}} = \frac{\text{scale interval (in.)}}{\text{log height (ft)}}$$

The foregoing ratio is solved to determine the scale interval, and this distance is uniformly marked off on a straight rule to define the desired log-height spacings. The Merritt hypsometer is a useful aid for estimating tree heights by log intervals, but it is not generally reliable for precise work. Where heights must be recorded to 1- or 2-ft intervals, an Abney level or clinometer of comparable accuracy should be used. For trees less than 50 ft tall, *direct* linear measurement of tree heights may be feasible by using jointed magnesium-alloy tubing having brightly colored stripes at 1- or 2-ft intervals. This technique may be particularly applicable in coniferous plantations where vehicular access is possible.

5-8 Total versus merchantable heights. Total tree height is the linear distance from ground level to the upper tip of the tree crown. The tip of the crown is easily defined when trees have conical shapes, but it may not be readily discernible for deciduous trees having irregular or round-topped crowns. Thus the measurement of total height is more applicable to coniferous trees having *excurrent* branching characteristics than to broad-leaved deciduous trees with *deliquescent* branching patterns. Recording of total heights is preferred to merchantable lengths on permanent sample plots when tree-growth measurements are based on periodic remeasurements of the same trees. Here, measurement of the entire stem is likely to be more objective and less subject to errors of judgment than heights measured to an ocularly selected merchantable top. In regions where trees more than 150 ft tall occur in dense stands, it may be virtually impossible to view both the crown tip and base of the tree from a single ground observation point. In such instances, tree tallies by merchantable lengths may provide the only practical alternative.

Merchantable tree height refers to the usable portion of the tree stem, i.e., the part for which volume is computed or the section expected to be utilized in a commercial logging operation. For smooth, straight stems, merchantable height may be simply defined as the length from an assumed stump height to an arbitrarily fixed upper-stem diameter. Exact location of the upper diameter limit may require considerable proficiency in ocular estimation, perhaps including occasional checks with an upper-stem dendrometer.

When upper limits of stem merchantability are not dictated by branches, crook, or defect, minimum top diameters may be chosen as a percentage of dbh. With sawtimber-sized trees, for example, minimum top diameters may be set at approximately 60 per cent of dbh for small trees, 50 per cent of dbh for medium-sized trees, and 40 per cent of dbh for large trees. This procedure, more often applied to conifers than to hardwoods, rationally presumes that the larger the dbh, the rougher the upper stem of a tree. Thus top-log scaling diameters will be larger for mature or old-growth trees than for smaller, second-growth stems. When merchantable heights are tallied for inventory purposes, minimum top diameters must be selected in accordance with the particular volume table to be used (Chap. 6). Failure to observe this precaution may result in highly inaccurate estimates of individual tree volume.

5-9 Sawlog merchantability for irregular stems. For many hardwood species, minimum top diameters and sawlog merchantability are regulated by tree form, branches, stem roughness, or defect (rotten cull material). Some typical stem forms that may be encountered in sawlog height determination are illustrated in Fig. 5-5. Bole sections designated as *upper stem* refer to sound portions unsuitable for sawlogs but usable for lower grade products such as fence posts or pulpwood. Limbs and sound cull material are considered unmerchantable because of roughness, form, or size. Following is a brief description prepared by the U.S. Forest Service for each tree pictured:

A: SAWTIMBER TREE: Sawlog length terminates at 9-inch top d.o.b. Meets minimum qualifications of a 12-foot sawlog. Upper stem portion contains no cull and terminates at 4 inches d.o.b. Sawlog length is recorded as 12 feet; bole length as 21 feet.

B: SAWTIMBER TREE: Sawlog portion terminated by limbs at 13 inches d.o.b. Contains no cull and meets minimum grade specifications. Both bole length and sawlog length are 14 feet. Portion between whorls of limbs is large enough in diameter but not in length to qualify as upper stem (i.e., it is less than 4 feet long).

C: ROTTEN CULL TREE: Although sawlog portion is 20 feet long, a 13-foot section of rotten cull prevents utilization of a log meeting minimum grade specifications; thus the entire sawlog portion is culled. Because more than half the volume in that portion is rotten, the tree is classed as a rotten cull.

D: SAWTIMBER TREE: Sawlog portion terminates because of branching at 15-inch top d.o.b. Right-hand fork is too limby to qualify as upper stem, but 7 feet of left-hand fork qualifies as upper stem.

E: ROUGH TREE: Sawlog top terminates by branches 11 feet above crooked butt. No sawlog meeting minimum requirements present.

F: SAWTIMBER TREE: Despite sound cull in the sawlog portion due to butt swell, a 12-foot sawlog is present. Seven feet of right-hand fork qualifies as upper stem. Left-hand fork does not qualify because of crook.

G: TWO SAWTIMBER TREES: Because lowest fork is below dbh, each fork is appraised and recorded as a separate tree. The lower 14-foot section in the left-hand fork meets requirements for a sawtimber tree. A 6-foot portion of the largest stem in upper fork qualifies as upper stem material. In the main right-hand fork, a 13½-foot sawlog plus a 9-foot sawlog (with an intervening 1-foot section of sound cull) is recorded as 23 feet of sawlog length.

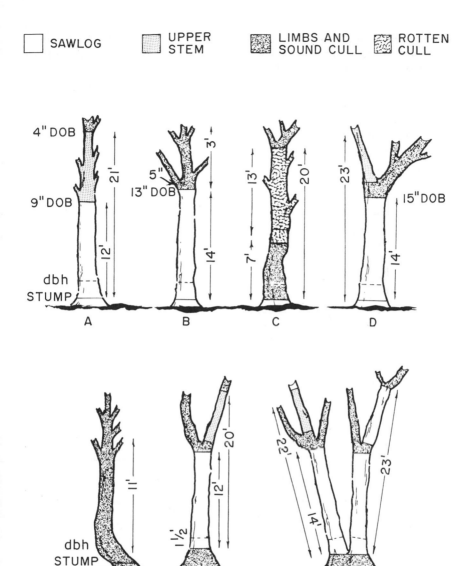

SAWLOG   UPPER STEM   LIMBS AND SOUND CULL   ROTTEN CULL

FIG. 5-5   Merchantable height limits for irregular bole forms. *Reprinted from the "Forest Survey Handbook,"* 1964.

5-10 Tree tallies. As outlined in subsequent chapters, it is essential that neat, concise, and accurate records be maintained when trees are measured and tallied in the field. Foresters have generally adopted the dot-dash system for indicating the number of trees tallied. The first four tallies are made by forming a small square with four pencil dots; the next four tallies are indicated by drawing successive lines between the dots to make a completed square, and the ninth and tenth tallies are denoted by diagonals placed within the square. A simplified tally form illustrating this technique is shown in Fig. 5-6.

dbh (INCHES)	TREE HEIGHT CLASSES (FEET)					TREE TOTALS
	20	40	60	80	100	
10	∴					3
12	⠙	⠶				6
14	⠄	⠙	⊓	⠂⠂		13
16		⠂⠂	⊠⠙	⊠	⠂⠂	27
18	⠄	⠂⠂	⠙	⊡		17
20			⠄	⠙	⬱	16
TREE TOTALS	6	10	24	23	19	**82**

DOT – DASH   TALLY   METHOD

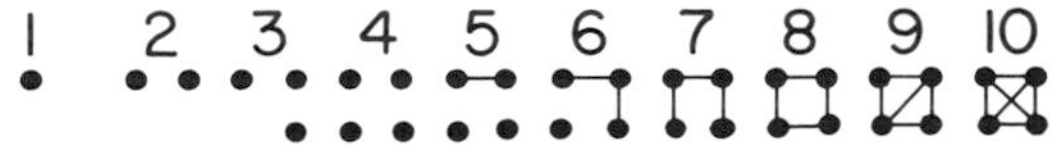

FIG. 5-6 Sample tally of standing trees by dbh and height classes.

Field tallies should always be made in pencil, because inked recordings tend to smear and become illegible when record sheets get wet. Erasures can be avoided by circling erroneous tallies; partial erasures often result in confusion and lead to later errors in office computations, particularly when several different persons are required to decipher field tabulations. Tally sheets, including pertinent locational headings, should be filled out completely *in the field*—not several hours later back at headquarters. Organization is just as important in field record keeping as it is in office bookkeeping.

TREE FORM EXPRESSIONS

5-11 Taper tables. Because trees taper, often irregularly, from stump to top, it is necessary to make some evaluation of stem form in the construction and application of tree volume tables. The rate of tree taper varies not only by species but also by age, dbh, and tree height. If a series of diameter measurements are taken at intervals along the bole, average taper rates may be derived for groups of trees characterized by a particular shape or form category. Such tabulations are referred to as *taper tables,* and they are commonly compiled according to generalized form classes, irrespective of tree species.

TABLE 5-1 Upper-log Taper (Inches) by 16-ft Logs

Dbh, in.	2-log tree	3-log tree		4-log tree		
	2d log	2d log	3d log	2d log	3d log	4th log
10	1.4	1.2	1.4			
12	1.6	1.3	1.5	1.1	1.4	1.9
14	1.7	1.4	1.6	1.2	1.5	2.0
16	1.9	1.5	1.7	1.2	1.6	2.1
18	2.0	1.6	1.8	1.3	1.7	2.2
20	2.1	1.7	1.9	1.4	1.8	2.4
22	2.2	1.8	2.0	1.4	2.0	2.5
24	2.3	1.8	2.2	1.5	2.2	2.6
26	2.4	1.9	2.3	1.5	2.3	2.7
28	2.5	1.9	2.5	1.6	2.4	2.8
30	2.6	2.0	2.6	1.7	2.5	3.0
32	2.7	2.0	2.7	1.7	2.5	3.1
34	2.8	2.1	2.7	1.8	2.5	3.3
36	2.8	2.1	2.8	1.8	2.6	3.4
38	2.9	2.1	2.8	1.9	2.6	3.4
40	2.9	2.2	2.8	1.9	2.7	3.4

SOURCE: C. Mesavage and J. W. Girard, "Tables for Estimating Board-foot Content of Timber," U.S. Forest Service, Washington, D.C., 1946. 94 pp. (Table abridged)

An example of upper-log taper rates is shown in Table 5-1. For specified dbh and merchantable height classes, average stem taper is shown for each successive 16-ft log above the butt section. It will be noted that both tree age and species are ignored. This particular table is the basis for construction of widely adopted Girard form-class volume tables discussed in Chap. 6. Improbable as it may seem, these taper rates were originally compiled from *ocular* estimates of about 2,000 trees of assorted species in the anthracite region of Pennsylvania. They were later modified and extended on the basis of ocular estimates of about 20,000 additional trees throughout the South.

The comparison of tree bole forms with various solids of revolution (cylinders, paraboloids, etc.) may be expressed in numerical terms as *form factors.* Such ratios are derived by dividing stem volume by the volume of a chosen solid. However, as form factors cannot be computed until essential stem diameters are obtained, it has become customary to express stem configuration in terms of *form quotients* derived directly from the diameter ratios themselves. In most instances, form quotients are computed as the ratio of some selected upper-stem diameter to dbh (Fig. 5-7). As a result, values are always less than unity and are usually expressed (or implied) in percentage terms.

5-12   Girard form class. This form quotient is computed as the ratio between stem diameter, *inside bark,* at the top of the first 16-ft log and dbh, *outside bark.* With a log trimming allowance of 0.3 ft and a 1-ft stump, the upper-stem measurement is taken 17.3 ft above ground. As an example, a tree with a first-log scaling diameter of 16.0 in. and a dbh of 20.0 in. has a Girard form class of $16 \div 20 = 0.80$ or 80 per cent.

Sawtimber volume tables based on Girard form class assume that trees having the same diameter and merchantable height will have similar, though not necessarily identical, rates of taper in the sawlog portion *above the first log.* It is thereby implied that all volume differences in trees of the same diameter and merchantable height may be attributed largely to taper variations occurring *in the first log.* Girard form-class tables are *composite* volume tables; i.e., they are compiled independently of tree species and are applicable to both coniferous and broad-leaved trees.

For swell-butted species such as cypress and tupelo gum, dn measured 1.5 ft above the pronounced swell should be substituted for dbh in computing Girard form class. Measurement of the scaling diameter remains at 17.3 ft above ground; thus the two diameters may be only 6 to 10 ft apart in some cases. For trees deformed by chipped turpentine faces at dbh, the normal diameter should be measured just above the highest face. Although the diameter here will be smaller, form class will be higher, resulting in a compensating volume increase. The d.i.b. at the top of the first log should always be located 16.3 ft above the point where the tree will be cut.

5-13   Form point. Unlike other expressions of tree taper, form point is based on a height ratio rather than a diameter relationship. To determine form point, the observer ocularly selects the center of gravity of the tree crown, i.e., the position on the stem that presents the greatest wind resistance. The height of this point above ground, expressed as a per cent of total tree height, is the numerical value of form point (Fig. 5-7).

The correlation between form point and stem taper is based on the theory that the development of bole form is dependent on the mechanical stresses to which a tree is subjected. Tree height, diameter, age, and species are considered important factors only to the extent that they affect crown shape and development. Stresses caused by wind pressures are presumed to "induce" the tree to develop its taper so that resistance to shear is presented equally at all points along the stem.

In practice, form point is sometimes used strictly for field classifications of tree taper, and later these values are translated into a different expression, such as Girard form class, for determining tree volume. The principal advantage of the form-point concept over other form expressions seems to be the ease of estimation, rather than superior prediction of stem taper. The first 10 in. of a standard engineer's scale, graduated in tenths, provides an ideal "percentage ruler" for measuring form point. With the rule held vertically, the observer positions himself at a sighting distance where total tree height is exactly spanned by the full 10 in. or 100 scale graduations. After the point of greatest crown resistance is ocularly selected, its height above ground can be read directly from the scale to the nearest per cent or form point.

5-14 Absolute and normal form quotients. These tree form expressions are based on ratios of mid-stem diameters and dbh. For absolute form quotient, the upper-stem diameter is taken midway between dbh and the tree top; for normal form quotient, the upper diameter is measured at a point halfway between ground level and the top. Although d.o.b. ratios are indicated in Fig. 5-7, form quotients may also be computed from inside-bark relationships. The latter measurements are more difficult to obtain in the field, but their use will provide a more accurate indication of actual stem taper and associated volume.

Absolute form quotient is generally favored over normal form quotient as an expression of tree form. With normal quotients, upper-stem diameters are taken progressively closer to dbh as shorter trees are encountered. For a tree only 9 ft tall, admittedly an extreme example, the two diameters would occur at the same point on the stem. This problem, of course, is largely eliminated with absolute form quotient. In reality, neither of these form quotients are enthusiastically endorsed, because of problems arising from accurate location and measurement of the upper-stem diameters.

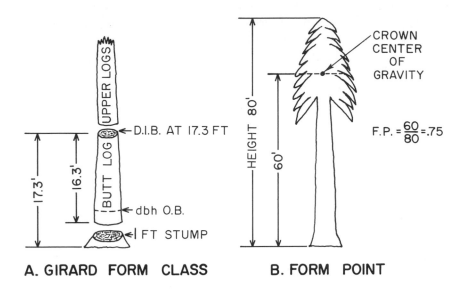

A. GIRARD FORM CLASS

UPPER LOGS

← D.I.B. AT 17.3 FT

BUTT LOG

17.3'

16.3'

← dbh O.B.

←1 FT STUMP

B. FORM POINT

CROWN
CENTER
OF
GRAVITY

HEIGHT 80'

60'

$F.P. = \dfrac{60}{80} = .75$

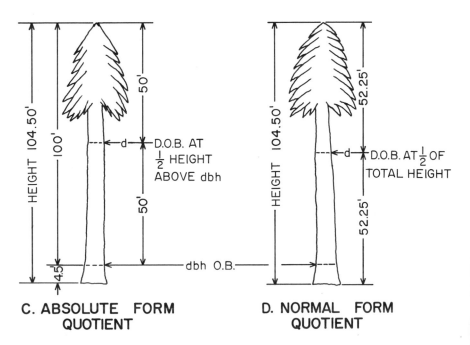

C. ABSOLUTE FORM QUOTIENT

HEIGHT 104.50'

100'

50'

50'

4.5'

d → D.O.B. AT $\frac{1}{2}$ HEIGHT ABOVE dbh

← dbh O.B. →

D. NORMAL FORM QUOTIENT

HEIGHT 104.50'

52.25'

52.25'

d → D.O.B. AT $\frac{1}{2}$ OF TOTAL HEIGHT

FIG. 5-7 Points of tree measurement for determining various form factors.

5-15 Importance of form measurements. Most foresters prefer form expressions based on relatively accessible measurements, a factor that has probably contributed to the popularity of Girard form class. Even here, the diameter measurement at 17.3 ft can rarely be ocularly estimated with precision and consistency; thus it is usually better to have a carefully *measured sample* of a few stems rather than rough estimates of form class for each tree tallied. Obtaining reliable inside-bark measurements at the top of the first 16-ft log implies the use of ladders or climbing irons—an expensive and time-consuming task. As an alternative, however, d.o.b. may be determined with an upper-stem dendrometer and converted to inside-bark readings by applying bark-thickness ratios developed from samples of felled trees (Judson, 1964).

For all tree form expressions discussed here, higher form quotient values indicate less stem taper and correspondingly greater tree volume. For a given species, form quotients are lowest for open-grown trees with long live crowns and highest for forest-grown trees with relatively short crowns. Thus for given soil and site conditions, stand density has an indirect effect on tree taper rates. When using Girard form-class values, the difference between one class and another (e.g., 79 versus 80) amounts to approximately 3 per cent in terms of merchantable tree volume.

PROBLEMS

5-1 Number 20 standing trees of varying diameters. Ocularly estimate each dbh to the nearest inch. Then, in order, remeasure diameters with (a) Biltmore stick, (b) diameter tape, and (c) calipers. Tabulate all measurements according to tree number on a single tally sheet. Using the average of two caliper readings as a standard, obtain plus or minus deviations for the other three diameter estimates. Discuss your findings and preferences in a brief written report.

5-2 Number 20 standing trees of varying total or merchantable heights. In order, obtain heights by (a) ocular estimation, (b) Merritt hypsometer, (c) Abney level, and (d) any other available clinometer. Tabulate and analyze findings as in problem 5-1, using Abney readings as the measurement standard.

5-3 Construct a Biltmore stick and Merritt hypsometer for your own arm reach. Graduate the rule by 1-in.-diameter classes and for height intervals most commonly used in your locality.

5-4 Number 5 to 10 standing trees (preferably mature conifers), and determine for each (a) Girard form class, (b) form point, (c) absolute form quotient, and (d) normal form quotient. If available, use an upper-stem dendrometer rather than ocular estimates for obtaining out-of-reach diameters. Which form expression is most easily derived in the field and which is most commonly used in your region?

REFERENCES

Avery, T. Eugene
1959. An all-purpose cruiser stick. *J. Forestry* **57**:924–925. illus.

Belyea, Harold C.
1931. Forest measurement. John Wiley & Sons, Inc., New York. 319 pp., illus.

Ferree, M. J.
1946. The pole caliper. *J. Forestry* **44**:594–595.

Grosenbaugh, L. R.
1963. Optical dendrometers for out-of-reach diameters: A conspectus and some new theory. *Forest Sci. Monograph* 4. 47 pp., illus.

Hunt, Ellis V., Jr.
1959. A time and accuracy test of some hypsometers. *J. Forestry* **57**:641–643.

Judson, George M.
1964. Inexpensive and accurate form-class estimates. *U.S. Forest Serv., Southern Forest Expt. Sta. Res. Paper SO*-11. 6 pp., illus.

Mesavage, Clement
1965. Definition of merchantable sawtimber height. *J. Forestry* **63**:30–32. illus.

——— **and Girard, J. W.**
1946. Tables for estimating board-foot content of timber. U.S. Forest Service, Government Printing Office, Washington, D.C. 94 pp.

Shipman, R. D.
1962. Girard vs. Horn form-class estimation on sweetgum. *J. Forestry* **60**:343–344. illus.

Spurr, Stephen H.
1952. Forest inventory. The Ronald Press Company, New York. 476 pp., illus.

U.S. Forest Service
1964. Forest survey handbook, review draft. Washington, D.C. 90 pp., illus.

Wheeler, P. R.
1962. Penta prism caliper for upper-stem diameter measurements. *J. Forestry* **60**:877–878. illus.

CHAPTER **6**
VOLUMES OF STANDING TREES

SIMPLE GRAPHICAL TECHNIQUES

6-1 The two-variable graph. The presence of a meaningful relationship between two variables can be quickly and clearly depicted by plotting paired values on simple cross-section paper (Figs. 4-6 and 4-7). Ordinary numerical tabulations can be immediately visualized, interpreted, and trends established. Furthermore, errors and abnormal values are easily detected, and minor irregularities in a relationship may often be eliminated by the drawing of a smooth curve through a series of plotted points.

In the plotting of graphical data, independent variables are placed on the horizontal or x axis, and dependent variables are plotted along the vertical or y axis. Measurements along the x axis are known as *abscissas;* those on the y axis are termed *ordinates*. Graduations for the x and y axes need not be identical; instead, each scale may be expanded to the maximum degree in keeping with the ranges of data that must be accommodated. Though not absolutely essential, it is often desirable to arrange each scale to show the graph origin, i.e., the "zero-zero" coordinate point. Other general rules of graphical presentation are as follows:

1 Scale units and complete identifications of variables should be clearly lettered on each axis. All labels should be oriented for easy reading, i.e., as illustrated by the graphs in this chapter.

2 Plotted points should be denoted by dots or small circles, with point weights written above or to one side.

3 Freehand curves may be sketched in as guides, but all final curves should be drawn with the ruling edge of a flexible spline or French curve.

4 Each graph should carry a "Figure number" and a complete descriptive title.

6-2 The fitting of freehand curves. Although both straight lines and curves may be fitted to a series of plotted points by the solution of mathematical equations, it is often simpler or more expedient to "balance" freehand curves by graphical methods. The weight (number of observations) represented by each plotted point is carefully noted, and a "trial curve" is lightly sketched; special care should be taken to ensure that the trial curve conforms to the expected relationship between the two variables involved.

Next, the curve is arbitrarily divided into two parts, with each portion including about one-half of the total number of samples represented. Each half of the curve is balanced separately by computing *vertical deviations* from each point to the trial line. For example, a point having a sample weight of 3 might appear four squares below the trial line; its deviation is therefore 3 times −4 or −12. Points located *above* the trial line carry *plus* deviations.

When all positive and negative deviations have been computed, each end of the trial curve should be in approximate balance; i.e., minus and plus totals should be roughly equal. In many cases, deviations must be computed for several trial curves before the desired condition of equilibrium can be attained. The final curve should not be drawn until each half of the curve can be separately balanced. For some relationships, it is desirable to record deviations for each half of the curve in one corner of the finished graph.

6-3 Curve transformation. In many instances, graphical relationships that logically have a curvilinear trend can be purposely adjusted or "transformed" into straight-line patterns. The principal advantages are that straight lines are more easily fitted to a set of plotted points than are curves, especially when a mathematical equation is used for fitting the line, and interpolations or extrapolations of graphed variables are made simpler when straight lines are employed.

Figure 6-1 provides an elementary illustration of how a curvilinear relationship can be easily transformed into a straight line. In the upper graph, the dependent variable is log volume in cubic feet, and the inde-

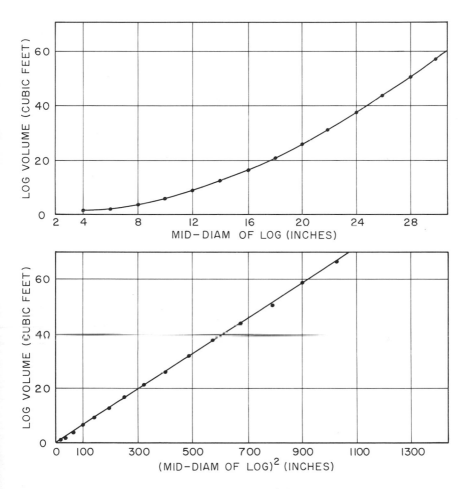

FIG. 6-1 The transformation of a curve to a straight line by changing graduations on the x axis.

pendent variable is log diameter in inches. As expected, the plotted points follow a rising curvilinear pattern. Such a trend could be predicted in advance, because the doubling of log diameter will increase log cubic volume about four times.

An analysis of the formula for the volume of a cylinder or Huber's formula for log volume (Chap. 3) indicates that log volume is directly related to BA or to *diameter squared*. Thus in the lower portion of Fig. 6-1, cubic volumes have been graphed over squared log diameters, and the expected straight-line pattern of plotted points results. A similar pattern could have been produced by retaining the original measures of log diameter on the abscissa and by graduating the ordinate in terms of the *square root* of cubic log volumes.

The foregoing illustrations presume the use of simple cross-section paper that is uniformly divided into equal squares. When one or more of the variables to be plotted is based on squared relationships, however, it may be desirable to use logarithmic or semilogarithmic paper. With this special type of graph paper, one or both axes are printed on a logarithmic scale, a feature that often facilitates the transformation of curves to straight lines.

TYPES OF TREE VOLUME TABLES

6-4   Purpose of volume tables.   A volume table is a tabulation that provides the average contents for standing trees of various sizes and species. Volume units most commonly employed are board feet, cubic feet, cords, or cubic meters. Volumes may be listed for the merchantable sawlog portion of the stem only, for both sawlog and cordwood top sections, or for the entire stem including the stump.

Board-foot volume tables are usually based on existing log rules; thus they can never be more reliable than the log rule selected as a basis for their construction. The principal objective in compiling such tables is to obtain a board-foot estimate for standing trees that would correspond with the volume obtained if the same trees were felled, bucked, and scaled as logs. Thus such tables are used in timber estimating as a means of ascertaining the volume and value of standing trees in a forested tract. This procedure is referred to as timber *cruising*.

6-5   Local versus standard volume tables.   The principal variables ordinarily associated with standing tree volumes are dbh, stem length in terms of merchantable or total height, tree form or taper, species, and locality. Tree volume tables that are based on the single variable of dbh are commonly referred to as *local* volume tables; those that require the user to also obtain estimates of tree height and possibly form or taper are referred to as *standard* volume tables. These labels are often misleading, for they tend to imply that local volume tables are somehow inferior to standard volume tables. Such an assumption is not necessarily true, particularly when the local table in question is derived from a standard volume table.

Volume tables, whether of the local or standard variety, may also be classified as *species* tables or *composite* tables. In the first instance separate tables are constructed for each important timber species or groups of species that are similar in terms of tree form. On the other hand, composite tables are intended for application to diverse species, often including both conifers and hardwoods. To compensate for inherent differences in stem taper and volume between various species groups, provision is usually made for additionally measuring tree form, or correction factors are developed for various species. Otherwise, composite tables will overestimate volumes for some trees while significantly underestimating volumes of others.

The main disadvantage of species tables is the large number of species encountered in most regions. When it is not feasible to construct separate tables for each species, those of similar taper and shape must be grouped together within specified localities. To avoid such difficulties, composite tables utilizing some measurement of tree form in lieu of species differentiation have been adopted in several sections of the United States.

STANDARD VOLUME TABLES

6-6 Use of form-class volume tables. The underlying theory and measurement of Girard form class have been discussed in the previous chapter (Sec. 5-12). Form-class volume tables based on this concept of butt-log taper are among the most widely accepted standard tables in Eastern United States. The biggest disadvantages in using these tables are (1) the almost universal tendency toward rough estimates of form class rather than actual measurements and (2) the wide variations in upper-stem form that cannot be adequately accommodated by measuring butt-log taper only. The fact that each change in form class (as from 77 to 78) accounts for about 3 per cent of merchantable tree volume should serve as a precaution against purely ocular estimates of this independent variable. On the other hand, when reliable upper-stem dendrometers are made generally available to cruisers, most of the objections to form-class tables for board-foot estimates will be removed.

Standard board-foot volume tables have been compiled from International, Scribner, and Doyle log rules for form classes of 65 to 90 (Mesavage and Girard, 1946). Table 6-1, based on form class 80 and the International rule, provides an abridged example of the format employed. The user must first determine the form class of the tree; then only dbh and sawlog length in 16-ft logs and half logs are needed to derive merchantable board-foot volumes. In most published versions, these tables cover a dbh range of 10 to 40 in. (by 1-in. classes) and a height range of one to six logs.

6-7 Compilation of form-class tables. In the original tabulation of the Mesavage-Girard form-class tables, the scaling diameter of the butt log is derived from the estimated or measured form class. Thus for a 20-in.-dbh three-log tree of form class 80, the scaling diameter of the first log is 0.80×20 or 16.0 in. Scaling diameters for all upper logs are derived from a single taper table, an abridged version of which appears in the preceding chapter (Table 5-1). For the tree in question, a taper rate of 1.7 in. is assigned to the second log and 1.9 in. to the third log.

TABLE 6-1 Standard Volume Table, International $\frac{1}{4}$-in. Rule, Form Class 80*

Dbh, in.	Volume by 16-ft logs, bd ft			
	1	2	3	4
10	39	63	80	
12	59	98	127	146
14	83	141	186	216
16	112	190	256	305
18	144	248	336	402
20	181	314	427	512
22	221	387	528	638
24	266	469	644	773
26	315	558	767	931
28	367	654	904	1,096
30	424	758	1,050	1,272
32	485	870	1,213	1,480
34	550	989	1,383	1,691
36	620	1,121	1,571	1,922
38	693	1,256	1,772	2,167
40	770	1,403	1,977	2,432

* From C. Mesavage and J. W. Girard, 1946.

Reference to the International $\frac{1}{4}$-in. rule for 16-ft logs indicates a scale volume of 181 bd ft for the 16-in. butt log. For the second log, the scaling diameter is 16.0 minus 1.7 or 14.3 in., and the log scale is 142 bd ft. For the third log, the scaling diameter is 14.3 minus 1.9 or 12.4 in., and the log scale is 104 bd ft. By totaling the scale values for the three logs $(181 + 142 + 104)$, the standing tree volume of 427 bd ft is derived. This simple construction technique is illustrated in Fig. 6-2, and the calculated tree volume may be verified by reference to Table 6-1.

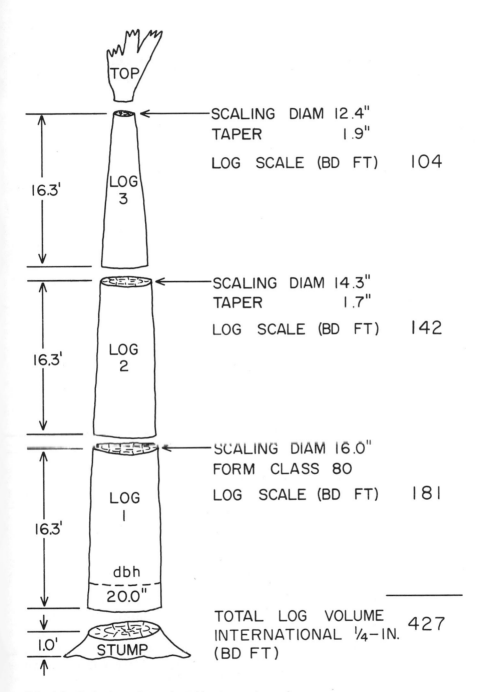

SCALING DIAM 12.4"
TAPER   1.9"

LOG SCALE (BD FT)   104

SCALING DIAM 14.3"
TAPER   1.7"

LOG SCALE (BD FT)   142

SCALING DIAM 16.0"
FORM CLASS 80

LOG SCALE (BD FT)   181

TOTAL LOG VOLUME
INTERNATIONAL ¼-IN.   427
(BD FT)

FIG. 6-2 Derivation of merchantable tree volume for
Mesavage-Girard form-class tables.

As pointed out in Chap. 5, the rates of upper-log taper used for these form-class tables were derived solely from *ocular* estimates. Even though the tables have been widely accepted in the United States, sizable errors in volume may result when the upper-log taper of a particular species differs appreciably from those listed in Table 5-1.

6-8 Selecting a standard volume table. For most timber inventories and forest management plans, the forester has a wide selection of standard volume tables available for possible use. The choice of a reliable table requires careful scrutiny and an objective evaluation. To determine whether a particular table is suitable for a given inventory project, these and other questions might be appropriately asked:

1 For what species, locality, and site classes was the table developed?
2 How many sample trees formed the basis for table construction?
3 Who is the author or publisher of the table?
4 What type of height and form measurements are required?
5 Are merchantability limits and units of volume suitable for the project at hand?
6 How were tree volumes originally obtained in deriving the table?
7 What method of table construction was used?
8 What evidence of table accuracy and reliability is available?

In consideration of item 8, standard volume tables are ordinarily accompanied by some statement of accuracy. If the table was constructed by multiple regression analysis, some evaluation may be given of the statistical error attributed to the sample used in compiling the table (Bryan and McClure, 1962). For tables constructed by graphical methods, the *aggregate difference* is often used as a measure of accuracy. This value is computed as the difference between the sum of original sample tree volumes and volumes of the same trees as read from the table. The aggregate difference, expressed as a per cent of original volume, should not generally exceed ±2 to 5 per cent. In compiling composite volume tables for the Lake states, Gevorkiantz and Olson (1955) have stated that "it is doubtful whether an accuracy better than ±2 per cent of gross volume will ever be required from a volume table or should even be anticipated with complete assurance. . . ."

6-9 Constructing standard volume tables. Although a number of mathematical and graphical methods have been used for constructing standard volume tables in the past, the preferred approach today is by multiple regression analysis. Independent variables such as dbh, BA, stem length, form, site, and species are analyzed to determine their relative value in predicting the dependent variable of tree volume. Regression equations involving several independent variables and hundreds of sample observations can be quickly and efficiently solved by use of electronic computers. Manual solution of such problems has become a rarity, particularly when three or more independent variables are being evaluated.

Another recent trend in the construction of standard volume tables has been the concept of complete tree utilization (Young, 1964). Instead of separate tables being developed for sawlog and cordwood portions of the tree, cubic volume or weight equations are computed for the entire stem (sometimes including stump, roots, and limbs). Subsequently, volumes for selected merchantable stem sections can be converted to desired units such as board feet or cords. In using such tables, the timber cruiser may merely record total height for each standing tree; nevertheless, upper-stem diameter limits are inherently implied for each part of the tree having a different standard of merchantability. As the workaday forester is rarely assigned the task of compiling standard volume tables, detailed procedures are not given here. Techniques of multiple regression analysis are treated extensively in standard statistical references.

LOCAL VOLUME TABLES

6-10 Advantages and limitations. Volume tables based on the single variable of dbh may be constructed from existing standard volume tables or from the scaled measure of felled trees. Such tables are particularly useful for quick timber inventories, because height and form estimates are not required and trees can be tallied by species and dbh only. Elimination of the subjective classifications of height and form also tends to assure greater uniformity in volume estimates, particularly when two or more field parties are cruising within the same project area.

Construction of volume tables based on dbh alone presumes that a definitive height-diameter relationship exists for the species under consideration, i.e., that trees of a given diameter class tend to be of similar height and form. If this is true, all trees in a given dbh class can be logically assigned the same average volume. Height-diameter or volume-diameter relationships can often be established for hardwood or coniferous species that grow under uniform site conditions. When soils and topography are notably varied, it is usually necessary to construct local tables for each broad site class encountered.

Volume tables based on dbh alone are sometimes compiled for inventories of relatively small areas, but this is not an essential condition; in some instances, "local" tables may be as widely applicable as standard volume tables. Thousands of tree samples may be represented by some local tables. The exact number of sample measurements required depends upon characteristics of the tree species involved, variability of soil-site conditions, and the desired geographic area of application. From 30 to

100 samples are usually considered a minimum number for small tracts, depending on the range of diameter classes to be included in the final table.

6-11 Constructing a local table from measurements of felled trees. To obtain tree volumes essential for this procedure, measurements may be obtained from felled trees on logging operations or by "scaling" standing trees with a reliable upper-stem dendrometer (Chap. 5, Sec. 5-5). Sample trees should be selected in an unbiased manner and a sufficient number of measurements made to span the desired range of dbh classes for each species involved.

For each sample tree, measurements should be obtained of (1) dbh to the nearest 0.1 in., (2) tree volume in desired units, and (3) total tree height. The last item, though not actually needed for constructing the table, serves as a useful indication of the sites or geographic areas to which the table may be applied. To illustrate the procedure of table construction, the following data were collected for 32 felled red pines:

Dbh class, in.	No. of sample trees	Average dbh, in.	Average volume Scribner rule, bd ft	Average total height, ft
10	6	9.7	30	40
11	4	11.4	45	47
12	3	12.1	70	55
13	6	13.3	90	58
14	1	14.0	125	60
15	3	14.9	145	62
16	5	16.2	200	70
17	2	17.0	230	70
18	2	18.3	260	72
	32		1,195	

On standard cross-section paper, average tree volume in board feet was plotted over average dbh in inches (Fig. 6-3). Each point was weighted by the number of trees represented, and a balanced curve was drawn according to the method outlined in Sec. 6-2. Tree volumes were then read from the curve for each 1-in.-dbh class and incorporated into a local volume table (Table 6-2). Average total heights of sample trees are also shown in the table for information of the user. As a check on the fit of the volume curve to the plotted points, the aggregate difference was computed by subtracting curved volumes from average field volumes. The total difference of 55 bd ft, expressed as a per cent of

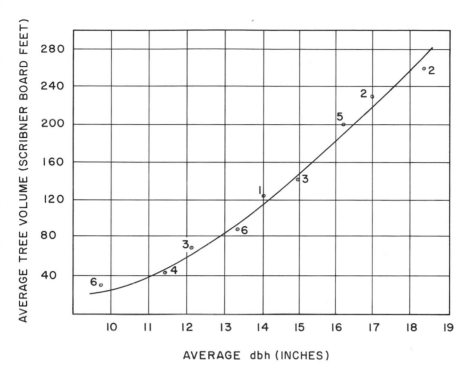

FIG. 6-3   Tree volume—dbh relationship for 32 red pines
in Chippewa County, Michigan.

TABLE 6-2 Local Volume Table for Red Pines in Chippewa County,
Michigan, 1960*

Dbh class, in.	Tree volume, bd ft	Average total height, ft
10	28	40
11	40	47
12	60	55
13	84	58
14	116	60
15	150	62
16	185	70
17	220	70
18	257	72

* Based on measurements of 32 felled trees. Tree volumes were
derived from the Scribner log rule. Aggregate difference: −4.6
per cent.

original field volumes, resulted in an aggregate difference of minus **4.6** per cent.

6-12   Limitations of felled-tree data.   The foregoing method of constructing a local volume table works reasonably well when felled trees of representative sizes are available for measurement. However, some biometricians have expressed the opinion that felled trees rarely make up a typical sample of standing trees, because they represent a different population or have distinctive characteristics that influenced their volume and thus caused them to be cut. If this theory is correct and felled trees are nonrepresentative samples, local volume tables derived from such data would be biased and unreliable. As an alternative, tree volumes might be obtained from random samples of standing trees, or tables might be constructed from height-diameter relationships as described in the next section.

6-13   Constructing a local table from a standard volume table.   This method of deriving a local volume table is dependent on a well-established height-diameter relationship and the existence of a reliable standard table from which volumes may be interpolated. Field measurements of 50 to 100 merchantable or total heights, spanning the desired range of tree dbh classes, should be obtained from the selected project area. If the standard volume table to be used is based on merchantable heights, field measurements must be carefully taken to identical top diameters or merchantability limits. An example of tree data for **62** loblolly pine follows:

Dbh class, in.	Average merchantable height, ft	No. of sample trees
8	20	3
10	28	2
12	38	6
14	43	4
16	48	9
18	50	6
20	53	3
22	55	7
24	60	4
26	55	5
28	58	10
30	63	3
		62

From the foregoing tabulation, average merchantable heights were plotted over corresponding dbh classes; a balanced curve was then graphically fitted to the plotted points (Fig. 6-4). Next, average heights were read from the curve for each 1-in.-dbh class. These two variables were used to interpolate board-foot volumes from the Mesavage-Girard standard volume tables (form class 78, International ¼-in. log rule). The completed local volume (Table 6-3) includes the average heights read

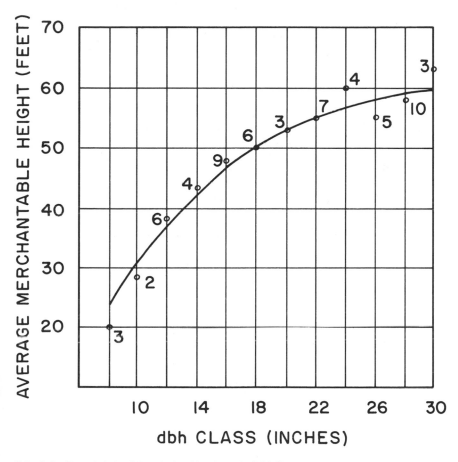

FIG. 6-4   Tree height–dbh relationship for 62 loblolly
pines in Oconee County, Georgia.

from the curve as an indication of the site conditions to which the table may be safely applied.

CUMULATIVE TALLY SHEETS

6-14   Tallies based on local volume tables.   One of the more common methods of handling field records of standing trees has been illustrated by the dot-dash tally scheme in Fig. 5-6. When greater efficiency is desired in obtaining quick estimates of standing tree volumes, cumulative tally sheets can be easily derived from local or standard volume tables. A local volume table can be incorporated directly into the field tally without modification by designating separate columns for (1) dbh class, (2) tree volume, (3) tree tally, and (4) tree volume times tree tally. The summation of column 4 provides an immediate total of all volume tallied for a given species.

A special advantage of cumulative tallying is that the proper volume table must be selected *in advance* of field data collection. This requirement minimizes the chances of selecting an unsuitable volume table when office computations are performed by personnel other than those who collect the field measurements.

6-15 Tallies based on standard volume tables. An example of a cumulative tally sheet derived from the Mesavage-Girard form-class tables is illustrated by Table 6-4. This particular form is designed for tallying

TABLE 6-3 Local Volume Table for Loblolly Pines in Oconee County, Georgia, 1965*

Dbh class, in.	Tree volume, bd ft	Average merchantable height from curve, ft
10	58	31
11	78	34
12	102	38
13	130	40
14	158	42
15	198	45
16	237	47
17	278	48
18	322	50
19	375	52
20	425	53
21	484	54
22	546	55
23	608	56
24	664	57
25	749	58
26	820	58
27	890	58
28	971	59
29	1,052	59
30	1,146	60

* Height-diameter relationship based on measurements of 62 trees. Tree volumes were derived from the International $\frac{1}{4}$-in. log rule, form class 78.

sawtimber-sized trees by 2-in.-dbh classes and 8-ft log intervals. Board-foot volumes are based on form classes 78 to 80, International $\frac{1}{4}$-in. log rule. Values actually printed in this cumulative tally sheet are in hundreds of board feet per acre and are based on a presumed use of $\frac{1}{5}$-acre sample plots. The method of coding volumes may be illustrated

TABLE 6-4 Cumulative Volume Tally Sheet for $\frac{1}{5}$-acre Sample Plots

Dbh, in.	Hundreds of board feet per acre by 16-ft logs														
	1			$1\frac{1}{2}$			2			$2\frac{1}{2}$			3		
12	3	6	9	4	8	12	5	10	15	6	12	17			
	11	14	17	16	20	24	20	25	30	23	29	34			
14	4	8	12	6	11	16	7	14	21	8	16	24	9	18	27
	16	20	24	22	28	33	28	35	42	33	41	49	36	45	54
16	5	10	16	7	15	22	9	18	27	11	21	32	12	25	37
	21	26	32	29	37	44	36	45	54	43	53	64	49	62	74
18	7	14	20	9	19	28	12	24	35	14	28	42	16	32	48
	27	34	40	38	47	56	47	59	70	56	70	83	64	80	96
20	8	17	26	12	24	35	15	30	44	18	35	52	20	40	60
	34	42	51	47	59	71	59	74	88	70	88	105	80	100	121
22	10	21	31	14	29	44	18	36	54	22	43	64	25	49	74
	42	52	63	58	72	87	72	90	109	86	108	129	99	124	148
24	13	25	38	17	35	52	22	43	65	26	51	77	30	59	89
	50	63	76	69	86	104	86	108	129	102	128	154	119	148	178
26	15	30	45	20	41	61	25	51	76	30	60	91	35	70	105
	60	75	90	82	102	123	102	127	152	121	151	181	140	174	209
28	17	35	52	24	48	72	30	60	90	35	70	106	41	81	122
	70	87	104	96	120	143	119	149	179	141	176	212	162	203	244

SOURCE: U.S. Forest Service. Volumes per acre are based on the International $\frac{1}{4}$-in. log rule.

by reference to the block designed for 12-in.-dbh trees having a height of one 16-ft log. The number 3 appearing in the first cell of this block implies a volume of 300 bd ft per acre. It was derived by multiplying the volume of one 12-in.-dbh one-log tree (e.g., 56 bd ft) by 5 (assuming a ⅕-acre plot tally) and rounding off the result to the nearest 100 bd ft. Thus $5 \times 56 = 280$ or 300 bd ft. The value of 300 is then coded back to 3 for placement in the table.

In using this type of table, each tree tally is recorded by drawing a diagonal line through consecutive cells of the table. Referring again to the 12-in.-dbh one-log block, a tally of four trees of this size would result in marking through the cells designated as 3, 6, 9, and 11. The *last value* marked is the cumulative volume; therefore, if the tally was made on a single ⅕-acre sample plot, the value of 11 would denote 1,100 bd ft per acre in 12-in.-dbh one-log trees. If several plot tallies are recorded on the same sheet, volume summaries must be divided by the number of ⅕-acre plots represented.

When a large tree tally causes all cells within a block to be crossed out, the cells can be double marked by using opposite diagonals, horizontal lines, vertical lines, circles, and so on. To avoid difficulties in separating tree species, it is desirable to use a different cumulative sheet for each species tallied. The principal advantages of this type of cumulative tally are that volumes can be quickly summarized at the end of each working day, and hours of tedious office tabulations may be avoided.

TREE-WEIGHT TABLES

6-16   Field tallies by weight.   The continued emphasis on weight scaling as a basis of payment for pulpwood and sawlogs will eventually result in field tallies based on tree weights rather than on various units of volume. It is only logical that standing trees should be measured in terms of the same units as those on which log purchases and sales are transacted.

An example of a tree-weight table for standing timber is shown by Table 6-5. For each dbh and total height class, merchantable tree weights of bark and wood are given in pounds. Actually, any ordinary volume table can be converted to a weight basis if weight/volume equivalents can be reliably established. For example, if it has been determined that a standard stacked cord of pine pulpwood weighs 5,500 lb, a standing tree having a merchantable volume (including bark) of 0.1 cd would be assigned a weight of 550 lb. The same technique can be used to convert board-foot volume tables, provided acceptable weight equivalents are derived. As previously outlined, Table 4-4 provides sawlog weight approximations for a number of commercial timber species.

TABLE 6-5 Tree-weight Table for Planted Slash Pines*

Dbh, in.	Total tree height, ft											
	20	25	30	35	40	45	50	55	60	65	70	75
	Weight, lb											
5		32	45	64	82	100	119	137	155			
6	42	67	94	120	146	173	199	226	252	279		
7		115	151	187	223	259	295	331	367	403	439	
8			217	264	311	358	405	452	499	546	593	640
9				351	411	470	530	589	649	708	768	827
10					522	596	669	743	816	890	963	1,037
11					646	734	824	913	1,001	1,090	1,179	1,268
12					781	887	992	1,098	1,204	1,310	1,416	1,521

* From McGee, 1959. Merchantable weights shown include bark and wood to a 4-in. top diameter.

PROBLEMS

6-1 Using Huber's formula, compute cubic volumes of all 10-ft logs from 8 to 24 in. in diameter, by 1-in. classes. (Assume diameters are inside bark at middle of logs.) On standard cross-section paper, plot (a) log volumes over mid-diameters of logs and (b) square roots of log volumes over mid-diameters of logs. Fit a smooth curve to each set of plotted points, and explain reasons for curve differences.

6-2 Assume that the following values were derived from the scaled measure of 31 ponderosa pines in northern Arizona. Construct a local volume table from this data according to the procedure outlined in Sec. 6-11.

Dbh class, in.	No. of sample trees	Average dbh, in.	Average volume, cu ft
12	1	12.2	36.1
13	3	12.7	49.0
14	1	14.2	60.6
15	3	15.4	67.2
16	2	15.8	73.1
17	6	17.0	86.7
18	4	18.1	98.7
19	2	19.2	121.0
20	1	20.0	114.5
21	5	21.4	142.2
22	3	21.8	165.7

6-3 From the following measurements of 37 white pines in western North Carolina, construct a local volume table based on a height-diameter relationship as described in Sec. 6-13. Use Mesavage-Girard tables (form class 79) for interpolation of volumes.

Dbh class, in.	Average merchantable height, ft	No. of sample trees
6	12	8
8	17	7
10	23	4
12	35	5
14	44	3
16	49	4
18	53	1
20	56	4
22	61	1
		37

6-4 Construct a cumulative tally sheet from an appropriate standard tree volume table. Diagram the sheet on cross-section paper, and provide for at least eight dbh classes and four to eight height classes. Allow space for the tally of 9 to 12 trees in each dbh-height block. The table may be constructed for individual tree tallies *or* designed for a specific plot size as illustrated by Table 6-4.

6-5 Convert an existing standard volume table into a tree-weight table. Use local weight/volume equivalents, if available. Otherwise, obtain values from either Table 3-1 or Table 4-4.

REFERENCES

Anderson, H. E.
1955. Preliminary western redcedar cubic form class volume tables for Southeast Alaska. *U.S. Forest Serv., Alaska Forest Res. Center Tech. Note* 28. 12 pp.

———
1956. Cubic foot volume tables for spruce and hemlock poletimber. *U.S. Forest Serv., Alaska Forest Res. Center Tech. Note* 29. 1 p.

Avery, T. Eugene, and Herrick, A. M.
1963. Field projects and classroom exercises in basic forest measurements. University of Georgia Press, Athens. 151 pp., illus.

Bickford, C. Allen
1951. Form-class volume tables for estimating board-foot content of northern conifers. *U.S. Forest Serv., Northeast. Forest Expt. Sta. Paper* 38. 33 pp., illus.

Bryan, M. B., and McClure, Joe P.
1962. Board-foot and cubic-foot volume computing equations for southeastern tree species. *U.S. Forest Serv., Southeast. Forest Expt. Sta. Paper* 145. 10 pp., illus.

Gevorkiantz, S. R., and Olson, L. P.

1955. Composite volume tables for timber and their application in the Lake States.. *U.S. Dept. Agr., Tech. Bull.* 1104. 51 pp.

Hallin, William

1941. Volume and taper tables for old growth coastal redwood. U.S. Forest Service, California Forest Experiment Station. 79 pp.

Honer, T. G.

1964. The use of height and squared diameter ratios for the estimation of merchantable cubic foot volume. *Forestry Chron.* **40**(3):324–331.

Johnson, Floyd A.

1955. Volume tables for Pacific Northwest trees. *U.S. Dept. Agr., Forest Serv. Handbook* 92. 122 pp.

McGee, C. E.

1959. Weight of merchantable wood with bark from planted slash pine in the Carolina Sandhills. *U.S. Forest Serv., Southeast. Forest Expt. Sta. Note* 128. 2 pp.

Mesavage, C.

1947. Tables for estimating cubic-foot volume of timber. *U.S. Forest Serv., Southern Forest Expt. Sta. Occasional Paper* 111. 70 pp.

———— **and Girard, J. W.**

1956. Tables for estimating board-foot content of timber. U.S. Forest Service, Washington, D.C. 94 pp.

Romancier, Robert M.

1961. Weight and volume of plantation-grown loblolly pine. *U.S. Forest Serv., Southeast. Forest Expt. Sta. Note* 161. 2 pp.

Schnur, G. Luther, and Lane, Richard D.

1950. Aids for computing tree volumes in Illinois. *U.S. Forest Serv., Central States Forest Expt. Sta. Tech. Paper* 115. 26 pp., illus.

Taylor, R. F.

1950. Cubic form class volume tables for Southeast Alaska. *U.S. Forest Serv., Alaska Forest Res. Center Tech. Note* 6. 12 pp.

Young, H. E.

1964. The complete tree concept—a challenge and an opportunity. *Proc. Soc. Am. Foresters,* Denver, Colo., pp. 231–233.

————, **Strand, Lars, and Altenberger, R.**

1964. Preliminary fresh and dry weight tables for seven tree species in Maine. *Maine Agr. Expt. Sta. Tech. Bull.* 12. 76 pp., illus.

CHAPTER ˙ 7

SPECIALTY WOOD PRODUCTS

7-1   Specialty products defined.   As arbitrarily applied in this chapter, specialty wood products encompass an agglomeration of logs, bolts, roundwood, timbers, and stumps that are distinctive because of their shapes, sizes, quality, measurement standards, or intended use. Aside from veneer logs, the items included here may be additionally classified as products purchased in individual units (i.e., piece products such as poles or railroad ties) or products purchased in bulk form (e.g., mine timbers and fuel wood).

VENEER LOGS

7-2   Size and quality standards.   Illogical as it may appear, veneer logs are ordinarily measured and purchased in terms of board-feet log scale. To compensate for the fact that size and quality standards are more stringent than for most sawlogs, a premium price is paid for logs of veneer quality. This price may sometimes amount to two or three times the price paid for logs that are sawed into yard lumber. Although grading specifications for veneer logs vary widely, quality requirements are based largely on species, log diameter, and freedom from defects such as crook, knots, bird peck, worm holes, ring shake, stains, and center rot.

For most hardwood species, veneer logs must have a minimum scaling diameter of 14 in.; preferred lengths range from 6 to 16 ft, plus trim

FIG. 7-1   Yellowpoplar and red gum logs purchased by a Georgia veneer plant. *U.S. Forest Service photograph.*

allowance. Acceptable logs are commonly graded as no. 1 or no. 2, depending on size and quality; logs grading poorer than no. 2 may be culled and rejected. Sellers can expect top prices for veneer logs only when wood is freshly cut and free from sap stains or discolorations that result from prolonged exposure (Fig. 7-1).

7-3   Computing yields from veneer logs.   Instead of scaling veneer logs in terms of board feet, it would be more realistic to compute their contents in cubic feet or calculate expected yield in terms of veneer sheets of a given thickness. For rotary-cut veneers obtained from sound logs, output can be closely estimated from the difference in BA between two cylinders—one based on the d.i.b. of the veneer bolt at the small end and the other based on a presumed core diameter. Thus the maximum surface area of rotary-cut veneer to be expected from a sound wood cylinder may be computed by

$$\text{Veneer yield in square feet} = \frac{B - b}{T} W$$

where B = BA of log at small end, sq ft
b = BA of residual core, sq ft
T = veneer thickness, thousandths of ft
W = sheet width (log length), ft

For excessively tapered logs, actual yields may be greater than that indicated, because some veneer is obtained from material outside the presumed right cylinder. On the other hand, yields may be less for logs having interior defects. Nevertheless, for sound logs the formula will provide predictions that are much more reliable and realistic than scale methods based on board feet.

PRODUCTS PURCHASED IN INDIVIDUAL UNITS

7-4 Poles and piling. These are roundwood products selected primarily for strength, durability (or capability for preservative treatment), and resistance to exposure and mechanical stresses. Along with several other piece products, they are grouped according to distinct classes and price grades on the basis of species, dimensions, straightness, and freedom from defects.

The principal species utilized for poles are southern pines, western redcedar, western hemlock, northern white cedar, lodgepole pine, and Douglas fir. As a rule, poles are marketed under specifications compiled by the American Standards Association (Williston, 1957). Poles are grouped into one of 10 size classes, depending on length, minimum top circumference, and minimum circumference 6 ft from the butt end. Standard dimensions for three commonly used species are given in Table 7-1.

Wood piling may be of any species that will withstand driving impact and support the loads imposed. Specifications are based on intended use, straightness, uniformity of taper, soundness, and dimensions (length, minimum top diameter, and both minimum and maximum diameters at 3 ft from the butt end). Most piling, especially if used in salt water, is pressure-treated with creosote as protection against shipworms.

TABLE 7-1 Dimensions of Douglas Fir, Western Hemlock, and Southern Pine Poles

Class:		1	2	3	4	5	6	7	8	9	10
Minimum circumference at top, in.:		27	25	23	21	19	17	15	18	15	12
Length of pole, ft	Ground line distance from butt, ft*	Minimum circumference at 6 ft from butt, in.									
16	3½										No butt requirement
18	3½			26.5	24.5	21.5	19.5	18.0			
20	4	31.5	29.5	27.5	25.5	22.5	21.0	19.0		No butt requirement	
22	4	33.0	31.0	29.0	26.5	23.5	22.0	20.0			
25	5	34.5	32.5	30.0	28.0	24.5	23.0	21.0			
30	5½	37.5	35.0	32.5	30.0	26.0	24.0	22.0	No butt requirement		
35	6	40.0	37.5	35.0	32.0	28.0	26.0	24.0			
40	6	42.0	39.5	37.0	34.0	30.0	27.5	25.5			
45	6½	44.0	41.5	38.5	36.0	31.5	29.0	27.0			
50	7	46.0	43.0	40.0	37.5	33.0	30.5	28.5			
55	7½	47.5	44.5	41.5	39.0	34.5	32.0	29.5			
60	8	49.5	46.0	43.0	40.0	36.0	33.5				
65	8½	51.0	47.5	44.5	41.5	37.0	34.5				
70	9	52.5	49.0	46.0	42.5	38.5					
75	9½	54.0	50.5	47.0	44.0	39.5					
80	10	55.0	51.5	48.5	45.0						
85	10½	56.5	53.0	49.5							
90	11	57.5	54.0	50.5							
95	11	58.5	55.0	51.5							
100	11	60.0	56.0	52.5							

* The figures in this column are intended solely for use whenever a definition of groundline is necessary in order to apply specification requirements relating to scars, straightness, etc.

Piling is purchased at a stated price per linear foot for specified dimensions, and value accrues rapidly with increasing length and desired taper characteristics. Standard specifications for round timber piling are available from the American Society for Testing Materials (Williston, 1957). In general, poles and piling must be peeled at the time of cutting. Therefore, the woodland owner anticipating the sale of such roundwood should carefully study the purchaser's requirements before trees are severed from the stump.

7-5 Fence posts. Posts are round, split, or sawed piece products ranging from about 3 to 8 in. in diameter. Lengths are usually 7 to 8 ft, though some posts are as long as 20 ft. If posts are split and untreated, they are preferably made from durable species such as various cedars, redwood, white oak, or catalpa. Those that are peeled, seasoned, and treated with preservatives are commonly made from red oak, southern pines, western pines, and Douglas fir (Fig. 7-2).

FIG. 7-2 Peeled fence posts banded together for preservative treatment. *U.S. Forest Service photograph.*

Posts may be cut from trees too small for efficient utilization as pulpwood or from the top sections of pulpwood and sawlog trees. If preservative treatment is required, posts are peeled either when cut or at concentration yards. The worth of posts as stumpage (standing trees) may be as little as 3 to 10 cents each; following seasoning and preservative treatment, they may retail for 40 cents to $1 each. To foresters who are somewhat less than cost conscious in their work routine, this price differential should provide a vivid lesson in "value added by processing and manufacture."

7-6 Railroad ties. The principal species used for railroad crossties are red and white oaks, Douglas fir, gums, and southern pines (Panshin,

FIG. 7-3 Peeled pine poles and railroad ties awaiting preservative treatment. *U.S. Forest Service photograph.*

Harrar, et al., 1950). Today, most ties utilized by leading railroads are sawed rather than hand-hewed and pressure-treated with preservatives to prolong service life (Fig. 7-3). Red oak is a preferred species, because it is dense, strong, easily treated, and possesses superior resistance to mechanical wear. There are seven standard classes of crossties, based on width and thickness, with the largest size (class 6) bringing the highest market price (Table 7-2). Ties for standard gauge railroads are 8, 8½, or 9 ft long.

TABLE 7-2 Standard Sizes for Railroad Crossties

| Tie class or size | Sawed or hewn top, bottom, and sides | |
	Thickness, in.	Width on top, in.
0	5*	5*
1	6	6
2	6	7
3	6	8
4	7	8
5	7	9
6	7	10

* Not acceptable for standard-gauge ties. Crossties are normally 8, 8½, or 9 ft long.

Before felling trees intended for conversion into railroad ties, the forester should check with local buyers or railroad agents about acceptable timber species and quantities that can be marketed. Trees of hardwood species are preferably cut in fall or winter when seasoning progresses slowly and there is less chance for end-checking of logs, sap stains, and incipient decay. Ties must be straight grained, with ends cut square and all bark removed. Defects such as bark seams, decay, splits, shakes, holes, and unsound knots are not permitted in high-grade ties.

Expected yields of crossties from standing trees or logs can be computed by diagraming various tie dimensions within circles representing cross-sectional areas of logs. The technique is analogous to that of determining the size of inscribed square timbers (Sec. 3-14) or constructing a diagram log rule (Sec. 4-5). Tabulations of predicted yields by tie class and log size are referred to as *tie log rules*. Such rules are of considerable aid in evaluating alternative product uses for standing timber.

PRODUCTS PURCHASED IN BULK FORM

7-7 Mine timbers. More than three-fourths of the mine timbers used in the United States and Canada are cut from assorted hardwoods such as beech, maple, hickory, ash, poplar, gum, and oak. Depending on local custom and requirements, mine timbers may be round, split, hand-hewed, or sawed. Because dimensions vary from place to place, the following specifications are merely indicative of size ranges encountered.

Mine props are round timbers used as supports for roofs and sides of tunnels; they range from 4 to 14 in. in diameter and 3 to 12 ft long. *Lagging* is round timber about 3 in. in diameter and 7 ft long; it is used behind props and caps to form the sides and roofs of tunnels. *Caps* are hewed or sawed timbers of various sizes that are placed across the tops of paired props as a support for roof lagging. *Sills* are hewed or sawed foundations for props, ranging from 8 to 12 in. across the widest face and of varied lengths. *Mine ties* are ordinary track ties 4 to 5 in. wide on the face and 3 to 5 ft long.

Mine timbers are commonly purchased on a green weight basis, though certain sawed items (e.g., mine ties) may be handled as piece products or measured in terms of board feet. Round and untreated mine props may be sold without removal of bark. Mine timbers are used primarily in areas where coal, iron ore, copper, lead, zinc, and silver are extracted. Thus the principal markets are found in regions producing large quantities of these minerals.

7-8 Stumps for the wood naval-stores industry. In Southeastern United States, residual stumps of old-growth longleaf and slash pines are utilized for the extraction of turpentine, rosin, and various pine oils. Only heartwood (sometimes referred to as *lightwood*) is valuable; hence wood producers prefer older stumps from which all sapwood has been removed by weathering and decay. Stumps and taproots are "pushed" out of the ground with large bulldozers equipped with coarsely toothed blades. Then they are loaded onto trucks or railroad cars for transport to one of more than a dozen steam-and-solvent extraction plants in Alabama, Florida, Georgia, Louisiana, or Mississippi (Fig. 7-4).

Pine stumpwood is purchased by the ton, and where stumps are readily accessible, profitable removal operations may be conducted for yields as low as 1 ton (five to eight average stumps) per acre. In general, stump lands are classed as "operable" if the area will support harvesting equipment during average seasons, can be worked without undue damage to live trees, and the stumpwood tract size is 25 acres or larger.

Inventories or cruises of pine stumps are accomplished by use of sample strips or plots similar to those designed for tallies of live timber (Chap. 9). Tracts are designated as operable, timber-locked, inaccessible, or nonproductive, and stumps are tallied by three to five ground-line diameter categories. Foresters concerned with inventories or leases of stumpwood may obtain prices and additional specifications from wood naval-stores extraction plants.

7-9 Bolts and billets. Bolts are short sections of logs, usually less than 8 ft long (e.g., veneer bolts). When bolts are split or sawed lengthwise, they are called billets. Collectively, bolts and billets are used for such products as cooperage, excelsior, handles, vehicle parts, shingles, baseball bats, pencils, and matches. A variety of hardwood and coniferous species are utilized. For example, white oak is used for tight cooperage, hickory for handles, western redcedar for shingles, ash for baseball bats, and white pine for matches.

In general, bolts and billets are shorter than 8 ft in length, less than 12 in. in diameter, and must be made up of high-quality materials.

FIG. 7-4   Loading pine stumps for transport to a naval-stores extraction plant. *Courtesy of Hercules Powder Company.*

However, exact size and grade requirements are so diversified that accurate specifications must be obtained locally. Bolts under 12 in. in diameter are usually measured and sold in terms of stacked cords; those 12 in. and larger may be scaled in board feet. Billets may be sold by piece counts, short cords, or standard cords.

7-10 Fuel wood. Firewood, primarily a farm woodlot product, is usually measured and sold in terms of stacked "short cords." As with pulpwood, the amount of solid wood contained depends on stick size, straightness, and care in stacking. Common stick lengths are 12, 18, and 24 in.; accordingly, a 4×8-ft face cord occupies approximately 32, 48, or 64 cu ft of space. Fuel wood may be sold round or in split sections, and bark is not ordinarily removed.

Firewood is usually cut and utilized locally, for its sale value will not support high transportation costs. As a result, a wide variety of species are utilized, with preference given to dense hardwoods such as oak, hickory, beech, birch, maple, ash, and elm. The heavier species weigh about 2 tons per cd and in a dry condition will provide about as much heat as a short ton of coal or 200 gal of domestic fuel oil (USDA, 1958). Retail prices for firewood are largely dependent on labor and transportation costs in a given locality; the intrinsic value of the wood itself is minimal by comparison.

SALES OF STANDING TIMBER

7-11   Stumpage value.   The sale value of standing timber is known as its stumpage value. For a given species, size (volume), and quality of timber, stumpage prices are highest when trees are accessible (easily logged) and located near concentration yards or primary markets. If a forest owner participates in harvesting, his income from the enterprise is increased in accordance with the value added by cutting, loading, and hauling to wood dealers or directly to mills. To determine *which* trees to sell and when to sell them, foresters must be intimately acquainted with local markets and prevailing prices, and they should learn to anticipate seasonal or periodic fluctuations in demands for various types of stumpage. Only by becoming thoroughly familiar with specifications for various wood products can the forest manager expect to realize consistently high returns from timber sales.

7-12   Methods of selling standing timber.   For handling sales of stumpage, trees to be cut (or those to be left standing) should be marked, or a cruise should be made by species and product designations. High-value trees, such as those to be utilized for veneer logs or poles, should be logged first. This cutting may be followed by removal of sawlogs, specialty bolts and billets, and tie logs. Finally, residual tops and smaller trees may then be converted into pulpwood, round mine timbers, fence posts, or fuel wood. Relative values of these products are dictated by local markets, and failure to observe rational priorities in cutting operations may severely penalize the seller of standing timber.

If the forest owner has made a reliable inventory or if timber is to be removed by clearcutting, sales may be made on a lump-sum basis. As with all business transactions, this is a reasonable approach provided both buyer and seller are well informed as to market values and volume of wood involved. In other instances, sale prices may be based on marked trees, on minimum diameter or merchantability limits, or on log scale as determined after trees are cut and skidded to a landing.

7-13   Timber-sale contracts. For most sales of standing timber, even for small tracts of low-value species, it is desirable to draw up a simple written agreement to protect both buyer and seller and to avoid unnecessary misunderstandings in the transaction. A timber sale contract contains sections on (1) location and description of timber, (2) prices and terms of payment, (3) utilization standards and related conditions of timber removal, and (4) procedures for settling disputes. The sample contract that follows, intended primarily for farmers and small woodlot owners, is reproduced from a bulletin of the USDA.

SAMPLE TIMBER-SALE AGREEMENT

_____, of _____, _____,
      (I or we) (Name of Purchaser)   (Post Office)   (State)
hereinafter called the purchaser, agree to purchase from _____ of
                                                                                              (Seller's Name)
_____, _____, hereinafter called the seller, the designated
      (Post Office)   (State)
trees from the area described below.

   I. DESCRIPTION OF SALE AREA:
          (Describe by legal subdivisions, if surveyed)

  II. TREES DESIGNATED FOR CUTTING: (Cross out A or B—use only one clause)

  A. All _____ trees marked by the seller, or his agent, with paint spots below
                    (species)
          stump height; also dead trees of the same species which are merchantable for

          _____.
          (Kind of forest products)

  B. All _____ trees merchantable for _____ which
                  (species)   (Kind of forest products)
          measure _____ inches or more outside the bark at a point not less than
          6 inches above the ground, also other _____ trees marked with paint spots
                                                                        (species)
          below stump height by the seller or his agent.

 III. CONDITIONS OF SALE:

  A. The purchaser agrees to the following:
          1. To pay the seller the sum of $_____ for the above-described trees and
               to make payments in advance of cutting in amounts of at least $_____
               each.
          2. To waive all claim to the above-described trees unless they are cut and
               removed on or before _____.
                                                  (Date)
          3. To do all in his power to prevent and suppress forest fires on or threatening
               the Sale Area.

4. To protect from unnecessary injury young growth and other trees not designated for cutting.

5. To pay the seller for undesignated trees cut or injured through carelessness at the rate of \$_____ each for trees measuring 10 to _____ inches in diameter at stump height and \$_____ each for trees _____ inches or over in diameter.

6. To repair damage caused by logging to ditches, fences, bridges, roads, trails or other improvements damaged beyond ordinary wear and tear.

7. Not to assign this agreement in whole or in part without the written consent of the seller.

B. The seller agrees to the following:

1. To guarantee title to the forest products covered by this agreement and to defend it against all claims at his expense.

2. To allow the purchaser to use unmerchantable material from tops of trees cut or from trees of _____ species for necessary logging improvement free of charge, provided such improvements are left in place by the purchaser.

3. To grant the freedom of entry and right-of-way to the purchaser and his employees on and across the area covered by this agreement and also other privileges usually extended to purchasers of stumpage which are not specifically covered, provided they do not conflict with specific provisions of this agreement.

C. In case of dispute over the terms of this agreement we agree to accept the decision of an arbitration board of three selected persons as final. Each of the contracting parties will select one person and the two selected will select a third to form this board.

Signed in duplicate this _____ day of _____ 19___

_____
(Witness)

_____
(Witness)

_____
(Purchaser)

_____
(Seller)

PROBLEMS

7-1 Compile a veneer log rule by use of the formula presented in Sec. 7-3. Assume a bolt length of 4, 6, or 8 ft, and compute veneer yields for logs 14 to 36 in. in diameter, by 2-in. classes. Base your table on any standard veneer thickness from $\frac{1}{28}$ in. to $\frac{1}{8}$ in.

7-2 Determine minimum log diameters that are required to produce crossties of the seven sizes listed in Table 7-2.

7-3 Assume you have 100 standing trees of a species that might theoretically be utilized for veneer, lumber, poles, or crossties in accordance with the following rules. For purposes of this example, further assume that all 100 trees are identical to the sketch in Fig. 6-2, that is, 20 in.; three logs or 48 ft of merchantable length; form class 80. Based on actual or assumed stumpage prices in your locality, compute the value of the standing timber if:

(a) All 100 trees are fully utilized for lumber, with 25 per cent of the yield in select lumber grades and 75 per cent in common lumber grades. Compute tree volumes by the International $\frac{1}{4}$-in. log rule.

(*b*) All butt logs are used for no. 1 veneer bolts (4 or 8 ft long); all second logs are used for no. 2 veneer bolts, and all top logs are used for lumber of common grades.

(*c*) Forty trees are converted into 45-ft poles of a class determined by Table 7-1, and the remaining 60 trees are utilized for lumber as in item *a*.

(*d*) All butt logs are used for no. 1 veneer logs as in item *b*, and all second and third logs are converted into the largest 8-ft crossties feasible (ignore waste from slabbing tie logs).

7-4 Investigate current retail prices for fuel wood in your locality. What is the average price per cubic foot or per standard cord? Estimate the stumpage value of fuel wood per standard stacked cord, and express this as a per cent of market price. Then compare the price paid for a standard stacked cord of pulpwood (fob mill) in your locality with the retail price of the equivalent amount of fuel wood. Can you supply rational reasons for the differences noted?

REFERENCES

Association of American Railroads
1954. Specifications for cross ties. C. & M. Section, Engineering Division, Chicago, Ill. 14 pp., illus.

Ffolliott, Peter F., and Barger, Roland L.
1965. A method of evaluating multiproduct potential in standing timber. *U.S. Forest Serv., Rocky Mt. Forest and Range Expt. Sta. Res. Paper RM*-15. 24 pp., illus.

McKinley, T. W.
1953. Veneer tables: Surface feet tabulations for rotary cut and special veneers. *J. Forestry* **51**:826–827.

Panshin, A. J., Harrar, E. S., Baker, W. J., and Proctor, P. B.
1950. Forest products: Their sources, production, and utilization. McGraw-Hill Book Company, New York. 549 pp., illus.

U.S. Department of Agriculture
1958. Measuring and marketing farm timber. *U.S. Forest Serv., Wash. D.C. Farmers' Bull.* 1210. 33 pp., illus.

Williston, Hamlin L.
1957. Pole grower's guide. *U.S. Forest Serv., Southern Forest Expt. Sta. Occasional Paper* 153. 34 pp., illus.

CHAPTER 8
BASIC STATISTICAL METHODS

8-1 Introduction. To the practicing forester, an understanding of statistical techniques and sampling methods has become as important as a knowledge of dendrology or type mapping. Whether he is attempting to design an efficient timber inventory or merely comprehend a scientific article, a background in statistics is essential. Because forestry students usually have one or more statistics courses prior to work in forest mensuration, this chapter is intended only as a brief review of applied techniques. Emphasis is placed on how to handle routine computations and (to a lesser degree) how to interpret the meaning of certain statistical quantities. Derivations and theory are purposely avoided, because they are best treated in textbooks devoted strictly to these subjects.

The reader is reminded that the procedures discussed in this chapter were not designed specifically for the solution of forestry problems. On the contrary, they are standard statistical methods which have merely been adapted for application to forest-oriented situations.

PROBABILITY AND DECISION MAKING

8-2   Rules for calculating probabilities.   For purposes of discussion, probability may be defined as the expected relative frequency with which an event takes place "in the long run." If an observed event A is expected to occur x times in n trials, the expected probability or relative frequency is

$$P(\text{A}) = \frac{x}{n}$$

For example, if a balanced coin is tossed in an unbiased fashion, one would expect to obtain *heads* about 50 per cent of the time; i.e., the *expected* probability is 0.50. If the same coin is tossed 100 times and heads occur only 41 times, the *observed* probability or relative frequency of heads is $^{41}/_{100}$ or 0.41. Still, the likelihood of getting *heads* on any given toss is 0.50, and "over the long run" (thousands of unbiased tosses) one would expect the observed relative frequency to closely approximate 0.50.

Coin flipping is an example of an *independent* event; i.e., the occurrence of heads or tails on one toss has no predictable effect on the outcomes of subsequent tosses. As the expected probability of obtaining heads on a single toss is $\frac{1}{2}$, the probability of obtaining two heads (or two tails) in a row is $\frac{1}{2} \times \frac{1}{2} = \frac{1}{4}$ or one chance in four. Thus for two *independent* events, the probability that both will occur is the *product* of their individual probabilities.

As another example of events that are apparently independent, assume that the probability of owning a bicycle is 0.17, the probability of having red hair is 0.04, and the probability of being a college student is 0.21. If the assumption of independence is correct, the probability that a randomly selected individual will be a red-headed college student with a bicycle is $0.17 \times 0.04 \times 0.21$ or 0.001428 (roughly 14 chances in 10,000). These events have been referred to as *apparently* independent, because truly independent happenings are difficult to establish, except by statistical design and randomization.

If the occurrence of one event A precludes the occurrence of some other event B and vice versa, A and B are said to be *mutually exclusive*. In a single appearance at bat, a baseball player may walk or hit safely but cannot do both. If the probability of drawing a walk is 0.104 and the probability of a safe hit is 0.310, the probability that the player will *either* draw a walk *or* hit safely is $P(0.310) + P(0.104) = 0.414$ (roughly 41 chances in 100). Thus for mutually exclusive events, the probability that at least one *or* the other will occur is the *sum* of their individual probabilities.

Probabilities are always positive numbers, and they range between 0 and 1. The probability that the earth will continue to revolve on its axis for another year is unknown but assumed to be 1.0. If this is true, the probability that it will not do so is 0. Nevertheless, there are few events that can be described in such absolute terms. When the probability of an event happening is 0.75 (three times in four) the probability that it will *not* occur is $1 - 0.75$ or 0.25 (one chance in four).

Foresters who employ statistical procedures must learn to accept the fact that they are dealing with probabilities and not with certainties. Even when we say that we are 95 per cent confident that the volume of a timber stand falls within specified limits, there are still 5 chances in 100 that it does not!

8-3 Probability, risk, and uncertainty. The usefulness of probability calculations in rational decision making can be demonstrated by a simple exercise:

As supervisor of planting operations on the Wildwood National Forest, you must decide whether to plant red pine or white pine in an area that has been periodically visited by the white pine weevil. Your decision will be based on the likelihood of a severe insect outbreak during the first 10 years after planting. On the basis of past records, you have the following information: if you plant red pine, you can expect a return on the investment of $28 per acre after 10 years, irrespective of a weevil attack; if you plant white pine, the return will be $46 per acre if there is no weevil attack but only $13 per acre if a severe infestation occurs. The alternatives and possible outcomes may be schematically represented in a two-way table:

Alternative	Expected returns, weevil attack	Expected returns, no weevils
Plant red pine	$28	$28
Plant white pine	$13	$46

When risks and uncertainties of this nature are faced, a logical or rational decision is one having the highest mathematical expectation, i.e., the greatest *expected* return. It is obvious in this example that if a weevil attack is practically certain, red pine should be planted. On the other hand, white pine is the logical choice if one can be sure that no attack will take place. But what if the probability of a weevil attack is 0.60? This is equivalent to a probability of $1 - 0.60 = 0.40$ that no attack will take place. The *expected* returns are computed as

Red pine: 0.60 ($28) $+$ 0.40 ($28) $=$ $28.00
White pine: 0.60 ($13) $+$ 0.40 ($46) $=$ $26.20
For the stated level of probability, expected returns differ by only

$1.80 per acre. The forester of a conservative nature would nevertheless plant red pine because (1) it shows the greatest expected return and (2) it is not subject to white pine weevil damage. However, the forester with a "gambler instinct" might select white pine because he is willing to accept the 4 in 10 chance that no weevil attack will take place. Thus the computation of *expected* profits does not provide an automatic decision; it merely supplies additional data from which a rational decision may be made.

Returning to the foregoing case, if the probability of a weevil attack is presumed to be 0.35, expected returns are:

Red pine: 0.35 ($28) + 0.65 ($28) = $28.00

White pine: 0.35 ($13) + 0.65 ($46) = $34.45

Here the results are more clear cut. The expected difference of $6.45 per acre would probably convince even the conservative administrator that white pine is the wiser alternative. However, the discerning reader will realize that the real key to the value of such computations is the establishment of reliable probability values for application to routine decisions. The risk incurred by accepting a numerical value for the likelihood of a weevil attack is no different from that incurred in deciding whether to water a parched lawn or irrigate a nursery when the weather forecast indicates a 50 per cent chance of rain. In essence, this use of probabilities is a means of "hedging" expected gains against expected losses in such a way that the probabilities help the decision maker control his risks objectively. Such procedures may be applied to logging engineering problems (Dane, 1965) and to other forestry decisions.

8-4 Factorial notation, permutations, and combinations. When very few events are involved, various outcomes can be simply counted; in other instances, special mathematical formulas are helpful. Assume, for example, that a four-volume set of books is placed upright on a shelf in a completely random order. The number of possible *arrangements* (permutations) of n things is n factorial (designated as $n!$) or $n! = (n)(n-1)(n-2) \ldots (2)(1)$. For our four books, this is $4! = (4)(3)(2)(1) = 24$. Because the books can be shelved in 24 possible ways, the probability of their being put in correct order is 1 out of 24.

A useful formula for calculating the number of possible *different events* (combinations) involving a things, b things, $\ldots$, z things, is $n = (a)(b)(c) \ldots (z)$. As an illustration, suppose a forest cover-type map is to be prepared to depict six species composition classes, five tree-height classes, three stand-density classes, and three soil-site conditions. The total number of possible cover types is $n = (6)(5)(3)(3) = 270$ combinations.

As described in foregoing instances, the term *combination* implies that two combinations are composed of different items; the sets *ABC, ABD,* and ACD are all different combinations. By contrast, the term *permutation* denotes the arrangement of a set of items. The sets ABC, ACB, and BAC are all the same combination, but they are different permutations. It is therefore obvious that a given population will have many more permutations than combinations. To illustrate this point, it may be presumed that one wishes to determine how many slates of officers (permutations) and how many different committees (combinations) of 4 individuals each can be selected from a group of 10 persons.

The number of *permutations* or arrangements of r items that can be formed from a total of n items is computed as $n!/(n-r)!$. For our example, this is $10!/6! = 5{,}040$ slates of officers. In most inventory situations, the forester is concerned more with combinations of sampling units than with permutations.

The number of different *combinations* of r items that can be formed from a total of n items is computed as $n!/r!(n-r)!$. In this example $r = 4$ and $n = 10$; therefore

$$\text{Combinations} = \frac{10!}{4!\,6!} = \frac{10 \cdot 9 \cdot 8 \cdot 7 \cdot 6 \cdot 5 \cdot 4 \cdot 3 \cdot 2 \cdot 1}{(4 \cdot 3 \cdot 2 \cdot 1)(6 \cdot 5 \cdot 4 \cdot 3 \cdot 2 \cdot 1)}$$

$$= 210 \text{ committees}$$

STATISTICAL CONCEPTS

8-5 Necessity for sampling. For most inventories of standing timber and associated forest conditions, a 100 per cent tally of all trees and stand characteristics is not economically feasible. Furthermore, the time required for a complete enumeration of large tracts would render the data obsolete by the time they could be amassed, collated, and summarized. As a result, some form of partial measurement or sampling is dictated. Careful measurement of 5 to 10 per cent of the units in a population will frequently give more reliable information than rough estimates obtained from the entire population.

Aside from time and cost factors, sampling is also necessary when testing procedures are destructive. All tree seeds cannot be evaluated in germination tests, because there would be none left for sowing. Similarly, the breaking strength of all plywood panels cannot be measured; otherwise there would be no panels available for marketing. In business and industry as well as in forestry, sampling is an accepted means of obtaining information about populations that cannot be subjected to a complete census. The ultimate objective of all sampling is to obtain reliable data from the population sampled. How well this objective is met depends on items such as the rule by which the sample is drawn, the care exercised in measurement, and the degree to which bias can be avoided (Sec. 1-6).

8-6 Populations, parameters, and variables. A population may be defined as the aggregate of all arbitrarily defined sampling units. If a square ⅕-acre plot is designated as a sampling unit, a 100-acre tract comprises a population of 500 such units (if they are defined on a mutually exclusive basis).

Constants that describe the population as a whole are termed *parameters*. For the foregoing population of five hundred ⅕-acre plots, the mean number of trees per plot is one parameter. On forest inventory projects, the desired parameter may be mean BA per acre, volume per acre, total volume of merchantable standing trees, past growth in volume, forest acreage by cover-type classes, and so on.

Populations are generally classed as being *finite* or *infinite*. A finite population is one for which the total number of sampling units can be reliably expressed as a finite number. The number of ¼-acre plots in a tract of land, Douglas fir stems in a cutting compartment, or members in the Society of American Foresters are examples of finite populations.

Infinite populations are those in which the sample units are not denumerable (countable). Also, populations from which samples are selected and replaced after each drawing may be regarded as equivalent to infinite populations. From a practical viewpoint, all the 5-in. balsam firs in Canada or all the white oak leaves in Missouri may be regarded as if they were infinite populations. As described in later sections of this chapter, the distinction between these two classes of populations becomes important when a relatively large number of sample units are drawn from a finite population. In statistical notation, finite population size is denoted by N, and the number of sampling units observed is indicated by n.

Without a measurable degree of variation in forest characteristics such as tree size, volumes, and values, there would be no forest sampling problems. Any characteristic that may vary from one sampling unit to another (for example, dbh, height, form, or tree volume) is referred to as a *variable*. Variables that may occupy any position along a measurement scale are termed *continuous* variables. Tree height, weight, and volume are conceptually continuous variables, as are air temperature, wind velocity, and atmospheric pressure.

Discrete variables are those commonly described by simple counts (discrete integers). We are often interested in a proportion having a given attribute, and this proportion is a ratio of two discrete variables (counts). Examples are number of tree seedlings per acre, number of cones per tree, or number of white pines infected with blister rust out of the total number of white pines. Most of the statistical procedures described in this chapter are applicable to continuous variables.

8-7 Frequency distributions. The frequency distribution defines the relative frequency with which different values of a variable occur in a population. Each population has its own distinct type of distribution. If the form of the distribution is known, it is possible to predict what proportion of the individuals are within any specified limits.

The most common distribution forms are the normal, binomial, and Poisson. The normal distribution is associated with continuous variables, and it is the form most used by foresters. The arithmetic techniques for handling data from normally distributed populations are relatively simple in comparison with methods developed for other distributions. Regardless of the distribution followed by a given variable, the means of large samples from the distribution are expected to have a distribution that approaches normality. Consequently, estimates and inferences may be based on this assumption.

ELEMENTARY COMPUTATIONS

8-8 Mode, median, and mean. All three of these values are sometimes referred to as *averages* or measures of central tendency. The *mode* is defined as the most frequently appearing value or class of values in a set of observations. The *median* is the middle value of the series of observations when they have been arranged in order of magnitude, and the arithmetic *mean* is simply the arithmetic average of the set of observations. For a majority of statistical analyses, the mean is the most useful value of the three. In populations that are truly normally distributed, values for the mode, the median, and the mean are identical.

Following are observations of diameters (in inches) taken on a sample of 26 trees. These values are listed haphazardly (as tallied) at the left and arranged in a frequency table at the right. In the frequency table, the indicated dbh is the midpoint of the diameter class.

Haphazard listing, dbh			Frequency table	
			Dbh	No. of trees
8	9	10	5	3
8	9	9	6	0
5	7	7	7	6
10	5	8	8	9
9	8	9	9	5
10	7	8	10	3
8	7	7		26
5	8	8		
7	8			
$n = 26$				

For this set of observations, 8 in. is the modal diameter class. This class is easily detected in the frequency table but is less discernible in the unorganized listing. If there had been nine trees in any other class as well as nine in the 8-in. class, the distribution would have been termed *bimodal*. When three or more values have the same frequency or when each value appears only once, no apparent mode can be specified.

The *median* position is found by adding 1 to the number in the sample and dividing by 2, that is, $(n + 1)/2$. With an odd number of observations, the median is merely picked out as the middle ranking value. Thus in a sample of seven observations ranked as 2, 4, 9, 12, 17, 24, and 50, the 12 is the median value. Had there been only six observations (eliminating the 50), the median *position* would have fallen between the 9 and 12. Its *value* would be recorded as the arithmetic average of these two numbers, or $(9 + 12)/2 = 10.5$. For the 26 tree diameters previously noted, the median position is $(26 + 1)/2$ or 13.5. As both the thirteenth and fourteenth values fall within the 8-in.-dbh class, the median value is recorded as 8 in.

It will be noted that both median and mode are unaffected by extreme values. Thus as measures of central tendency, the median and mode may be more informative than the arithmetic mean when a few extreme values are observed.

The sample *mean* or arithmetic average, commonly designated as $\bar{x}$, is computed from

$$\bar{x} = \frac{\Sigma x}{n}$$

where Σ = sum of (over entire sample)
x = value of an individual observation
n = number of observations in sample

For the 26 tree diameters under consideration, the *sample mean* is $204 \div 26 = 7.85$ in.

8-9 The range and average deviation. In a series of sample values, the *range* is merely the difference between the highest and the lowest value recorded. For the 26 tree diameters listed in Sec. 8-8, the range is therefore $10 - 5$ or 5 in. Although based solely on extreme values, the range is a useful indicator of the dispersion or variability of a set of observations, and it also has some utility in providing estimates of the standard deviation (Sec. 8-11).

The *average deviation*, though largely supplanted by the standard deviation, provides an easily computed measure of the dispersion of individual variables about their sample mean. It is computed as the arithmetic average of deviations from the mean (ignoring algebraic signs). Using the same symbols as in the previous section, the formula is

$$AD = \frac{\Sigma|x - \bar{x}|}{n}$$

Again referring to the 26 tree diameters in Sec. 8-8, the average deviation is calculated as

$$AD = \frac{27.20}{26} = 1.05 \text{ in.}$$

The calculated value indicates that the average deviation of the individual dbh measurements from their mean of 7.85 in. is 1.05 in. Although this measure of dispersion about the arithmetic mean is easily computed, it is not widely used for making statistical inferences. The average deviation was once often computed as a measure of the reliability of volume tables.

8-10 Standard deviation. The standard deviation is also a measure of the dispersion of individual observations about their arithmetic mean. In a normally distributed population, approximately two-thirds (68 per cent) of the observations will be within ± 1 standard deviation of the mean. About 95 per cent will be within 1.96 standard deviations and roughly 99 per cent within 2.58 standard deviations. In succeeding sections, the standard deviation will be used to evaluate the reliability of sample estimates.

The standard deviation of a population is a parameter, and it is commonly denoted by the Greek letter sigma (σ). The sample standard deviation is a statistic that is an estimate of the population parameter σ, and it is symbolized by s. Again employing the symbols previously identified, the estimated standard deviation is calculated from

$$s = \sqrt{\frac{\Sigma x^2 - (\Sigma x)^2/n}{n - 1}}$$

This is equivalent to the formula

$$s = \sqrt{\frac{\Sigma(x - \bar{x})^2}{n - 1}}$$

where $\bar{x}$ is the arithmetic mean, and $(x - \bar{x})^2$ is the squared deviation of an individual observation from the arithmetic mean.

The first formula is a shortcut version of the second and is easier to use for calculations. For the 26 measurements of tree diameters in Sec. 8-8, the standard deviation is

$$s = \sqrt{\frac{1,650 - (204)^2/26}{25}} = \sqrt{\frac{49.38}{25}} = 1.41 \text{ in.}$$

If the population sampled is normally distributed, it is expected that about two-thirds of the individual tree diameters will fall within ±1.41 in. of the population mean.

The *variance* of a population is merely the squared standard deviation. For sample data, the variance is denoted by s^2, and it must be computed first; then the standard deviation is derived by taking the square root of the variance as shown in the previous formula.

8-11 Estimating the standard deviation from the range. The sample standard deviation s is an estimate of the population standard deviation σ. The range R may also be used to estimate the population standard deviation. Snedecor (1956) has prepared a table showing the ratio of the population standard deviation to the range for various sized samples. For the sample of 26 observations illustrated here, the expected value of this ratio is about 0.25; that is, the population standard deviation is roughly one-fourth of the range. With a range of 5 in., the estimated standard deviation is 0.25 (5) or 1.25 in. (as compared with the computed value of 1.41 in.). Although this simple procedure provides a useful shortcut, it is not recommended except for samples of less than 10 individuals. This method of estimation has been used for illustrative purposes in Chap. 11, but more efficient estimates of the standard deviation are obtained by formula calculation.

Computation of the standard deviation and similar values can be tedious when large numbers of observations are involved; hence desk calculators or electronic computers should be utilized if available. Special tables for extracting square roots with desk calculators are included in the Appendix. Tables of squares and square roots (Comrie, 1960) are also valuable, particularly when calculations are performed by hand.

8-12 Coefficient of variation. The ratio of the standard deviation to the mean is known as the *coefficient of variation*. It is usually expressed as a percentage value. Because populations with large means tend to have larger standard deviations than those with small means, the coefficient of variation permits a comparison of relative variability about different-sized means. A standard deviation of 5 for a population with a mean of 15 indicates the same relative variability as a standard deviation of 30 with a mean of 90. The coefficient of variation in each instance would be 0.33 or 33 per cent.

For the 26 tree diameters in Sec. 8-8, the mean is 7.85, and the standard deviation is 1.41. The coefficient of variation CV from the sample is

$$CV = \frac{s}{\bar{x}}(100) = \frac{1.41}{7.85}(100) = 18\%$$

If the trees listed in Sec. 8-8 have a mean height of 32 ft and a standard deviation of 8 ft, the coefficient of variation for tree heights would be $(\%_{32})$ 100 or 25 per cent. Thus for this particular sample, it can be said that tree heights show more relative variation than tree diameters.

8-13   Standard error of the mean.   The standard deviation is a measure of the variation of individual sample observations about their mean. Inasmuch as individuals vary, there will also be variation among means computed from different samples of these individuals. A measure of the variation among sample means is the standard error of the mean. It may be regarded as a standard deviation among the means of samples of a fixed size n. As described in succeeding sections, the standard error of the mean can be used to compute confidence limits for a population mean or for determining sample size required to achieve a specified sampling precision.

Calculation of the standard error of the mean depends on the manner in which the sample was selected. For simple random sampling from a finite population, the formula for the estimated standard error of the mean $s_{\bar{x}}$ is

$$s_{\bar{x}} = \sqrt{\frac{s^2}{n}} \sqrt{\frac{N-n}{n}} = \frac{s}{\sqrt{n}} \sqrt{\frac{N-n}{n}}$$

The term $\sqrt{N-n/n}$ is referred to as the finite population correction; in this term, N denotes the population size, and n is the actual sample size. If the population is small or if the sample comprises more than 5 to 10 per cent of the population, the sample mean will probably be closer to the population mean than with infinite populations. As a result, the standard error of the mean will also be smaller. Thus the finite population correction serves to reduce the standard error of the mean when relatively large samples are drawn without replacement from finite populations.

If it is assumed that the 26 tree diameters in Sec. 8-8 were drawn from a population of only 200 stems, the standard error of the mean would be computed as

$$s_{\bar{x}} = \frac{1.41}{\sqrt{26}} \sqrt{\frac{200-26}{200}} = 0.28 \sqrt{0.87} = 0.28(0.93) = 0.26 \text{ in.}$$

This value indicates that if several samples of 26 units each were randomly drawn from the same population, the standard deviation among the sample means might be expected to be approximately 0.26 in. The value of the finite population correction is always less than unity, but it approaches unity when the sampling intensity is very low.

If less than 5 per cent of the population appears in the sample, the finite population correction can usually be omitted.

If the 26 tree diameters had been drawn from an infinite population or from one that was quite large in relation to the sample size, the standard error of the mean would have been computed simply as

$$s_{\bar{x}} = \frac{1.41}{\sqrt{26}} = 0.28 \text{ in.}$$

8-14 Confidence limits. It is recognized that sample means vary about the true mean of the population. The establishment of confidence limits provides a method of estimating what the probability is that a given sample mean might be more than some specified distance from the true mean. The standard error of the mean and a table of t values (Appendix) are used for setting up confidence limits. For simple random samples from normally distributed populations, the confidence limits for the population mean are computed by

$$\text{Mean} \pm t \text{ (standard error) or } \bar{x} - t\,s_{\bar{x}} \text{ to } \bar{x} + t\,s_{\bar{x}}$$

In using the Appendix table for the distribution of t, the column labeled df refers to *degrees of freedom,* which in the case of a simple random sample will be equal to one less than the sample size (that is, $n - 1$). The columns labeled *probability* refer to the level of odds demanded. If one wishes to state that the true mean falls within specified limits unless a 1-in-20 chance has occurred, the t values in the 0.05 column are used. If one wishes to establish confidence limits at the 99 per cent probability level, the 0.01 column in the t table is used, and so forth.

For the sample tree diameters previously listed, the estimated mean was 7.85 in., and the corrected standard error of the mean was ±0.26 in. Because only 26 samples were taken, there are $26 - 1$ or 25 df. The 95 per cent and 99 per cent t values are read from the Appendix table as 2.060 and 2.787, respectively. Confidence limits for these probabilities are as follows:

$P = 0.95: 7.85 - (2.06)(0.26)$ to $7.85 + (2.06)(0.26) = 7.31$ to 8.39 in.

$P = 0.99: 7.85 - (2.787)(0.26)$ to $7.85 + (2.787)(0.26) = 7.13$ to 8.57 in.

Therefore, if the 26 units were randomly selected from a normally distributed population, the true population mean lies between 7.31 and 8.39 in., unless a 1-in-20 chance has occurred in sampling. In other words, the population mean will be included in the interval unless this random sample is one of those which, by chance, yields a sample mean so far from the true population mean that the interval constructed from it will not include the mean. Such would happen, on the average, once in every 20 samples. Similarly, unless a 1-in-100 chance has occurred, the true mean is included in the interval of 7.13 to 8.57 in. It can be seen from these examples that the higher the probability level, the wider the confidence limits must be expanded.

The forester must remember that confidence limits and accompanying statements of probability account for *sampling variation only*. It is assumed that sampling procedures are unbiased, field measurements are without error, and no computational mistakes are included. If these assumptions are incorrect, confidence statements may be misleading.

8-15 Sampling intensity. To plan a timber inventory that is statistically and practically efficient, enough sample units should be measured to obtain the desired standard of precision—no more and no less. As an example, one might wish to estimate the mean volume per acre of a timber stand and have a 90 per cent probability of being within ±500 bd ft per acre of the true mean. A formula for computing the required sampling intensity may be derived by transforming the relationship for the confidence limits on the mean. Excluding the finite population correction, the formula may be expressed as

$$n = \frac{t^2 s^2}{E^2}$$

Where E is the desired half width of the confidence interval and other symbols are as previously described.

Solving this formula requires an estimate of the standard deviation (or variance), expressed *in the same units* as the desired precision E. This estimate may be obtained by (1) measuring a small preliminary sample of the population, (2) using the standard deviation obtained from previous sampling of the same or a similar population, or (3) deriving an approximation from the estimated range of sample values (Sec. 8-11). The first method is likely to be most reliable, if the expense of a preliminary survey can be accepted. In the example proposed earlier, assume that preliminary measurement of 25 field plots provided the following data:

$$n = 25 \text{ sample units}; \; df = 25 - 1 \text{ or } 24$$
$$\bar{x} = 4,400 \text{ bd ft per acre}$$
$$s = \pm 2,000 \text{ bd ft per acre}$$

The original objective was to be within ±500 bd ft per acre, with a confidence probability of 90 per cent. Accordingly, a t value of 1.711 is read from the Appendix table (probability column of 0.1 and 24 df). The *desired* half width of the confidence interval, $E = 500$, is substituted in the formula, along with the estimated standard deviation:

$$n = \left[\frac{(1.711)(2,000)}{500} \right]^2 = (6.84)^2 = 46.7 \text{ or } 47 \text{ sample units}$$

Apparently, 47 sample units will be required to attain the desired precision. Actually the number will be slightly less than 47, because there are 46 *df* now involved instead of the 24 assumed in the computation. The exact number of *df* can only be obtained by repeated trial-and-error solutions of the formula, because it depends on the number of sample units to be measured. Resolving the equation for the nearest value in the Appendix *t* table (40 *df*) provides this result:

$$n = \left[\frac{(1.684)(2,000)}{500}\right]^2 = (6.74)^2 = 45.4 \text{ or } 46 \text{ sample units}$$

Although the sample size was reduced by only 1 in this illustration, it could have been considerably greater if a *t* value for only 5 to 10 preliminary observations had been used. On the other hand, if the preliminary *t* value involves 30 or more *df* and the calculated sample size turns out to be even larger, further reduction of the *t* value is so small that it is unnecessary to resolve the formula.

8-16   The standard error as a per cent.   If the standard error of the mean is expressed as a per cent of the mean and an estimate of the coefficient of variation is available, the required sample size can be calculated from

$$n = \frac{(\text{coefficient of variation in per cent})^2}{(\text{standard error of mean in per cent})^2}$$

For a specified standard error of ±5 per cent and a coefficient of variation of 50 per cent, the number of sample units to be taken from an infinite population would be

$$n = \frac{(50)^2}{(5)^2} = \frac{2,500}{25} = 100 \text{ sample units}$$

The foregoing relationship has been used by Grosenbaugh (1952) in the compilation of Table 8-1. This table may also be used to determine the number of sample units required to achieve a specified half width of confidence interval. It is only necessary to look up the sample size appropriate for the specified percentage and multiply this value by the *square* of the selected *t* value.

With an estimated coefficient of variation of 50 per cent, for example, one might wish to determine the number of observations needed to estimate the population mean within ±5 per cent for a confidence level of 0.80. Table 8-1 indicates that 100 sample units are needed to provide a standard error of ±5 per cent. From the Appendix, the *t* value (infinite *df* and probability column of 0.2) is 1.282. Therefore, the total number of sample units required to achieve the specified precision in terms of the half width of the confidence interval is

$$(1.282)^2(100) = 164.4 \text{ or } 165 \text{ units}$$

8-17 Formula interpretations and precautions. A study of Table 8-1 reveals that sampling intensities are increased *four times* when (1) the coefficient of variation is doubled, as from 25 to 50 per cent, or (2) the specified standard error is reduced by one-half. These are important facts for consideration in balancing costs and desired precision on forest inventories.

The perceptive reader will note that forest *area* is a variable that does not appear in the sampling intensity formulas or in Table 8-1 when an infinite population is assumed. However, the *effect* of tract

TABLE 8-1 Number of Sample Units To Be Taken from an
Infinite Population*

Coefficient of variation, %	Specified per cent limit for standard error			
	$\pm 1\frac{1}{2}\%$	$\pm 5\%$	$\pm 10\%$	$\pm 20\%$
	Number of sample units			
5	12	1	1	1
10	45	4	1	1
15	100	9	3	1
20	178	16	4	1
25	278	25	7	2
30	400	36	9	3
35	545	49	13	4
40	712	64	16	4
45	900	81	21	6
50	1,112	100	25	7
55	1,345	121	31	8
60	1,600	144	36	9
65	1,878	169	43	11
70	2,178	196	49	13
75	2,500	225	57	15
80	2,845	256	64	16
85	3,212	289	73	19
90	3,600	324	81	21
95	4,012	361	91	23
100	4,445	400	100	25
125	6,945	625	157	40
150	10,000	900	225	57
175	13,612	1,225	307	77
200	17,778	1,600	400	100

* From Grosenbaugh, 1952.

size is partially included, because large areas tend to have greater variances (standard deviations) than small areas. Where sampling variation does *not* increase proportionately with increasing tract size (as in a uniform forest plantation), a fixed number of sample units may provide estimates that are almost as reliable for 1,000 acres as for 25 acres.

8-18 Expansion of means and standard errors. In most instances, estimates of means per sample plot are multiplied by a constant to scale the estimates to a more useful basis. If a forest inventory utilizes $\frac{1}{4}$-acre plots, for example, the mean volume per plot is multiplied by 4 to put the estimated mean on a per acre basis. Or, for a tract of 500 acres, the mean volume per plot would be multiplied by 2,000 (the number of possible $\frac{1}{4}$ acres in the tract) to estimate the total volume.

The rule to remember is that expansion of sample means must be accompanied by a similar expansion of standard errors. Thus if the mean volume per $\frac{1}{4}$-acre plot is 1,500 bd ft with a standard error of 60, the mean volume per acre is 4(1,500) $\pm$ 4(60) or 6,000 $\pm$ 240 bd ft. For a tract of 500 acres, the total volume would be expressed as 2,000(1,500) $\pm$ 2,000(60) or 3,000,000 $\pm$ 120,000 bd ft.

The foregoing examples presume the use of expansion factors having no error. However, sample-based estimates of area are (or should be) also accompanied by standard errors. Thus the expansion of per acre volume to total tract volume becomes one of deriving the product of volume times area and computing a standard error applicable to this product (Meyer, 1963). The computation may be illustrated by assuming *independent* inventories that produced the following estimates and standard errors for volume $\overline{V}$ and area A:

Mean volume: 18 $\pm$ 2 cd per acre

Tract acreage: 52 $\pm$ 1.5 acres

If these two estimates are independent (and only if they are), their product and its standard error may be computed by

$$\overline{V}A \pm \sqrt{\overline{V}^2 s_A{}^2 + A^2 s_{\overline{V}}{}^2}$$

where $\overline{V}$ = estimated mean volume per acre

A = estimated number of acres

$s_{\overline{V}}$ = standard error of mean volume per acre

s_A = standard error of area estimate

Substituting the sample problem data, the total volume and its standard error are

$$18(52) \pm \sqrt{(18)^2(1.5)^2 + (52)^2(2)^2} = 936 \pm 107.45 \text{ cd (tract total)}$$

8-19 Effect of plot size on variability. At a given scale of measurement, small sample plots usually exhibit more relative variability (i.e., have a larger coefficient of variation) than large plots. The variance in volume per acre on $\frac{1}{4}$-acre plots is usually larger than the variance in volume per acre on $\frac{1}{2}$-acre plots but slightly smaller than that for $\frac{1}{5}$-acre plots. The relation of plot size to variance changes from one population to another. In general, large plots tend to have less relative variability, because they average out the effect of tree clumps and stand openings. In uniform populations (e.g., plantations), changes in plot size have little effect on variance. In nonuniform populations, the relation of plot size to variance depends on how clumps of trees and open areas compare to the sizes of plots.

Although plot sizes have often been chosen on the basis of experience, the objective should be the selection of the most efficient size. Usually, this is the smallest size commensurate with the variability produced. Where the coefficient of variation has been determined for plots of a given size, the coefficient of variation for different-sized plots may be estimated by a formula suggested by Freese (1962):

$$(CV_2)^2 = (CV_1)^2 \sqrt{\frac{P_1}{P_2}}$$

where CV_2 = estimated coefficient of variation for new plot size
$\quad\quad CV_1$ = known coefficient of variation for plots of previous size
$\quad\quad P_1$ = previous plot size
$\quad\quad P_2$ = new plot size

If the coefficient of variation for $\frac{1}{5}$-acre plots is 30 per cent, the estimated coefficient of variation for $\frac{1}{10}$-acre plots would be computed as

$$(CV_2)^2 = (30)^2 \sqrt{\frac{0.2}{0.1}} = 900(1.414) = 1,272.6$$

$$CV_2 = \sqrt{1,272.6} = 36 \text{ per cent}$$

The coefficients of variation of 36 per cent for $\frac{1}{10}$-acre plots versus 30 per cent for $\frac{1}{5}$-acre sample units may now be compared as to relative *numbers* of plots needed. Assume, for example, that the $\frac{1}{5}$-acre plots produced a sample mean of 4 cd per plot, which is equivalent to 20 cd per acre. The sample standard deviation is 30 per cent of this value or ±6 cd per acre. If these data lead us to believe that the required sample size will be roughly 30 units, the total number of $\frac{1}{5}$-acre plots needed to estimate the mean volume per acre within ±2 cd at a probability level of 95 per cent ($t = 2.045$ for 29 df) are estimated as

$$n = \left[\frac{(2.045)(6)}{2} \right]^2 = (6.14)^2 = 37.7 \text{ or } 38 \text{ plots}$$

The reader should note that it is necessary to have the standard deviation and the allowable error in the same units before substitution in the formula. In this instance, these values are ± 6 and ± 2 cd per acre, respectively. For comparison with the preceding results, the standard deviation for $\frac{1}{10}$-acre plots, expressed on a per acre basis, would be $0.36(20) = \pm 7.2$ cd per acre. The number of $\frac{1}{10}$-acre plots required to meet the previous standards of precision would be

$$ n = \left[\frac{(2.045)(7.2)}{2} \right]^2 = (7.36)^2 = 54.2 \text{ or } 55 \text{ plots} $$

The choice between thirty-eight $\frac{1}{5}$-acre plots versus fifty-five $\frac{1}{10}$-acre plots is a decision that now rests on the relative time or costs involved. Some aspects of sampling "efficiency" are discussed in the next section.

8-20 Relative efficiencies of sampling plans. Viewed from the standpoint of a consumer's "best buy," the most efficient timber inventory is one that produces the greatest precision for the money expended. This may be conveniently translated into an efficiency index based on the product of the squared standard error (expressed as a per cent of the mean) and the cruising time required (Mesavage and Grosenbaugh, 1956). To illustrate, the following results of five inventories of the same tract may be considered:

Inventory plan	Mean (bd ft/acre)	Standard error of mean, %	Time, hr	(Standard error, %)^2 × time	Efficiency (rank)
A	2,800	8	8	512	2
B	2,750	7	11	539	3
C	3,080	7	10	490	1
D	2,640	12	6	864	5
E	2,975	9	8	648	4

In this example, inventory plan C proved most efficient (rank 1), because of the lowest product of squared per cent standard error and time. Although cruise B was equally precise (7 per cent standard error) it ranked third in overall efficiency because of the larger time factor. If this method of ranking timber cruises appears to penalize estimates with large standard errors, it should be remembered that halving a standard error requires not merely twice as many sampling units but *four times as many* (Sec. 8-17). On the other hand, time is regarded as a linear variable, because reducing time by one-half is expected to lower cruising costs proportionately.

COMMON SAMPLING DESIGNS

8-21 Systematic sampling. The method of selecting the units to be included in a sample is referred to as the *sampling design*. Four common designs are shown in Fig. 8-1. Foresters have traditionally employed systematic or mechanical plot arrangements, because sample units are easy to locate and "they appear to provide a more typical or representative picture" of stand conditions. Even when these arguments are true, however, the drawback is that no methods are available for reliably estimating variances (or standard errors) for systematic samples.

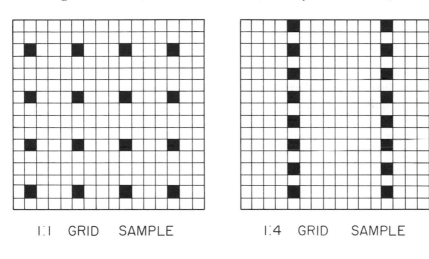

I:I   GRID   SAMPLE   I:4   GRID   SAMPLE

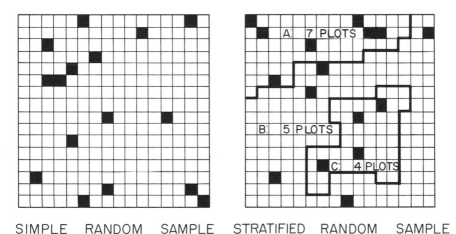

SIMPLE RANDOM SAMPLE   STRATIFIED RANDOM SAMPLE

FIG. 8-1 Four possible arrangements of 16 sample plots
          in a population composed of 256 square plots.

Rectangular spacings or square grid layouts may often yield more efficient estimates than simple random samples of the same intensity, but this gain cannot be evaluated and statistically defended by the formulas and techniques described earlier in this chapter. These techniques have presumed the employment of random samples and therefore cannot be logically applied to systematic designs. The fact that systematic samples are often analyzed *as if they were* randomly selected is a violation of the basic theory. It tends to place the inventory forester in a "statistical no-man's-land."

In summary, there are good defenses for systematic sampling—unfortunately a random sampling analysis is not one of them. When an objective numerical statement of precision need not be appended to inventory estimates, however, systematic sampling may well provide the most precise estimate for the time (or money) expended.

8-22 Simple random sampling. All the statistical procedures previously discussed assume simple random sampling. By this approach, *every possible combination of sampling units* has an equal and independent chance of being selected. This is *not* the same as simply requiring that every sampling unit in the population have an equal chance of being selected. This latter requirement is met by many forms of restricted randomization and even by some systematic designs.

Allowing every possible combination of *n* sampling units an equal chance of being selected is easily accomplished. It is only necessary that at any stage of the sampling, the selection of a particular unit be in no way influenced by the other units that have been selected or will be selected on succeeding draws. To state it another way, the selection of any given unit should be completely independent of the selection of all other units. One way to do this is to assign every unit in the population a number and draw *n* numbers from a table of random digits (Appendix). A modification of this technique consists of drawing random intersection points in a coordinate system based on column and row numbers designating each plot (Fig. 8-2).

Sampling units may be selected with or without replacement. If selection is with replacement, each unit is allowed to appear in the sample as often as it is selected. In sampling without replacement, a particular unit is allowed to appear in the sample only once. Most forest sampling is without replacement.

8-23 Stratified random sampling. In stratified sampling, a population is divided into subpopulations of known size, and a random sample of at least two units is selected in each subpopulation. This approach has several advantages. If sample units are allocated among the strata wisely, the estimate of the population mean will be more precise than

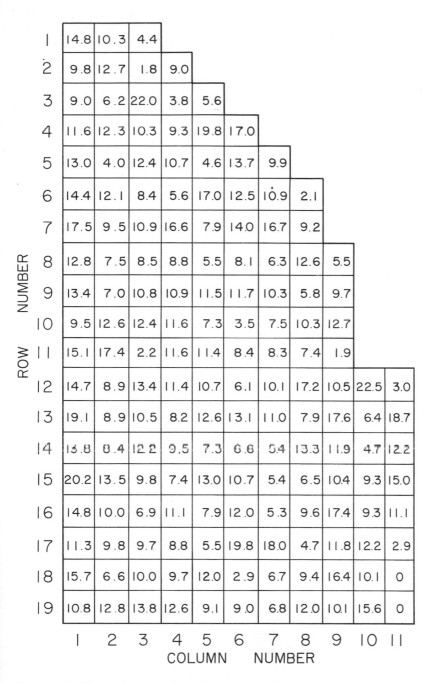

FIG. 8-2   Basal area in square feet of all trees 5.0 in. dbh and larger on square plots (60 × 60 ft) in a 13.6-acre woodlot.

that given by a simple random sample of the same size. Also, it may be desirable to have separate estimates for each subpopulation (e.g., for different timber types or administrative subunits). And it may be administratively more efficient to sample by subpopulations.

Establishment of various strata or subpopulations may be accomplished by using forest cover maps and aerial photographs or by presampling methods. A simplified approach to stratified random sampling is presented in Chap. 11.

8-24 Sampling for discrete variables. The formulas for estimates, standard deviations, confidence limits, etc. that were discussed in the previous sections apply to data that are on a continuous or nearly continuous quantitative scale of measurement. These methods may not be applicable if each unit observed is classified according to a qualitative attribute, such as alive or dead, deciduous or evergreen, forest or non-forest. Data such as counts in two mutually exclusive classes follow what is known as the binomial distribution, and slightly different statistical formulas are required. Determining the intensity for dot sampling to estimate proportions of area provides a useful example of sampling for discrete variables.

The number of dots to be counted for a given precision depends upon the proportion (or percentage) of the total area occupied by the most important classification to be recognized. For example, suppose area breakdowns are needed for 10 square miles photographed at a scale of 1:15,840. Estimated percentages in each area classification are as follows: forest, 25 per cent; agricultural lands, 60 per cent; urban areas, 10 per cent; and rivers and lakes, 5 per cent. Assuming that the most important category is agricultural land, the dot sampling intensity would be calculated on this basis. If a relatively large sample is to be measured, the approximate number of sample units required may be computed by this formula based on the binomial distribution:

$$n = p(1 - p) \left(\frac{t}{E}\right)^2$$

where n = total number of units (dots) that should be counted
  p = estimated proportion of the total area in the most important type classification (0.60 in this case)
  t = a constant related to the reliability required of the estimate or level of confidence probability (a t value of 1.96 used here denotes a confidence probability of 95 per cent)
  E = maximum permissible half width of confidence interval for the area in the most important category, expressed as a proportion of total area (in this case, E is set at ± 0.02)

Substituting the above values, we get

$$n = 0.60(1 - 0.60) \left(\frac{1.96}{0.02}\right)^2 = 2,305 \text{ dots}$$

Thus, if we are correct in the assumption that the true proportion of agricultural land is about 0.60, 2,305 dots should be randomly located within the area to ensure a 95 per cent confidence probability of obtaining a sample-estimated proportion that will be within ± 0.02 of the true proportion.

The principal drawback to the method is that the formula requires a prior knowledge of p, which is actually the value being sought. By definition, however, p always lies between 0 and 1, and the statistic $p(1 - p)$ reaches a maximum value of 0.25´when p is 0.50. Therefore, the maximum number of sample units required, regardless of what p is, may be computed by

$$n = 0.25 \left(\frac{t}{E}\right)^2$$

In contrast with the earlier solution, the original problem data are substituted in the "revised" formula

$$n = 0.25 \left(\frac{1.96}{0.02}\right)^2$$
$$= 2,401 \text{ dots, an increase of 96 dots over the first estimate}$$

The second approximation formula is recommended when it is difficult to estimate the proportion represented by the most important category in advance of the dot count. Setting this proportion at 0.50 assures at least the desired minimum precision for the most important classification; other categories are likely to be estimated with greater precision because of oversampling.

The reader is reminded that this method of determining dot-sampling intensity is *not* applicable for use in conjunction with systematic dot grids as discussed in Chap. 2. For the foregoing formulas to be applicable, dots must be selected by random location.

PROBLEMS

8-1 (*a*) What is the probability of obtaining a queen *or* a black card in a single draw from a standard deck of playing cards?
(*b*) What is the probability of getting five tails in a row when tossing a balanced coin?
(*c*) What are the chances of drawing three aces in a row from a standard deck of playing cards, if (1) cards are replaced after each draw and (2) cards are *not replaced* after each draw?

8-2 Give three examples of two independent events.

8-3 You must decide whether to hire a fire lookout for the summer on the Tahoe National Forest. His salary and per diem allowance will cost $1,000. Your decision will be based on the probability of a severe summer fire on the forest. Set up a two-way table of possible outcomes (Sec. 8-3) for computing expected gains or losses from the following data:

(a) If *no fires* occur and a lookout is *not hired,* you will save his salary of $1,000.

(b) If *no fires* occur and a lookout is *hired,* you will lose $800 (assuming the lookout will do about $200 worth of trail improvement work).

(c) If a severe *fire occurs* and a lookout is *not hired,* you will lose $3,000.

(d) If a severe *fire occurs* and a lookout is *hired,* you will lose $1,200.

Question: As you wish to minimize your expected losses, what would be your decision if the probability of a severe fire is 0.60?

Question: What would be your decision if the probability of a severe fire is 0.40?

8-4 (a) How many different ways (combinations) can a committee of 3 be selected from 11 men?

(b) How many arrangements (permutations) of three plots can be selected from an experimental planting having a total of nine plots?

8-5 Give four examples each of *continuous* and *discrete* variables that might be recorded on a forest inventory.

8-6 Using the Appendix table of random numbers, obtain a simple random sample of 16 plots from Fig. 8-2.

(a) Then compute the following statistics on a *per acre* basis for the plot data:

(1) range, (2) estimate of standard deviation from range, (3) arithmetic mean, (4) average deviation, (5) standard deviation and variance, (6) coefficient of variation (per cent), (7) standard error of the mean (corrected for finite population), (8) confidence limits for probability of 0.68, (9) confidence limits for probability of 0.95, and (10) number of plots that are needed to estimate the population mean within ±10 per cent, for a confidence probability of 90 per cent. (Compare computed result with value read from Table 8-1.)

(b) Assuming an estimated area of 13.6 acres with a standard error of ±0.5 acres, estimate the total tract volume and its standard error.

(c) Estimate the coefficient of variation if plot size is changed from $\frac{1}{12}$ acre to $\frac{1}{4}$ acre.

8-7 Rank these timber cruises in order of relative efficiency as in Sec. 8-20:

Cruise	Mean and standard error	Average time per sample, min
A	1,064 ± 98	4.3
B	1,405 ± 91	8.0
C	1,422 ± 108	5.4
D	1,583 ± 124	4.2
E	1,580 ± 164	3.6

8-8 Suppose a sample survey yields a mean of 150 and a standard error of the mean of 12. To reduce the standard error to a value of 6 (assuming no change in estimated variance) will require:

(*a*) Twice as many sample units

(*b*) Three times as many sample units

(*c*) Four times as many sample units

(*d*) Eight times as many sample units

(*e*) None of the previous answers is correct

8-9 Suppose you decide to interview **1,000** families on a sample survey. You assign each family to a density class according to the population density of the block in which they live and then randomly select a given number of families to be interviewed in each density class. Such sampling is called:

(*a*) Systematic sampling

(*b*) Cluster or area sampling

(*c*) Simple random sampling

(*d*) Stratified random sampling

(*e*) None of these

8-10 You wish to determine the proportion of forest land on an aerial photograph within ±5 per cent for a confidence probability of 0.90 ($t = 1.645$). Compute the number of dots that must be counted by using the "revised" formula in Sec. 8-24.

REFERENCES

Alder, Henry L., and Roessler, Edward B.
1962. Introduction to probability and statistics, 2d ed. W. H. Freeman and Company, San Francisco. 289 pp., illus.

Comrie, L. J.
1960. Barlow's tables of squares, cubes, square roots, cube roots, and reciprocals. Chemical Publishing Company, Inc., New York. 258 pp.

Dane, C. W.
1965. Statistical decision theory and its application to forest engineering. *J. Forestry* **63**:276–279.

Freese, Frank
1964. Linear regression methods for forest research. *U.S. Forest Serv., Forest Prod. Lab. Res. Paper FPL* **17**. 136 pp., illus.

————
1962. Elementary forest sampling. *U.S. Dept. Agr. Handbook* **232**, Government Printing Office, Washington, D.C. 91 pp.

————
1956. A guidebook for statistical transients. U.S. Forest Service, Southern Forest Experiment Station. 77 pp.

Grosenbaugh, L. R.
1965. Three-pee sampling theory and program "THRP" for computer generation of selection criteria. *U.S. Forest Serv., Pacific Southwest Forest and Range Expt. Sta. Res. Paper PSW*-21. 53 pp., illus.

————
1952. Shortcuts for cruisers and scalers. *U.S. Forest Serv., Southern Forest Expt. Sta. Occasional Paper* 126. 24 pp., illus.

Hasel, A. A.
1937. Arrangement of cruise plots to permit a valid estimate of sampling error. U.S. Forest Service, California Forest and Range Experiment Station. 13 pp., illus.

Mesavage, C., and Grosenbaugh, L. R.
1956. Efficiency of several cruising designs on small tracts in north Arkansas. *J. Forestry* **54**:569–576, illus.

Meyer, Walter H.
1963. Some comments on the error of the total volume estimate. *J. Forestry* **61**:503–507, illus.

Osborne, James G.
1942. Sampling errors of systematic and random surveys of cover-type areas. *J. Am. Statist. Assoc.* **37**:256–264, illus.

Seely, H. E.
1964. Canadian forest inventory methods. *Forest Res. Branch Can. Dept. Forestry, Publ.* 1068. 11 pp.

———
1961. Some investigations of forest sampling methods. *Forest Res. Branch Can. Dept. Forestry, Tech. Note* 111. 17 pp., illus.

Shiue, Cherng-Jiann
1960. Systematic sampling with multiple random starts. *Forest Sci.* **6**(1):42–50.

Snedecor, George W.
1956. Statistical methods, 5th ed. The Iowa State University Press, Ames, Iowa. 534 pp.

CHAPTER 9

TIMBER CRUISING WITH
SAMPLE STRIPS OR PLOTS

INTRODUCTION

9-1 The cruise and the cruiser. The primary purpose of a timber inventory is to determine, as precisely as available time and money will permit, the volume (or value) of standing trees in a given area. To attain this objective requires (1) a reliable estimate of the forest area and (2) measurement of all or an unbiased sample of trees within this area. Forest areas may be determined from boundary surveys, existing type maps, topographic quadrangle sheets, or aerial photographs. As methods of area measurement have been described in Chap. **2**, this chapter is devoted to the techniques of timber cruising. It goes without saying that no reliable timber inventory can be planned until the cruiser knows the location of all tract corners and boundary lines; recent aerial photographs and maps are therefore genuine assets for cruising in unfamiliar terrain.

The choice of a particular cruising system, often made at the forester's discretion, is generally governed by relative costs, size and density of timber, area to be covered, precision desired, number of men available for fieldwork, and the length of time allowed for the estimate. Other things being equal, the intensity of cruise (i.e., percentage of the total area sampled) will increase as the size of the tract decreases and as the value of the timber increases.

In earlier years, cruising timber was regarded more as an art than as a science, and patriarchs such as James W. Girard and Inman F. ("Cap") Eldredge were nationally known for their prowess in making "ocular estimates" of timber volumes. Even today, one of the most essential qualities for becoming a good timber cruiser is the ability to make careful observations, rational estimates, and responsible judgments. No matter how many hard and fast rules are set down to remove the human factor from timber estimating, the cruiser still has to make the decisions in the woods. And only the man on the ground with field experience and good judgment can decide what to do about unusual tree defects, merchantability limits, timber trespass, or inoperable stands.

9-2 Inventory objectives and precision standards. The organization, intensity, and precision required in a timber cruise are logically based on the planned use of information collected. Depending on primary objectives, timber surveys may be conveniently classified as (1) land acquisition cruises, (2) cruises for logging or timber sales, (3) management plan cruises or continuous forest inventory (CFI) systems, and (4) special surveys designed for evaluating conditions such as stand improvement needs, plantable areas, insect and disease infestations, or timber trespass.

For land acquisition or timber sales, the principal information desired is net volume and value of merchantable trees growing in operable areas. In simple terms, a stand is usually classed as "operable" when merchantable trees can be logged at a reasonable profit. Notations on timber quality, by species or species groups, are also commonly required. For land acquisition surveys, additional information is needed on soil or site quality, presence of nonmerchantable growing stock, and proximity of the tract with regard to mills or primary markets. Where timber values are relatively high, acquisition or sale inventories should be of an intensity that will produce estimates of mean volume per acre with standard errors of ±10 per cent or less (Table 8-1).

Management plan cruises, designed for providing information on timber growth, yield, and allowable cut, are no longer considered essential in all regions. In many instances, such cruises have been replaced by CFI systems that make use of permanent sample plots (Chap. 14). As a rule, both types of cruises are of low intensity (often less than 1 per cent of the area is sampled), and the information collected is primarily intended for top-level management decisions and long-range planning. As a result, inventory data are summarized by large administrative units rather than by cutting compartments or logging units.

Special surveys are so diversified that few general rules can be stipulated. For locating spot insect or disease infestations, a survey might merely consist of an accurate forest type map with "trouble areas" located visually from aerial observations. Similarly, understocked stands in need of planting might be mapped from existing aerial photographs (Chap. 11). In other instances, a 100 per cent tree tally might be made for determining the number and volume of trees suitable for poles, piling, or veneer logs. Special surveys are also required in timber trespass cases. The estimation of timber volumes removed from cutover areas is discussed in a later section of this chapter.

SPECIAL CONSIDERATIONS IN CRUISING

9-3 Methods of sampling. Except for those occasions when a complete tree tally may be justified, cruising is a sampling process. The cruise strips and plots described in this chapter are *area* samples, with the probability of sampling trees of a given size being dependent on the *frequency* with which that tree size occurs in the stand. With point-sample cruising (described in Chap. 10), the probability of sampling a given tree is proportional to its size or diameter.

In spite of the statistical difficulties associated with systematic sampling designs, such cruises are still employed frequently. Thus systematic spacings of sample strips and plots are described here in some detail. Forest type maps that were formerly compiled during the conduct of timber cruises are now derived mainly from aerial photographs. Mapping techniques are therefore deferred to Chap. 11.

9-4 Methods of tallying timber. In accordance with tree volume or tree-weight tables to be used, standing trees may be tallied by simple counts, by dbh and species only, or by various combinations of dbh, species, merchantable height, total height, form, individual tree quality classes, and so on. The dot-dash tally method, merchantable height limitations, and tree form expressions have been described in Chap. 5; cumulative volume tallies and field tallies by weight are covered in Chap. 6.

Neophyte cruisers should be particularly careful in estimating tree heights; upper limits of stem merchantability often change from one species or locality to another. When ocular estimates of tree heights are permitted, the conscientious cruiser will nevertheless "check his eye" by *measuring* every tenth or twentieth tree. Proficiency and consistency in cruising are dependent on constant checks of estimated techniques.

9-5 Estimates of tree defects and cull per cents. The question of what constitutes a "cull" log and merchantability standards for irregular tree stems has been outlined previously (Secs. 4-14 and 5-9). Learning to make proper allowance for defective trees encountered in cruising requires experience that can be gained only by (1) repeated practice in estimating standing tree defects and (2) observing the sawing and utilization of defective logs at various mills.

When entire trees are classed as culls, they are either omitted from the field tally or recorded by species and dbh in a separate column of the tally sheet. For merchantable trees with evidence of interior defects, deductions for unsound portions of the stem may be handled by one of the following techniques:

1 For *visible defects*, dimensions of tallied trees are reduced in proportion to the estimated amount of defect. Thus a 22-in.-dbh three-log tree might be recorded as an 18-in.-dbh tree with three logs or possibly as a 22-in.-dbh tree with 2½ logs. Refinements may be made in this technique by applying the cull per cent formulas for log volumes as suggested by Grosenbaugh (Sec. 4-13).

2 For *hidden defects*, all trees are tallied in the field as sound. After gross volumes have been computed, a flat percentage is deducted in proportion to the total amount of timber presumed to be defective. Although this method will usually produce more consistent results than individual tree allowances, the drawback is the difficulty of deciding *what percentage deductions* should be applied. Reliable ratios can be developed only by following samples of trees from the stump to the sawmill carriage; experience of this nature cannot be acquired in university classrooms.

9-6 The complete tree tally. Under limited circumstances when scattered, high-value trees occur on small tracts, a complete or 100 per cent tree tally may be feasible. Every tree of the desired species and size class may be measured, or the tally may be comprised of a 100 per cent *count* of all stems plus a subsample (every *n*th tree) of actual measurements. The choice of methods depends on the stumpage value of trees inventoried, allowable costs, and desired precision.

Advantages of the complete tree tally are as follows:

1 More accurate estimates of total volume are possible, because every tree can be tallied by species, dbh, height, and quality class.

2 Deductions for defect can be more accurately assessed, because cull percentages can be applied to individual trees as they are tallied.

3 It is not necessary to determine the exact area of the tract. Once boundaries have been located, the total estimate can be made without regard to area.

Disadvantages of the complete tree tally are:

1 High costs. Because of expense and time required, the 100 per cent cruise is usually limited to small tracts or to individual trees of extra high stumpage value.

2 Trees must often be marked as they are recorded to avoid omissions or duplications in the field tally. This requires additional time and/or added personnel.

9-7 Organizing the 100 per cent tally. For planning 100 per cent cruises of dense stands when large numbers of trees are tallied, a three-man crew is desirable. Two men serve as cruisers; the third tallies and acts as the chief of the party. If the area exceeds 10 acres in size, it is helpful to first lay out rectangles of about 4×10 chains by using stout cord or twine. Then, depending on topography and underbrush, parallel strips 1 to 2 chains wide can be traversed through each rectangle.

Fieldwork in dense stands proceeds most efficiently when it is feasible to merely count merchantable trees and restrict actual measurements to every tenth or twentieth stem. For pure stands that require little or no cull deductions, an alternative procedure might employ caliper measurements of dbh only for all stems, with volumes derived from local volume tables or cumulative tally sheets. To ensure that no trees are overlooked or tallied twice, cruisers should use "limesocks" to mark each stem at eye level on the side facing the unmeasured portion of the stand. In deciduous forests, complete stem tallies are preferably made during the dormant season when trees are leafless.

STRIP SYSTEM OF CRUISING

9-8 Strip-cruise layout. With this system, sample areas take the form of continuous strips of uniform width which are run through the forest at equally spaced intervals, such as 5, 10, or 20 chains. The sample strip itself is usually 1 chain wide, although it may be narrowed to $\frac{1}{2}$ chain in dense stands of young timber or increased to 2 chains and wider in scattered, old-growth sawtimber. Strips commonly run straight through the tract in a north-south or east-west direction, preferably oriented to cross topography and drainage at right angles (Fig. 9-1). By this technique, all soil types and timber conditions from ridge top to valley floor are theoretically intersected to provide a representative sample tally.

Strip cruises are usually organized to sample a predetermined percentage of the forest area. One-chain sample strips spaced 10 chains apart provide a 10 per cent estimate, and $\frac{1}{2}$-chain strips at 20 chain intervals produce a $2\frac{1}{2}$ per cent cruise (Table 9-1). The conversion of volume derived from the sample to total tract volume may be accomplished

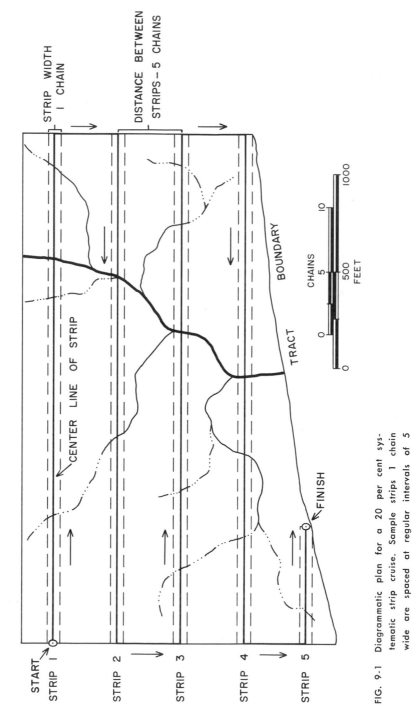

FIG. 9-1 Diagrammatic plan for a 20 per cent systematic strip cruise. Sample strips 1 chain wide are spaced at regular intervals of 5 chains.

TABLE 9-1 Examples of Cruising Intensities for 1-chain Sample Strip Widths

Distance between strip centerlines,		No. of strips per "forty"	Cruise per cent
ft	chains		
1,320	20	1	5
660	10	2	10
330	5	4	20
165	2½	8	40

by (1) dividing the cruising percentage into 100 or (2) dividing the total tract acreage by the number of acres sampled. The result is often termed the *cruise expansion factor* or *blow-up factor*.

9-9   Computing tract acreage from sample strips.   If the boundaries of a tract are well established, but the total area is unknown, a fixed cruising percentage may be decided upon, and the tract area can be estimated from the total chainage of strips comprising the sample. A 5 per cent cruise utilizing 1-chain strips at 20-chain intervals provides a good example. The centerline of the first sample strip is offset 10 chains from one corner of the tract (i.e., one-half the planned interval between lines), and parallel strips are alternately run 20 chains apart until the entire area has been traversed by a pattern similar to that shown in Fig. 9-1. If 132 lineal chains of sample strips are required, the area sampled is $(132 \times 1)/10 = 13.2$ acres. Because the strips were spaced for a 5 per cent estimate, the total tract area is approximately 20×13.2 or 264 acres. The expansion factor of 20 is also used to convert the sampled timber volume to total tract volume.

When trees are tallied according to forest types and acreages are desired for each type encountered, the preceding technique may also be used to develop these breakdowns. If the 132 lineal chains of strip were made up of 90 chains intersecting a coniferous type and 42 chains intersecting a hardwood type, sampled areas would be 9.0 and 4.2 acres, respectively. Applying the expansion factor of 20 would result in estimated areas of 180 acres for conifers and 84 acres for hardwoods.

9-10   Field procedure for strip cruising.   Accurate determination of strip lengths and centerlines on the ground requires that distances be chained rather than paced; thus a two-man crew is needed for reliable fieldwork. One man locates the centerline with a hand or staff compass and also serves as head chainman; the other cruises the timber on the sample strip and acts as rear chainman. Either person may handle the tree tally, depending on underbrush and density of the timber. The width of the sample strip is ordinarily checked by occasional pacing from the 2-chain tape being dragged along as a moving centerline. Trailer tapes may be used where slope corrections are necessary.

In an efficient cruising party, the compassman is always 1 to $1\frac{1}{2}$ chains ahead of the cruiser, and the sampling progresses in a smooth, continuous fashion. Experienced cruisers learn to "size up" tree heights well ahead, because there is a tendency toward underestimation when standing directly under a tree. At the end of each cruise line, the strip chainage should be recorded to the nearest link. Strip cruising can be speeded up appreciably by tallying tree diameters only and determining timber volumes from local volume tables.

When timber type maps are prepared as cruising progresses, strips are preferably spaced no more than 10 chains apart. There are few forest stands where the cruiser can map more than 5 chains to either side of the centerline without having to make frequent side checks to verify the trends of type boundaries, streams, trails, or fence lines. The preferred technique for mapping is to sketch cruise lines directly on a recent aerial photograph; approximate type lines and drainage can also be interpreted in advance of fieldwork. Then, during the conduct of fieldwork, type lines can be verified and cover types correctly identified with the photographs in hand (Chap. 11).

9-11 Pros and cons of strip cruising. The strip system of cruising is not as popular as in previous years. Its loss of favor is probably due to the facts that two-man crews are needed, and volume estimates are difficult to analyze statistically unless the tally is separated every few chains (resulting in a series of contiguous rectangular plots). In addition to items cited previously, the principal advantages claimed for strip cruising are:

1 Sampling is continuous, and less time is wasted in traveling between strips than would be the case for a plot cruise of equal intensity.
2 In comparison with a plot cruise of the same intensity, strips have fewer borderline trees, because the total perimeter of the sample is usually smaller.
3 With two men working together, there is less risk to personnel in remote or hazardous regions.

Disadvantages of strip cruising are as follows:

1 Errors are easily incurred through inaccurate estimation of strip width. Since the cruiser is constantly walking as he tallies, there is little incentive to leave the centerline of the strip to check borderline trees.
2 Unless tree heights are checked at a considerable distance from the bases of trees, they may be easily underestimated.

3 Brush and windfalls are more of a hindrance to the strip cruiser than to the plot cruiser.

4 It is difficult to make spot checks of the cruise results, because the strip centerline is rarely marked on the ground.

LINE-PLOT SYSTEM OF CRUISING

9-12 Plot sizes and spacings. As the name implies, line-plot cruising consists of a systematic tally of timber on a series of plots that are arranged in a rectangular or square grid pattern. Compass lines are run through the forest at uniform spacings, and plots of equal area are located at predetermined intervals along these lines. Plots are usually circular in shape, but they may also take the form of squares, rectangles, or triangles. In the United States, $\frac{1}{4}$- and $\frac{1}{5}$-acre circular plots are most commonly employed for sawtimber tallies; smaller plots are preferred for cruising poletimber or sapling stands. Radii for circular plots frequently used are given in Table 9-2.

TABLE 9-2 Radii for Several Sizes of Circular Sample Plots

Plot size, acres	Plot radius, ft	Plot radius, links
1	117.8	178.4
$\frac{1}{2}$	83.3	126.2
$\frac{1}{4}$	58.9	89.2
$\frac{1}{5}$	52.7	79.8
$\frac{1}{10}$	37.2	56.4
$\frac{1}{20}$	26.3	39.8
$\frac{1}{25}$	23.5	35.6
$\frac{1}{40}$	18.6	28.2
$\frac{1}{50}$	16.7	25.3
$\frac{1}{100}$	11.8	17.8
$\frac{1}{500}$	5.2	7.9
$\frac{1}{1000}$	3.7	5.6

As with the strip method, systematic line-plot inventories are usually planned on a per cent cruise basis. In Fig. 9-2, for example, $\frac{1}{5}$-acre plots are spaced at intervals of 4 chains on cruise lines that are 5 chains apart. As each plot "represents" an area of 20 square chains, the cruising percentage is computed as

$$\frac{\text{Plot size in acres}}{\text{Acres represented}} \times 100 = \frac{0.2 \text{ acre}}{2.0 \text{ acres}} \times 100 = 10 \text{ per cent}$$

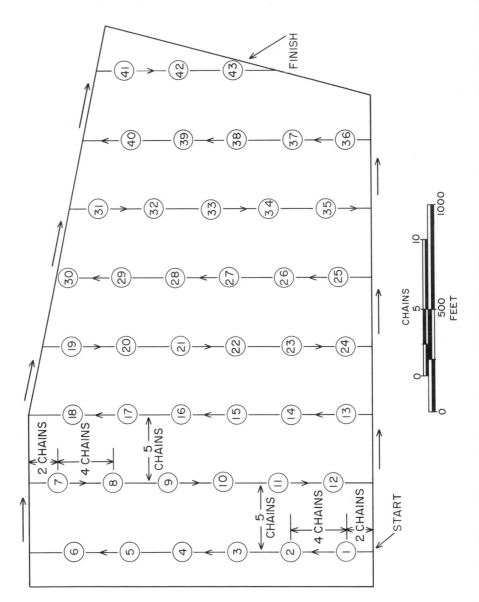

FIG. 9-2   Diagrammatic plan for a 10 per cent systematic
line-plot   cruise   utilizing   ⅕-acre   circular
samples.

By the same token, 10 per cent estimates may also be accomplished by spacing the same ⅕-acre plots at intervals of $2\frac{1}{2} \times 8$ chains, 2×10 chains, and so on. If a 1:1 square grid arrangement is desired, the intervals between both plot centers and compass lines would be calculated as $\sqrt{20}$ square chains or 4.47×4.47 chains. Similar computations can be made for other plot sizes and cruising intensities. Cruise expansion factors are calculated by the same methods described for strip cruises.

To cite another case example, a $2\frac{1}{2}$ per cent estimate utilizing $\frac{1}{10}$-acre plots might be desired for a tract whose exact area is unknown. As a $2\frac{1}{2}$ per cent cruise implies an expansion factor of 40, each sample plot must be located to represent 40 times its own area. For $\frac{1}{10}$-acre plots, the area represented is thus 4 acres or 40 square chains, and the samples might logically be spaced at intervals of 4×10 chains, 5×8 chains, or any other dimensions whose product is 40 square chains. If a total of 75 such plots is carefully located within the tract by chaining rather than pacing distances, the area sampled would be 7.5 acres and the total tract area approximately 7.5×40 or 300 acres. This method of area determination is not recommended when compass lines are paced.

Compass lines are usually run in the cardinal directions or perpendicular to the longest straight boundary of the forest property. When square or nearly square grid arrangements are employed, no allowances are necessary for orientation with respect to topography. However, compass lines should cross major drainage at right angles when lines are separated by more than three or four times the interval between plots. The spacing of plots on a given line may be any uniform interval, provided sample plot edges or perimeters do not overlap. Square grid arrangements tend to provide the most reliable estimates, but the greater number of cruise lines that are required sometimes mitigates against their use.

9-13 Combination or concentric plots. In localities where a variety of tree sizes and densities are encountered, concentric circular plots of different sizes may be employed in accordance with the character and distribution of the timber. From a given plot center, for example, saw-timber trees might be tallied on $\frac{1}{4}$- or $\frac{1}{5}$-acre circular samples, and a concentric plot of $\frac{1}{10}$ to $\frac{1}{20}$ acre might be the basis for poletimber tallies. Similarly, cordwood and saplings would be recorded on $\frac{1}{25}$- to $\frac{1}{40}$-acre samples and seedling counts made on $\frac{1}{100}$- to $\frac{1}{1000}$-acre plots. All plot radii originate from the same center stake, resulting in a target-like sampling pattern at each field location. This concept of sampling according to tree size classes bears some resemblance to point-sample cruising as described in Chap. 10.

When a single plot size is used for tree tallies, foresters have shown preference for $\frac{1}{5}$- or $\frac{1}{4}$-acre samples in most regions. However, recent studies in Arkansas and Georgia have shown that for second-growth stands of sawtimber, the optimum plot size is not larger than $\frac{1}{10}$ acre (Avery and Newton, 1965). For poletimber and cordwood sampling, plots of $\frac{1}{20}$ and $\frac{1}{25}$ acre often prove most efficient; i.e., they provide the greatest precision for the amount of field time required.

9-14 Field procedure for line-plot cruising. Line-plot cruising is ordinarily a one-man task, even though two or three men can sometimes be used efficiently. When cruising for land acquisition or timber sales or when tallying is relatively simple, two men cruising alone (or perhaps on adjacent lines) can usually accomplish more than two men working together on the same plots. With one-man crews, line directions are established with a hand compass, and intervals between sample plots are paced. Plot center locations for temporary samples are marked only when check cruises are to be made; in such cases, a wood stake or cairn provides a good reference point for plot relocation.

One of the more important considerations is the accurate determination of plot boundaries; as a minimum, four radii should be paced or measured to establish the sample perimeter. If an ordinary chaining pin is carried to denote plot centers, a steel tape or plastic line (with wire center) can be tied to the pin for one-man checks of plot radii. When trees appear to be borderline, the center of the stem (pith) determines whether they are "in" or "out."

Inaccurate estimation of plot radii is one of the greatest sources of error in using circular samples. The gravity of such errors is exemplified by the 2½ per cent cruise described previously; every stem erroneously tallied or ignored has its volume expanded 40 times. Thus the failure to include one tree having a volume of 300 bd ft will result in a final estimate that is 12,000 bd ft too low.

9-15 The effect of type changes. When a plot center happens to fall at a transition line that divides two different types, stand sizes, or area conditions (e.g., forest versus open land), a question arises as to whether the sample location should be shifted. If the cruise estimate is to be summarized by types and expansion factors for each type (including nonforest areas) are determined, the plot should be moved along the cruise line until it falls *entirely* within the type indicated by its original center location.

In contrast to the foregoing, plots should not be shifted if a single area expansion factor is to be used for deriving total tract volumes. Under these conditions, edge effects, type transition zones, and stand openings are typically part of the population; therefore a representative sample would be *expected* to result in occasional plots that are part sawtimber and part seedlings—or half timbered and half cutover land. To arbitrarily move these plot locations would result in a biased sample.

9-16 Plot tallies and intensity. Separate tally sheets are recommended for each plot location and species; tallies may be recorded as in strip cruising or handled by mark-sensed and prescored punch cards (Chap. 14). It is usually most efficient to begin the tally at a natural stand opening (or due north) and record trees in a clockwise sweep around the plot. When the tally is completed, a quick stem count made from the opposite direction provides a valuable check on the number of trees sampled.

The intensity of plot cruising is governed by the variability of the stand, allowable cruising costs, and desired standards of precision. When the coefficient of variation in volume per acre can be reliably estimated, Table 8-1 (though intended for random samples) will provide usable guides for deciding the number of plots needed for various standard errors. Fortunately, the trend is away from the concept of *fixed* cruising percentages, for it has been demonstrated that the "old reliable 10 per cent estimate" is not the paragon of precision that many foresters have presumed it to be. In the final analysis, the best endorsement for a given plot size and cruising intensity is an unbiased estimate of stand volume that is bracketed by reasonable confidence limits.

9-17 Merits of the plot system. The principal advantages claimed for line-plot cruising over the strip system are as follows:

1 The system is suitable for one-man cruising.
2 Cruisers are not hindered by brush and windfalls as in strip cruising, for they do not have to tally trees while following a compass line.
3 A pause at each plot center allows the cruiser more time for checking stem dimensions, borderline trees, and defective timber.
4 The tree tally is separated for each plot, thus permitting quick summaries of data by timber types, stand sizes, or area condition classes.

9-18 Timber volumes from stump diameters. In timber trespass cases, it may be necessary to determine the volume of trees illegally removed during a clandestine logging operation. As stem diameters cannot be measured at breast height, they must be estimated, by species or species groups, from available stump diameters. The conversion may be accomplished by use of specially prepared tables (Table 9-3), or they may be derived "on location" from sample measurements of trees left standing.

Once each dbh has been ascertained, volumes may be determined from local volume tables. Or, if tree tops have not been scattered, lengths of removed merchantable stems may be obtained by measuring distances between paired stumps and tops. With this additional information, volumes can be derived from standard tables. When the cutover area is too large for a 100 per cent stump tally, partial estimates based on sample plots may be used as in conventional cruising. The final volume summary should be accompanied by an appraisal of the stumpage value of timber removed, along with notes and photographs documenting damage to real property or to residual standing trees.

TABLE 9-3 Dbh Outside Bark in Inches in Relation to Stump Diameters

Stump d.o.b., in.	Stump height of yellow pine species, in.				Stump height of hardwood species, in.			
	6	12	18	30	6	12	18	30
	DBH in inches							
6	4	5	5	6	4	5	5	5
7	5	6	6	6	5	5	6	6
8	6	7	7	7	5	6	7	7
9	7	7	8	8	6	7	7	8
10	8	8	9	9	7	8	8	9
11	8	9	10	10	7	8	9	10
12	9	10	10	11	8	9	10	11
13	10	11	11	12	9	10	11	12
14	10	11	12	13	9	11	11	13
15	11	12	13	14	10	11	12	14
16	12	13	14	15	11	12	13	14
17	13	14	15	16	11	13	14	15
18	14	15	16	17	12	14	15	16
19	14	16	16	18	13	14	15	17
20	15	16	17	19	13	15	16	18
21	16	17	18	19	14	16	17	19
22	16	18	19	20	15	17	18	20
23	17	19	20	21	15	17	19	21
24	18	20	21	22	16	18	20	22
25	19	20	22	23	17	19	20	23
26	20	21	22	24	17	20	21	23
27	20	22	23	25	18	20	22	24
28	21	23	24	26	19	21	23	25
29	22	24	25	27	19	22	24	26
30	22	25	26	28	20	23	24	27
Basis: no. of trees	1,296	1,320	380	943	557	620	259	421

SOURCE: Research Note 43, U.S. Forest Service, Southeastern Forest Experiment Station, Asheville, N.C. July, 1953.

SUMMARIES OF CRUISE DATA

9-19 Stand and stock tables. Although total stand volume is a major objective of most forest inventories, such information is most useful when it is summarized by tree sizes and species groups. It is important to know that a given stand contains 1 million bd ft of timber, but it is more valuable to know how this volume is distributed among various species groups and diameter classes. Thus the compilation of stand and stock tables is often a prime requisite in summarizing cruising results.

A *stand table* is a tabulation of the total *number* of stems (or average number of stems per acre) in a stand or compartment, by dbh classes and species. A *stock table* lists the total *volume* of stems (or average volume per acre) in a stand, by dbh classes and species. As stock tables are derived from stand tables, they are sometimes combined into the same tabulation as shown by Table 9-4. This summary for mixed hard-

TABLE 9-4 Combined Stand and Stock Table for Mixed Hardwoods on a Tract of 107.2 Acres in Greene County, Georgia

Dbh, in.	No. of trees		Cubic-foot volumes*	
	Tract total	Per acre	Tract total	Per acre
5	1,195.5	11.2	1,730.4	16.1
6	1,432.6	13.4	3,767.6	35.1
7	1,455.1	13.6	5,667.8	52.9
8	1,150.6	10.7	6,294.4	58.7
9	1,128.0	10.5	8,379.0	78.2
10	1,082.9	10.1	10,622.4	99.1
11	823.4	7.7	11,142.7	103.9
Totals	8,268.1	77.2	47,604.3	444.0

* Cubic-foot volumes are inside bark of the merchantable stem to a variable top diameter not smaller than 3 in.

wood species includes oaks, gums, yellowpoplar, ash, and sycamore on a tract of 107.2 acres. Total numbers of trees and volumes are shown, as well as per-acre averages.

9-20 Faster office computations. The key to efficient handling of inventory data and reductions in tedious office computations is advance planning—beginning with the collection of field data. This means that cruising work should not begin until (1) inventory objectives have been clearly outlined and (2) the exact format of summary forms to be compiled from the cruise data is known. Failure to take cognizance of these elemental rules has resulted in thousands of man-hours wasted in the field and countless file cabinets stuffed with unused tabulations from ill-conceived surveys. Even when field travel costs are high, it is *not* more efficient to "go ahead and collect soil samples or deer-browse data while you're there," unless someone has definite plans for analysis of

TABLE 9-5 Local Volume Tables for Georgia Shortleaf-Loblolly Pines Incorporated into a Field Tally Sheet

Dbh class	Tree tally	Tree vol., cu ft	Plot vol., cu ft	Local cubic-foot volumes are outside bark to 4-in. top diameter.
5		0.4		
6		1.2		Local board-foot volumes derived from Scribner Log Rule, Form Class 78.
7		2.6		
8		4.5		
9		7.1		

				Tree vol., bd ft	Plot vol., bd ft
10		9.9			
11		13.4			
12		17.2		86	
13		20.7		110	
14		24.6		136	
15		28.9		168	
16		33.6		201	
17		39.7		242	
18		45.4		280	
19		51.6		326	
20		58.4		369	
21		65.7		426	
22		73.5		481	
Totals					
Per acre					

such information. As a simple illustration, it may be assumed that a forest supervisor requires a quick land acquisition cruise of 80 acres. Cubic-foot volumes are needed for all pines 5 in. dbh and larger, and board-foot volumes for trees 12 in. dbh and up. Stand and stock tables will also be required, and only 1 man-day is allotted for the entire task. Although the problem of work scheduling is not complex here, some rational thinking and planning are in order. Otherwise, the cruiser who immediately departs to spend 8 to 10 hr in the woods may be faced with additional hours of office computing that evening.

Allowing 1 hr for travel to and from the tract, a 10 to 15 per cent area sample of the 80-acre tract can probably be taken in 6 man-hours or less, depending on topography, underbrush, and character of the timber. Because only one species group will be tallied, cruising time can be considerably reduced if local volume tables are available and trees are recorded by dbh only. Table 9-5 provides the answer. Local cubic-foot and board-foot volumes have been combined with a simple tally sheet; once the fieldwork is done, the required stand tables are expanded directly from the "tree tally" column, and stock tables are derived from the "plot volume" column—a product of "tree tally times tree volume" for each dbh class. Tree heights are not specified, and their elimination from the tally saves valuable time in field estimating and office computations of volume. The result is that no superfluous data are collected, yet all project objectives are satisfactorily accomplished.

PROBLEMS

9-1 Compute the cruising per cents and expansion factors for the following systematic samples:
  (a) Strips ½ chain wide spaced 12 chains apart
  (b) Two 1-chain strips run through a section of land
  (c) Plots of 1/20 acre spaced at 2½ × 5 chains
  (d) Plots of ¼ acre spaced at 5 × 15 chains

9-2 (a) If you space 2-chain strips at 10-chain intervals through a square quarter section of land and tally 155 MBF on the sample, what would be the total volume on the entire tract?
  (b) If you space ⅕-acre circular plots at 5 × 10 chains through a tier of six forties, and the volume tallied on the sample is 41.5 MBF, what would be the total volume on the entire tract?
  (c) How many lineal chains of sample strips 1 chain wide would you run through a township to obtain a 2½ per cent cruising intensity?
  (d) If you made a 0.05 per cent inventory of the total land area of your own state, how many ¼-acre circular plots would be required? For a square grid arrangement of samples, what would be the distance (in chains) between plots?

9-3 For the same plot sizes shown in Table 9-2, compile a similar tabulation for *square* sample plots. In lieu of plot radii, show the length of one side of the squares in feet and links.

9-4 Design a 10 to 20 per cent strip cruise for a local forest tract of 25 to 100 acres. Follow this with a systematic plot cruise of the same intensity. On both cruises, tally trees by dbh only, and use local volume tables for deriving stand and stock tables. Compare the results of the two inventories with regard to ease of field travel, cruising time required, and volumes derived.

9-5 Prepare a table of stump diameter-dbh conversions for a major species in your locality. Obtain paired measurements of at least 100 trees, and summarize data as in Table 9-3.

REFERENCES

Avery, T. Eugene, and Newton, Roger
1965. Plot sizes for timber cruising in Georgia. *J. Forestry* **63**:930–932.

Beckwith, A. F., Dwight, T. W., and Leslie, A. P.
1964. Comparison of log scaling and timber cruising for determination of wood volumes. *Ontario Dept. Lands and Forests, Res. Report* 59. 54 pp., illus.

Bickford, C. Allen
1961. Stratification for timber cruising. *J. Forestry* **59**:761–763.

Bruce, Donald, and Schumacher, Francis X.
1950. Forest Mensuration, 3d ed. McGraw-Hill Book Company, Inc., New York. 483 pp., illus.

Dale, Jim E.
1961. A simplified method of computing cordwood volumes in the woods. *J. Forestry* **59**:191–193.

Girard, James W., and Gevorkiantz, Suren R.
1939. Timber cruising. U.S.D.A., Forest Service, Washington, D.C. 160 pp., illus.

Johnson, F. A., and Hixon, H. J.
1952. The most efficient size and shape of plot to use for cruising in old-growth Douglas-fir timber. *J. Forestry* **50**:17–20. illus.

Kendall, R. H., and Sayn-Wittgenstein, L.
1960. A rapid method of laying out circular plots. *Forestry Chron.* **36**:230–233. illus.

McCormack, J. F.
1953. D.b.h. in relation to stump diameter at various heights for southern yellow pines and hardwoods. *U.S. Forest Serv., Southeast. Forest Expt. Sta. Res. Note* 43. 2 pp.

Vimmerstedt, J. P.
1957. Estimating d.b.h. from stump diameter in southern Appalachian species. *U.S. Forest Serv., Southeast. Forest Expt. Sta. Res. Note* 110. 2 pp.

CHAPTER **10**

POINT-SAMPLE TIMBER CRUISING

A NEW ANGLE TO CRUISING

10-1 The concept of point sampling. In its most elementary form, point sampling is merely a method of selecting trees to be tallied on the basis of their *sizes* rather than by their frequency of occurrence. Sample "points," somewhat analogous to plot centers, are randomly or systematically located within a forested tract, and a simple prism or angle gauge that subtends a fixed angle of view is used to "sight in" each tree dbh. Tree boles close enough to the observation point to completely fill the fixed sighting angle are tallied; stems too small or too far away are ignored. Thus the probability of tallying any given tree is proportional to its BA, and consequently more time is spent on larger, high-value trees than is the case with conventional strip or line-plot cruising.

The concept of point sampling was developed and first reported in

1948 by Walter Bitterlich, a forest engineer of Salzburg, Austria. The introduction and adoption of the method in North America were largely due to the efforts of Lewis R. Grosenbaugh, a biometrician with the U.S. Forest Service. Grosenbaugh recognized the potentialities of the angle-gauge idea and expanded it into a complete inventory system that has largely supplanted strip and line-plot cruising in many regions. In the United States, the technique is usually referred to as the *Bitterlich system* or simply as *point sampling*. These two terms are generally favored over *variable-plot sampling* or *plotless cruising*.

10-2   The basal area approach.   Point sampling does not require measurements of either plot areas or tree diameters. If a predetermined basal area factor (BAF) of 10 sq ft per acre is assumed and a total of 75 trees is tallied on 15 sample points, the average of five trees per point multiplied by 10 provides a BA estimate of 50 sq ft per acre. The well-established relationship between tree BA and volumes also makes it feasible to use point sampling for obtaining conventional timber inventory data when "counted" trees are recorded by merchantable or total height classes.

10-3   Selecting a sighting angle.   BA conversion factors are dependent on the sighting angle (or "critical angle") arbitrarily selected. The sight-

TABLE 10-1 Common Basal Area Factors and Angle Sizes Used in
Point Sampling

Basal area factor	Angle size, min	Angle size, diopters	Ratio (tree diameter to plot radius)	Plot radius factor
1	32.94	0.96	1/104.4	8.696
2	46.59	1.36	1/73.8	6.149
3	57.06	1.66	1/60.2	5.021
4	65.89	1.92	1/52.2	4.348
5	73.66	2.14	1/46.7	3.889
10	104.18	3.03	1/33.0	2.750
15	127.59	3.71	1/26.9	2.245
20	147.34	4.29	1/23.3	1.944
25	164.73	4.79	1/20.9	1.739
30	180.46	5.25	1/19.0	1.588
35	194.92	5.67	1/17.6	1.470
40	208.38	6.07	1/16.5	1.375
50	232.99	6.79	1/14.8	1.230
60	255.23	7.44	1/13.5	1.123

SOURCE: Hovind and Rieck, 1961.

ing angle chosen, in turn, is largely based on the average size and distribution of trees to be sampled. Furthermore, from the standpoint of subsequent volume computations, it is desirable to select a sighting angle having a BAF that can be expressed as a whole number rather than as a fractional number.

In Eastern United States, a predetermined sighting angle of 104.18 min (BAF of 10 sq ft per acre) is commonly used in second-growth sawtimber or dense pole-timber stands. Critical angles of 73.66 min (BAF 5) and 147.34 min (BAF 20) are often employed for light-density pole stands and for large, old-growth sawtimber, respectively. With small, scattered stems, the sighting angle is narrowed so that it will extend farther out for trees of minimum diameter; conversely, where large tree diameters are common, the angle is enlarged to reduce excessively heavy field tallies.

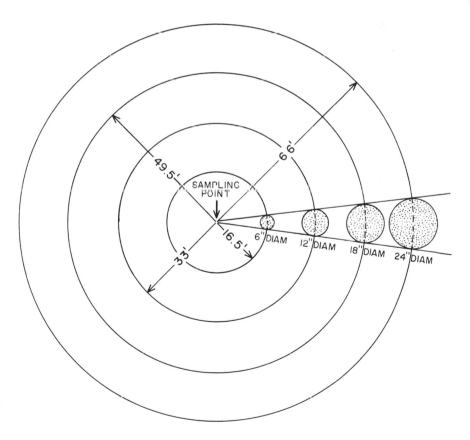

FIG. 10-1 Ratio of tree diameter to plot radius for
BAF 10. *Adapted from Hovind and Rieck,*
1961.

Depending on the region, average tree size, and amount of underbrush restricting line-of-sight visibility, the BAF is usually chosen to provide an average tally of 5 to 12 trees per sample point. In Western United States where larger timber predominates, a BAF of 20 to 60 is in common use. For "West Side" Douglas fir, a BAF of 40 might be regarded as typical, but an instrument with a BAF of 20 would be more frequently encountered in sampling stands of "East Side" ponderosa pine.

10-4   Plot radius factor.   To illustrate the meaning of BA conversions listed in Table 10-1, a sighting angle of 104.18 min (BAF 10) may be presumed. As this angle can also be defined by placing a 1-in. horizontal intercept on a sighting base of 33 in. (column 4 of Table 10-1), it follows that all trees located no farther than 33 times their diameter from the sample point will be tallied. Accordingly, a 1-in. dbh tree must be within 33 in. of the point, a 12-in.-dbh tree will be tallied up to 396 in. (33.0 ft) away, and a 24-in. or 2-ft-dbh tree will be recorded up to a distance of 66 ft (Fig. 10-1). This 1:33 ratio of tree diameter to plot radius, a constant for the specified angle of 104.18 min, has a value of 2.75 ft (33 ÷ 12) when expressed as a "plot radius factor." Thus for each full inch added to stem diameter, a tree can be 2.75 ft farther from the sample point and still be tallied.

HOW POINT SAMPLING WORKS

10-5   Imaginary tree zones.   As the plot radius factor for BAF 10 has been developed in the preceding section, all subsequent explanations of point-sampling theory and tree volume conversions in this chapter will presume a sighting angle of 104.18 min and a BAF of 10 sq ft per acre. Nevertheless, the underlying principles discussed may be applied to any other angle or BAF.

Because each tree "sighted in" must be within 33 times its diameter of the sample point to be tallied, it is convenient to presume that all trees are encircled with imaginary zones whose radii are exactly 33 times the diameter of each tree stem. All these imaginary circles that encompass a given sampling point on the ground represent trees to be tallied (Fig. 10-2). Thus the probability of tallying any given tree is proportional to its stem BA. A 12-in. dbh has four times the probability of being counted as a 6-in.-dbh stem. Stated in another way, the chances of tallying one 12-in.-dbh tree are the same as that of encountering four 6-in.-dbh trees.

10-6   Equality of trees on a per acre basic.   For the sighting angle of 104.18 min, each tallied tree (regardless of its size or relative position to the sampling point) represents 10 sq ft of BA on a *per acre basis.*

The reason for this is that each stem and its imaginary zone "represent" a definite part of an acre and a specific number of trees per acre, depending on its size. The derivation of values for 6-in.- and 12-in.-dbh trees in Table 10-2 provides an explanation or "proof" of this theory.

Considering the 6-in. dbh first, its imaginary "plot" radius is read from Table 10-2 as 16.50 ft. This hypothetical zone represents an imaginary plot of 0.0196 acre around each 6-in.-dbh stem (column 3 of

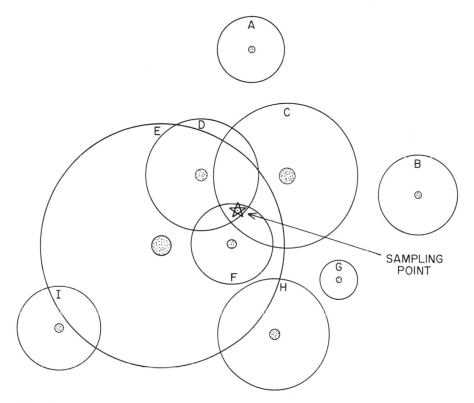

FIG. 10-2   Imaginary zones proportional to stem diameter and encircling each tree determine
which trees will be tallied at a given point.
Adapted from Hovind and Rieck, 1961.

Table 10-2). By dividing 0.0196 into 1.00 acre, it can be seen from column 4 that there can be 51.02 such areas fitted into a single acre. Thus when one 6-in.-dbh tree is tallied, it is tacitly assumed that there are 51.02 such stems per acre. Accordingly, the BA of a 6-in.-dbh tree (0.196 sq ft from column 5), multiplied by 51.02 trees per acre, yields the "constant" BAF of 10 sq ft *per acre* (column 6).

For 12-in.-dbh stems, the imaginary plot radius is 33.00 ft, and the

TABLE 10-2 Derivation of the Basal Area Factor of 10 Sq Ft Per Acre for Point Sampling

Tree dbh, in. (1)	Imaginary plot radius, ft (2)	Imaginary plot size, acres (3)	Trees per acre,* no. of stems (4)	Basal area per tree, sq ft (5)	Basal area per acre, sq ft (6)
4	11.00	0.0087	114.94	0.087	10
6	16.50	0.0196	51.02	0.196	10
8	22.00	0.0349	28.65	0.349	10
10	27.50	0.0545	18.35	0.545	10
12	33.00	0.0785	12.74	0.785	10
14	38.50	0.1069	9.35	1.069	10
16	44.00	0.1396	7.16	1.396	10
18	49.50	0.1767	5.66	1.767	10
20	55.00	0.2182	4.58	2.182	10
22	60.50	0.2640	3.79	2.640	10
24	66.00	0.3142	3.18	3.142	10
26	71.50	0.3687	2.71	3.687	10
28	77.00	0.4276	2.34	4.276	10
30	82.50	0.4909	2.04	4.909	10
32	88.00	0.5585	1.79	5.585	10
34	93.50	0.6305	1.59	6.305	10
36	99.00	0.7069	1.41	7.069	10
Method of calculation	dbh × 2.75	$\dfrac{\pi r^2}{43,560}$	$\dfrac{1.00}{\text{plot size}}$	$0.005454D^2$	column 4 × 5

* Exact value for number of trees per acre may vary slightly, depending upon number of decimal places expressed for imaginary plot size.

implied plot size is 0.0785 acre. Only 12.74 trees per acre are assumed— approximately one-fourth the number of 6-in.-dbh trees expected. However, 12-in.-dbh trees have four times the BA of 6-in.-dbh stems, and this value (0.785 sq ft) from column 5, multiplied by 12.74 trees per acre, again produces a BA of 10 sq ft per acre. The same "proof" applies to all other tree sizes encountered when sampling with a BAF 10 angle gauge.

INSTRUMENTS FOR POINT SAMPLING

10-7 The stick-type angle gauge. This simple, horizontal angle gauge often consists of a wooden rod with a peep sight at one end and a metal intercept at the other. To establish a sighting angle of 104.18 min (BAF 10), an intercept 1 in. wide on a 33-in. sighting base can be easily improvised. Gauges for other factors can be constructed according to ratios provided in Table 10-1. Regardless of the ratio desired, the sighting base should be at least 24 in. long; otherwise, it is difficult to keep both the intercept and the tree in focus simultaneously.

When the stick gauge is used, all tree diameters larger than the defined angle are counted; those smaller are ignored. Trees that appear to be exactly the same size as the intercept should be checked by measuring their exact dbh and distance from the sampling point. The product of dbh and the appropriate plot radius factor (2.75 for BAF 10) determines whether the tree is "in," "out," or a borderline case. Truly borderline trees are rare, but if they are encountered, they should be tallied as ½ tree.

With a stick gauge, the observer's eye represents the vertex of the sighting angle; hence the stick must be pivoted or revolved about this exact point for a correct tree tally. When properly calibrated for use by a particular individual, the stick gauge may be just as accurate as other more expensive point-sampling devices. In dense sapling or pole stands and where heavy underbrush is encountered, the stick gauge is often easier to use than more sophisticated relascopes or prisms.

10-8   The Spiegel relascope.   This is a versatile, hand-held instrument developed for point sampling by Walter Bitterlich. It is a compact and rugged device that may be used for determining BA per acre, upper-stem diameters, tree heights, horizontal distances of 66 and 99 ft with correction for slope, and measurement of slope on per cent, degree, and topographic scales. Sighting angles are provided for factors of 5, 10, 20, or 40, and the instrument automatically corrects each angle for slope. The base has a tripod socket for use when especially precise measurements are desired.

Establishment of sighting angles with the Spiegel relascope is somewhat analogous to measuring distances with transit and stadia rod; the principal difference is that the relascope subtends a horizontal angle, and the transit and stadia system is based on a vertically projected angle. The Spiegel relascope is complex in design but relatively simple to use. Its principal disadvantages are that it is relatively expensive and lacks the optical qualities for good sighting visibility on dark and rainy days.

10-9   The wedge prism.   A properly ground and calibrated prism is merely a tapered wedge of glass that bends or deflects light rays at a specific offset angle. When a tree stem is viewed through such a wedge,

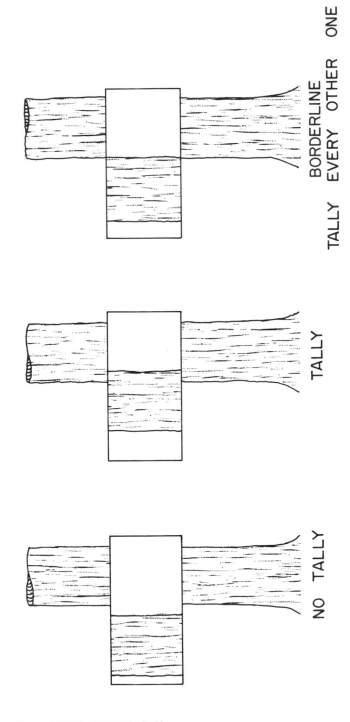

NO TALLY

TALLY

BORDERLINE
TALLY EVERY OTHER ONE

FIG. 10-3 Use of the wedge prism for point sampling.
Adapted from Bruce, 1955.

the bole appears to be displaced, as if seen through a camera range finder. The amount of offset or displacement is controlled by the prism strength, measured in diopters. As one prism diopter is equal to a right angle displacement of one unit per 100 units of distance, a 3.03-diopter prism will produce a displacement of one unit per 33 units of distance, i.e., a critical angle of 104.18 min. Other prism-strength relationships are given in Table 10-1.

Field use of the prism requires that it be held precisely over the sampling point at all times, for this point and *not the observer's eye* is the pivot from which the stand is "swept" by a 360° circle. All tree stems not completely offset when viewed through the wedge are counted; others are not tallied (Fig. 10-3). Trees that appear to be borderline should be measured and checked with the appropriate plot radius factor *before* arbitrarily deciding to tally every other borderline stem.

The prism may be held at any convenient distance from the eye, provided it is always positioned directly over the sampling point. Proper orientation also requires that the prism be held in a vertical position and at right angles to the line of sight; otherwise, large errors in the tree tally may result (Fig. 10-4).

The wedge prism is simple, relatively inexpensive, portable, and as accurate as other angle gauges when properly calibrated and used. Some sighting difficulties are found in dense stands where displaced bole sections offset into one another, and special corrections must be applied when slopes of 15 per cent and greater are encountered. However, the latter disadvantage may be cited for all point-sampling devices except the Spiegel relascope.

10-10 Calibration of prisms or angle gauges. Precision-tested prisms and angle gauges should be used whenever feasible, because a BAF of *exactly* 5, 10, or 40 is conducive to faster computations than such values as 4.9, 9.8, or 39.5 (Sec. 10-3). Prisms ground to within ±1 min of a specified angle are desired, for such deviation will usually result in a maximum error of about 2 per cent for a BAF 10 prism.

Where inexpensive prisms or angle gauges are employed and the exact BAF is unknown, such devices should be carefully calibrated. As individual eyesights may vary appreciably, it may even be desirable to calibrate *all instruments* (regardless of price or supposed precision) for each cruiser's own sighting habits or peculiarities.

To calibrate a prism or angle gauge, a target of known width (for example, 1.0 ft) is set up against a contrasting background. With the angle gauge or prism in proper orientation, the observer backs away from the target until the target exactly fills the sighting angle (or until the prism image is displaced as shown for the "borderline" tree in Fig.

10-3). The exact distance from target to instrument is then measured and the BAF computed by this relationship:

$$BAF = 10{,}890 \left(\frac{W}{D}\right)^2$$

where W is the target width in feet, and D is the distance to target in feet.

The foregoing formula is not exact when a flat target is used in calibration but only when the target is a circular cross section with diameter W.

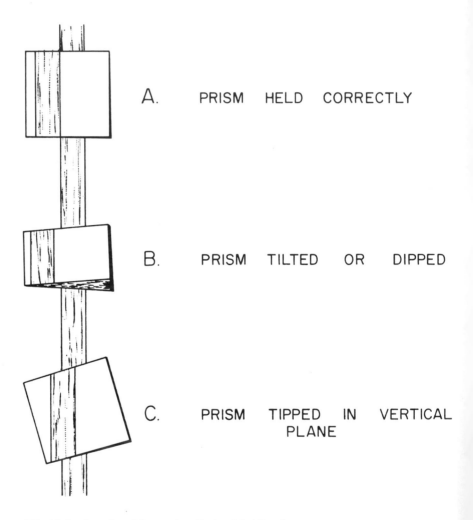

A. PRISM HELD CORRECTLY

B. PRISM TILTED OR DIPPED

C. PRISM TIPPED IN VERTICAL
PLANE

FIG. 10-4   Correct and incorrect methods of holding the
wedge prism. *Adapted from Hovind and
Rieck,* 1961.

With small critical angles, however, this simple approximation is usually satisfactory, because of the near equality of sine and tangent functions for narrow angles. For reliable results, the instrument should be mounted on a plane table, tripod, or vise and several readings made of the horizontal distance to the target. When a fractional BAF is derived, conversions similar to those in Table 10-2 should be prepared to simplify subsequent inventory computations.

10-11 Corrections for slope. Unless the Spiegel relascope is used to establish sighting angles, corrections must be made in point sampling when slope is 15 per cent or greater, that is, a 15-ft rise or drop in elevation per 100 horizontal feet (Stage, 1959).

When the wedge prism is used, an approximate on-the-ground compensation for slope can be made by tilting the top edge of the prism through the estimated slope angle—at right angles to the line of slope.

TABLE 10-3 Slope Correction Table for Point Sampling*

Maximum per cent of slope at sampling point	Maximum degrees of slope at sampling point	Multiply tree count by—
15	6.75	1.01
20	9.00	1.02
25	11.25	1.03
30	13.50	1.04
35	15.75	1.06
40	18.00	1.08
45	20.25	1.10
50	22.50	1.12
55	24.75	1.14
60	27.00	1.17
65	29.25	1.19
70	31.50	1.22
75	33.75	1.25
80	36.00	1.28
85	38.25	1.31
90	40.50	1.34
95	42.75	1.38
100	45.00	1.41

* This correction for tree count, BA, and volume per acre is true only when it is assumed that in this sampling procedure a proportionate number of trees will be added when the slope distance is corrected to the true horizontal distance. For all practical purposes, however, tree count, BA, and volume can be corrected by using the above multipliers.
SOURCE: Hovind and Rieck, 1961.

With angle gauges such as the stick type, the unadjusted field tally can be corrected by (1) measuring the slope at right angles to the contour in per cent or degrees and (2) applying corresponding correction factors to BA or volume per acre estimates from Table 10-3. The amount of slope is usually measured with an Abney level.

10-12 Doubtful trees, limiting distances, and bias. Most cruisers possess some degree of observer bias when "sighting in" doubtful trees. In a strict sense, borderline trees occur only when the distance from the sampling point to the stem center is precisely equal to tree dbh times plot radius factor. Therefore, if doubtful trees are regularly checked by careful measurement, the borderline tree is rarely encountered.

To encourage regular field checks of doubtful trees and speed up the

TABLE 10-4 Horizontal Limiting Distances in Feet for BAF 10 Point-sampling Instruments

Dbh, in.	0.0	0.1	0.2	0.3	0.4	0.5	0.6	0.7	0.8	0.9
5	13.75	14.02	14.30	14.57	14.85	15.12	15.40	15.67	15.95	16.22
6	16.50	16.77	17.05	17.32	17.60	17.87	18.15	18.42	18.70	18.97
7	19.25	19.52	19.80	20.07	20.35	20.62	20.90	21.17	21.45	21.72
8	22.00	22.27	22.55	22.82	23.10	23.37	23.65	23.92	24.20	24.47
9	24.75	25.02	25.30	25.57	25.85	26.12	26.40	26.67	26.95	27.22
10	27.50	27.77	28.05	28.32	28.60	28.87	29.15	29.42	29.70	29.97
11	30.25	30.52	30.80	31.07	31.35	31.62	31.90	32.17	32.45	32.72
12	33.00	33.27	33.55	33.82	34.10	34.37	34.65	34.92	35.20	35.47
13	35.75	36.02	36.30	36.57	36.85	37.12	37.40	37.67	37.95	38.22
14	38.50	38.77	39.05	39.32	39.60	39.87	40.15	40.42	40.70	40.97
15	41.25	41.52	41.80	42.07	42.35	42.62	42.90	43.17	43.65	43.72
16	44.00	44.27	44.55	44.82	45.10	45.37	45.65	45.92	46.20	46.47
17	46.75	47.02	47.30	47.57	47.85	48.12	48.40	48.67	48.95	49.22
18	49.50	49.77	50.05	50.32	50.60	50.87	51.15	51.42	51.70	51.97
19	52.25	52.52	52.80	53.07	53.35	53.62	53.90	54.17	54.45	54.72
20	55.00	55.27	55.55	55.82	56.10	56.37	56.65	56.92	57.20	57.47
21	57.75	58.02	58.30	58.57	58.85	59.12	59.40	59.67	59.95	60.22
22	60.50	60.77	61.05	61.32	61.60	61.87	62.15	62.42	62.70	62.97
23	63.25	63.52	63.80	64.07	64.35	64.62	64.90	65.17	65.45	65.72
24	66.00	66.27	66.55	66.82	67.10	67.37	67.65	67.92	68.20	68.47
25	68.75	69.02	69.30	69.57	69.85	70.12	70.40	70.67	70.95	71.22
26	71.50	71.77	72.05	72.32	72.60	72.87	73.15	73.42	73.70	73.97
27	74.25	74.52	74.80	75.07	75.35	75.62	75.90	76.17	76.45	76.72
28	77.00	77.27	77.55	77.82	78.10	78.37	78.65	78.92	79.20	79.47
29	79.75	80.02	80.30	80.57	80.85	81.12	81.40	81.67	81.95	82.22
30	82.50	82.77	83.05	83.32	83.60	83.87	84.15	84.42	84.70	84.97

sampling process, it is helpful to compile tables of limiting distances in advance of fieldwork. These are easily prepared by multiplying various tree diameters by the appropriate plot radius factor (Table 10-4). For maximum utility, such tables should be expressed in feet and links.

When brush or other obstructions make it necessary to move from the sampling point to view certain stems, special care must be exercised to maintain the correct distances from obscured trees. Failure to maintain proper distance relationships can result in sizable errors in the tally, especially when using a large BAF.

10-13 Choice of instruments. In summary, the selection of a point sampling sighting gauge is largely a matter of balancing such factors as costs, efficiency, and personal preferences. All the devices described here will provide a reliable tree tally if they are properly calibrated and carefully used. Accordingly, the following generalizations will be primarily useful to the newer advocates of point sampling:

1 When steep slopes are regularly encountered, the Spiegel relascope is preferred.
2 For relatively flat topography, either the wedge prism or the stick gauge may be used. The prism is particularly desirable for persons who wear eyeglasses, because the vertex of the sighting angle occurs at the prism rather than at the observer's eye. However, the prism is difficult to use in dense stands due to displacement of stem sections into one another.
3 The simple stick gauge, though largely supplanted by the prism, is preferable in dense stands—especially if the cruiser does not wear spectacles. Cruisers who use point sampling only occasionally will find the stick gauge more reliable, because there are fewer ways for errors to result with this device than with the wedge prism.

VOLUME CONVERSIONS

10-14 Tree count and basal area. As previously described, each tree tallied in point sampling, *regardless of its diameter*, represents the same amount of BA on a per acre basis. BA per acre for any tract may thus be computed by this relationship:

$$\text{BA per acre} = \frac{\text{total trees tallied}}{\text{no. of points}} \times \text{BAF}$$

If the BAF is 10 and 160 trees are tallied at 20 sample points, the BA per acre would be $160/20 \times 10 = 80$ sq ft per acre. As with all cruising techniques, it is presumed that the counted trees are representative of the population sampled.

10-15 Derivation of tree volumes. Most cruisers are interested in volumes expressed in board feet, cubic feet, or cords rather than BA alone. When using point sampling, volume computations are handled differently from conventional cruising, because all sizes of trees have the same BA per acre. The variable of dbh (a function of BA) can therefore be ignored when only total volumes are required, and the field tally can be reduced to a simple stem count by height classes. Average stand volume per acre is determined by using ratios of the volumes of each height class to their respective BA. These ratios or volume factors can be quickly determined by use of the "per acre conversion factors" in Table 10-2 and the volume of one tree of a specified size. Volume per acre can thus be derived by this relationship:

$$\text{Volume per acre} = \frac{(\text{volume per tree})(\text{no. trees per acre})}{\text{no. of sample points}}$$

To illustrate the computation of volume per acre conversions, it may be assumed that cordwood factors are desired for 1-bolt (8 ft of merchantable height) trees in the Lake states by five tree diameter classes. Essential steps in deriving these converting factors can be illustrated in tabular form:

Merchantable height, ft	Corresponding dbh class, in.	Volume per tree, cd	Trees per acre (Table 10-2), no. of stems	Volume per acre, (column 3 × 4)
8	6	0.017	51.02	0.87
8	8	0.031	28.65	0.89
8	10	0.049	18.35	0.90
8	12	0.070	12.74	0.89
8	14	0.095	9.35	0.89

For the single 8-ft-height class listed, it will be noted that volume per acre conversions show very little change from one dbh class to another. Hence, unless stand tables are required, it is superfluous to break down the tally by diameter classes. As shown here, a volume factor of 0.9 cd will suffice for all 8-ft heights, irrespective of diameter changes. For other height classes, volume per acre factors might be computed as follows:

Merchantable height, ft	Corresponding dbh class, in.	Volume per tree, cd	Trees per acre (Table 10-2), no. of stems	Volume per acre, (column 3 × 4)
8	8	0.031	28.65	0.89 = 0.9
16	10	0.083	18.35	1.52 = 1.5
24	12	0.155	12.74	1.97 = 2.0
32	14	0.269	9.35	2.52 = 2.5
40	18	0.531	5.66	3.01 = 3.0
48	22	0.918	3.79	3.48 = 3.5

To review the foregoing computations, the height classes desired for field tallying are listed first in column 1. The average dbh that corresponds to each height class must be obtained from existing records or special field samples (column 2). With these two values known, the volume per tree (column 3) is read from any desired tree volume table. Number of trees per acre (column 4), based on the appropriate dbh class, may be read directly from Table 10-2 for BAF 10 conversions—or computed as described in Sec. 10-6. Finally, the volume per acre conversion (column 5) is simply a product of volume per tree and number of trees per acre.

10-16   Field tally by height classes.   The reason that point sampling appears to be such a simple method of deriving standing tree volumes is that most of the computational work is accomplished *in advance of the field tally*. When the volume per acre conversions are incorporated directly into the field tally form and trees are recorded by height classes only, a minimum of post-cruising calculations are necessary. Under these conditions, the field record essentially becomes a cumulative tally sheet and volumes can be speedily summarized (Table 10-5).

TABLE 10-5 Simplified Field Tally and Volume Summary for Point Sampling

Tract: La Crosse, Wisconsin	Timbered area: 40 acres
No. of points: 20	BAF: 10

Height class, ft	Tree tally, no. of stems	Volume per acre, cd	Tally × volume, cd
8	20	0.9	18.0
16	30	1.5	45.0
24	40	2.0	80.0
32	20	2.5	50.0
40	10	3.0	30.0
48	5	3.5	17.5
Totals	125 Trees		240.5 cd

$$\text{BA per acre} = \frac{125 \text{ trees}}{20 \text{ points}} \times 10 = 62.5 \text{ sq ft per acre}$$

$$\text{Average volume per acre} = \frac{240.5 \text{ cd}}{20 \text{ points}} = 12.025 \text{ cd per acre}$$

When stand and stock tables are needed and trees must also be listed by diameter classes, special cumulative tally sheets have been published (Thornton and Hutchison, 1958).

POINT-SAMPLE CRUISING INTENSITY

10-17 Comparisons with conventional plots. There is no fixed plot size when using point sampling; hence it is difficult to compute cruise intensity on a conventional area-sample basis. Each tree has its own imaginary plot radius (depending on the BAF used), and the exact plot size cannot be easily determined, even after the tally has been made. However, approximations can be made on the basis of the *average* stem diameter encountered at a given point.

Assuming an even-aged plantation with a single dbh class of 6 in. and a critical angle of 104.18 min, the area sampled would have a radius of 6 × 2.75 or 16.5 ft—equivalent to about $\frac{1}{50}$ acre. If the dbh class were doubled to 12 in., the effective sample area would quadruple to about $\frac{1}{12}$ acre. To sample a full $\frac{1}{5}$ acre, average dbh would have to be about 19 in.

From the foregoing, it follows that use of BAF 10 sample points in lieu of the same number of $\frac{1}{5}$- or $\frac{1}{4}$-acre plots will usually result in a tally of fewer trees. From a statistical standpoint, however, the selection of trees according to size rather than frequency may more than offset this reduction of sample size—and with an additional saving in time. Conversely, it must be remembered that smaller samples of any kind require larger expansion or blow-up factors. Thus when point sampling is adopted, the so-called borderline trees must always be closely checked, for the erroneous addition or omission of a single stem reduces the accuracy of any volume estimate by the amount of the BAF.

10-18 Number of sampling points needed. The only accurate method of determining how many point samples should be measured is to determine the standard deviation (or coefficient of variation) of BA or volume per acre from a preliminary field sample. When this has been done, sampling intensity may be derived from Table 8-1 or by formulas described in Secs 8-15 and 8-16. If the statistical approach is not feasible, the following rules of thumb will often provide acceptable results:

1 If the BAF is selected according to tree size so that an average of 5 to 12 trees are counted at each point, use the same number of points as $\frac{1}{5}$-acre plots.

2 With a BAF 10 angle gauge and timber that averages 12 to 15 in. in diameter, use the same number of points as $\frac{1}{10}$-acre plots.

3 For reliable estimates, never use fewer than 20 points in natural timber stands or less than 10 points in even-aged plantations.

10-19 Point samples versus plots. Of the numerous field comparisons of point sampling and plot cruising, one of the more extensive evaluations was made by the U.S. Forest Survey in Southeast Texas (Grosenbaugh and Stover, 1957). In this test, BAF 10 point samples were measured from the centers of 655 circular $\frac{1}{4}$-acre plots that were distributed throughout 12 counties. Volume per acre comparisons were made for BA, cubic-foot volumes, and board-foot volumes.

Differences in mean volumes by the two sampling methods were not significant at the 5 per cent level. Coefficients of variation for point sampling were only 7 to 12 per cent larger than for the $\frac{1}{4}$-acre plots, and standard errors were within 0.5 per cent of each other. It was estimated that 20 per cent more point samples would be needed to provide the same accuracy in cubic volume as derived from the plots; however, even with these additional samples the points could be measured in considerably less field time.

10-20 Attributes and limitations.   In summary, the principal advantages of point sampling over plot cruising are:

1 It is not necessary to establish a fixed plot boundary; thus greater cruising speed is possible.
2 Large, high-value trees are sampled in greater proportions than smaller stems.
3 BA and volume per acre may be derived without direct measurement of stem diameters.
4 When volume per acre conversions are developed in advance of fieldwork, efficient volume determinations can be made in a minimum of time. Thus the method is particularly suited to quick, reconnaissance-type cruises.

The main drawbacks to point sampling are:

1 Heavy underbrush reduces sighting visibility and cruising efficiency.
2 Because of the relatively small size of sampling units, carelessness and errors in the tally (when expanded to tract totals) are likely to be more serious than in plot cruising.
3 Slope compensation causes difficulties that may result in large errors unless special care is exercised. Similar difficulties are encountered in strip and line-plot cruising, of course.
4 Some problems arise in edge-effect bias when sampling very small tracts or long, narrow tracts.

PROBLEMS

10-1 Prepare a compilation similar to Table 10-2 for some BAF other than 10.
10-2 Construct (a) a stick-type angle gauge for an appropriate BAF in your locality or (b) a slope-compensating prism holder similar to the "Purdue point-sampling block" (Beers and Miller, 1964).
10-3 If feasible, establish 10 or more sampling points in a forested tract, and design a simple cruise to compare relative efficiencies of the stick-type angle gauge, the Spiegel relascope, and the wedge prism.
10-4 Prepare a table of limiting distances (similar to Table 10-4) in feet and links for a BAF other than 10.

10-5   Derive an appropriate set of cubic-foot or board-foot volume conversions for point sampling in your locality. Tabulate according to the format shown in Sec. 10-15.

10-6   Establish 20 to 50 marked sampling points in a local forest area. Make independent point-sample and circular plot cruises from the same plot centers. Compare results as to mean volumes, standard errors, average number of trees tallied per point, and cruising time per point.

REFERENCES

Afanasiev, Michael
1957. The Bitterlich method of cruising—Why does it work? *J. Forestry* **55**:216–217.

———
1958. Some results of the use of the Bitterlich method of cruising in an even-aged stand of longleaf pine. *J. Forestry* **56**:341–343.

Allen, R. H., and Mogren, E. W.
1960. Range-mean ratio of basal area as an indicator of Bitterlich sampling intensity in lodgepole pine. *Colo. State Univ. Coll. Forestry Res. Note* 13. 2 pp.

Avery, T. Eugene
1955. Gross volume estimation using "plotless cruising" in southeast Arkansas. *J. Forestry* **53**:206–207.

Beers, T. W., and Miller, C. I.
1964. Point-sampling: Research results, theory and applications. *Purdue Univ. Agr. Expt. Sta. Res. Bull.* 786. 56 pp., illus.

Bell, John F., and Alexander, Lucien B.
1957. Application of the variable plot method of sampling forest stands. *Oregon State Board Forestry Res. Note* 30. 22 pp., illus.

Bitterlich, W.
1948. Die Winkelzahlprobe. *Allgem. Forest-u. Holzw. Ztg.* **59**($\frac{1}{2}$):4–5.

Bruce, David
1955. A new way to look at trees. *J. Forestry* **53**:163–167. illus.

Cox, Paul
1961. A test of variable plot cruising in mixed stands on Latour State Forest. *Calif. Div. Forestry State Forest Note* 5. 6 pp.

Daniel, T. W., and Sutter, Harald
1955. Bitterlich's "Spiegelrelaskop"—a revolutionary general-use forest instrument. *J. Forestry* **53**:844–846. illus.

Deitschman, Glenn H.
1956. Plotless timber cruising tested in upland hardwoods. *J. Forestry* **54**:844–845.

Gould, E. M., Jr.
1957. The Harvard forest prism holder for point-sampling. *J. Forestry* **55**:730–731. illus.

Grosenbaugh, L. R.
1952. Plotless timber estimates—new, fast, easy. *J. Forestry* **50**:32–37. illus.

———
1955. Comments on "Results of an investigation of the variable plot method of cruising." *J. Forestry* **53**:734.

————— and Stover, W. S.
1957. Point-sampling compared with plot-sampling in southeast Texas. *Forest Sci.* 3:2–14.

Hovind, H. J., and Rieck, C. E.
1961. Basal area and point-sampling: Interpretation and application. *Wisconsin Conservation Dept. Tech. Bull.* 23. 52 pp., illus.

Hunt, Ellis V., Jr.
1961. Need a reliable point-sampling board foot factor?—Look in your files. *J. Forestry* 59:512–513.

—————, Baker, Robert D., and Biskamp, Lloyd A.
1964. Point-sampling from two angles. *Stephen F. Austin State Coll. Dept. Forestry Bull.* 6. 81 pp., illus.

Husch, Bertram
1955. Results of an investigation of the variable plot method of cruising. *J. Forestry* 53:570–574.

Kendall, R. H., and Sayn-Wittgenstein, L.
1959. An evaluation of the relascope. *Can. Dept. Northern Affairs and Nat. Resources Tech. Note* 77. 26 pp., illus.

Ker, J. W., Smith, J. H. G., and Walters, J.
1957. Observations on the accuracy and utility of plotless cruising. *Brit. Columbia Lumberman* (Nov.). 2 pp., illus.

Lemmon, Paul E.
1958. Aids for using wedge prisms. *J. Forestry* 56:767–768.

Morrow, Robert R.
1958. Computation of volume in the Bitterlich method of cruising. *J. Forestry* 56:41.

Myers, Clifford A.
1963. Point-sampling factors for southwestern ponderosa pine. *U.S. Forest Serv., Rocky Mt. Forest and Range Expt. Sta. Res. Paper* RM-3. 15 pp.

—————
1964. Volume tables and point-sampling factors for lodgepole pine in Colorado and Wyoming. *U.S. Forest Serv., Rocky Mt. Forest and Range Expt. Sta. Res. Paper* RM-6. 16 pp.

Stage, Albert R.
1959. A cruising computer for variable plots, tree heights, and slope correction. *J. Forestry* 57:835–836. illus.

—————
1958. An aid for comparing variable plot radius with fixed plot radius cruise designs. *J. Forestry* 56:593.

Thomson, George W., and Deitschman, Glenn H.
1959. Bibliography of world literature on the Bitterlich method of plotless cruising. Iowa State University, Agriculture Experiment Station. 10 pp.

Thornton, Philip L., and Hutchison, O. K.
1958. Cumulative-volume tally sheets for point-sampling. *U.S. Forest Serv., Central States Forest Expt. Sta. Note* 114. 2 pp.

Trappe, James M.
1957. Experience with basal area estimation by prisms in lodgepole pine. *U.S. Forest Serv., Pacific Northwest Forest and Range Expt. Sta. Res. Note* 145. 6 pp., illus.

CHAPTER 11
USES OF AERIAL PHOTOGRAPHS

INTRODUCTION TO PHOTO INTERPRETATION

11-1 How photographs can help. With a minimum of training, the forester can use aerial photographs to locate inventory plots and property boundaries, determine bearings and distances, identify classes of vegetation, and compile timber type maps. Additional experience will enable him to improve the efficiency of forest inventories by distributing field samples on the basis of photo stratifications. In some instances, he may even be able to estimate timber volumes directly from aerial photographs.

Although photo interpretation may make the forester's job easier, there are limitations. Accurate measurements of such items as tree diameter, form class, and stem defect are possible only on the ground. Aerial photographs are best employed to complement, improve, or reduce field-work rather than take its place.

Some of the basic techniques employed in forest photo interpretation are briefed in the pages that follow. Readers interested in a more comprehensive coverage of photogrammetric methods should refer to the manuals and textbooks listed at the end of the chapter.

11-2   Types of aerial photographs.   As a general rule, foresters are primarily concerned with *vertical photographs,* i.e., those taken with an aerial camera pointed straight down toward the earth's surface. Consecutive exposures in each flight line are overlapped about 60 per cent to allow three-dimensional study with a stereoscope. Although few (if any) aerial photographs are truly vertical views, they are usually presumed to be vertical when exposures are tilted no more than 3°. Unless otherwise specified, the terms *photo* and *photograph* as used in this chapter will denote vertical aerial photographs.

Oblique photographs are exposures made with the camera axis pointed at an angle between the vertical and the horizon. Although obliques are useful for panoramic views, they are not easily adapted to stereoscopic study; hence they are seldom used for forest inventory purposes in the United States and Canada.

Mosaics are assembled by cutting, matching, and pasting together portions of individual vertical exposures; the result is a large photograph that appears to be a single print. Controlled mosaics, i.e., those compiled at a uniform scale from ground reference points, provide good map approximations. However, controlled mosaics are quite expensive and cannot be viewed three-dimensionally. Except for pictorial displays, their use by foresters is limited.

11-3   Films and seasons for photography.   Two types of black-and-white aerial film are in common use: panchromatic and infrared. Infrared is usually modified by the use of a minus-blue filter that serves to reduce extreme contrast and improve image resolution. Panchromatic photography offers better resolution and lighter shadows but exhibits little tonal contrast among forest types. Modified infrared photography presents a maximum of contrast between conifers and deciduous hardwoods, but wet sites and shadows register in black, thus restricting interpretation.

In Western United States, where coniferous trees predominate, panchromatic film is more likely to be employed. Conversely, foresters managing eastern hardwoods often prefer infrared photography because of easier forest type separations. Figure 11-1 illustrates infrared and panchromatic exposures that were made simultaneously with a dual aerial camera system. These views can be seen three-dimensionally with a lens stereoscope.

If measurements are needed for deciduous species, both kinds of photog-

FIG. 11-1   Modified infrared (above) and panchromatic
photography made in the North Carolina
Piedmont during June. The dark-toned, uniform pattern at A is a pine plantation;
mixed pines and upland hardwoods are
shown at B, and a pure stand of hardwoods
is pictured at C. Mixed stands are difficult to
distinguish in the panchromatic stereogram.
Scale is 1,320 ft per in.

raphy are preferably taken during the growing season. Infrared usually
meets this requirement, as it is likely to be flown specifically for forestry
purposes. When panchromatic photographs have been taken in winter,
conifers can be distinguished from hardwoods, but interpretation of hardwood stand sizes is difficult. Modified infrared photography is occasionally available for tracts near large ownerships or national forests, but
many interpreters are limited to panchromatic photography available
from the USDA.

11-4 Photographic enlargements and papers. Most photos used by inventory foresters range in nominal scale from 1:12,000 to 1:20,000. Contact prints are standardized at the 9 × 9-in. size. Forest industries often contract for photography at 1:15,840 (4 in. per mile), and sizable areas in Western United States have been photographed at 1:12,000. Although enlargements can be obtained, they cost more, yield no additional detail, and cannot be viewed with simple stereoscopes. Contact prints are recom-

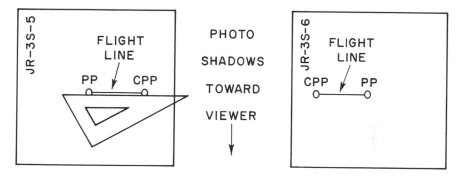

A. PRELIMINARY PHOTO ORIENTATION

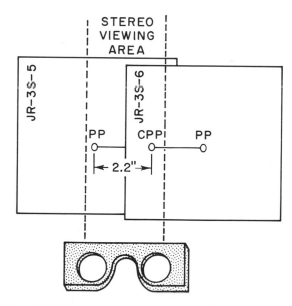

B. FINAL PHOTO ALIGNMENT

FIG. 11-2 Alignment of 9 × 9-in. contact prints for viewing with a lens stereoscope.

mended for general use, unless enlargements present definite advantages for transfer of photo detail to base maps.

Photographs can be obtained on either single- or double-weight papers. Single-weight papers are suitable for office use, conserve filing space, and are easy to handle under the lens stereoscope. Double-weight papers are preferred for field use, however, as they are less subject to dimensional changes and withstand handling better than single-weight papers.

11-5 Aligning prints for stereoscopic study. Photographic flights are planned so that prints will overlap about 60 per cent of their width in the line of flight and about 30 per cent between flight strips. For effective stereoviewing, prints must be trimmed to the nominal 9 × 9-in. size, preserving the four fiducial marks at the midpoint of each of the edges. The principal point PP is located by the intersection of lines drawn from opposite sets of fiducial marks. The conjugate principal points (CPPs or points that correspond to PPs of adjacent photos) are located by stereoscopic transfer from overlapping prints. Each photo thus has one PP and two CPPs, except that prints at the ends of flight lines have only one CPP.

To align the photographs for stereoscopic study, a print is selected and fastened down with shadows toward the viewer. The adjacent photo is placed with its CPP 2.2 in. from the corresponding PP on the first photo. With flight lines superimposed, the second photo is positioned. A lens stereoscope is placed with its long axis parallel to the flight line and with the lenses over corresponding photo images. In this way an overlapping strip 2.2 in. wide and nearly 9 in. long can be viewed by moving the stereoscope up and down the overlap area (Fig. 11-2).

BASIC MEASUREMENTS

11-6 Determining photographic scales. The vertical aerial photograph presents a true record of angles, but measures of horizontal distances vary widely with changes in ground elevations and flight altitudes. The nominal scale (as 1:20,000) is representative only of the datum, an imaginary plane passing through a specified ground elevation above sea level. Calculation of the average photo scale will increase the accuracy of subsequent photo measurements.

Aerial cameras in common use have focal lengths of 6, 8.25, or 12 in. (0.5, 0.6875, or 1.0 ft). This information, coupled with the altitude of the aircraft above ground datum, makes it possible to determine the representative fraction RF or natural scale:

$$RF = \frac{\text{focal length (ft)}}{\text{flying height above ground (ft)}}$$

The exact height of the aircraft is rarely known to the interpreter, however, and photo scale is more often calculated by this proportion:

$$RF = \frac{\text{photographic distance between two points (ft)}}{\text{ground or map distance between same points (ft)}}$$

As an example, the distance between two road intersections might be measured on a vertical photograph as 3.60 in. (0.30 ft). If the corresponding ground distance is measured as 3,960 ft, the representative fraction would be computed as

$$RF = \frac{0.30}{3,960.00} = \frac{1}{13,200} \text{ or } 1:13,200$$

It is not essential to calculate the scale of every photograph in a flight strip. In hilly terrain, every third or fifth print may be used; in flat topography, every tenth or twentieth may be used. Scales of intervening photos can be obtained by interpolation.

11-7 Compass bearings and distances. Although flight lines usually run north-south or east-west, few photographs are oriented exactly with the cardinal directions. For this reason, a reference line must be located before bearings can be determined. The method described is used by field teams on the U.S. Forest Survey:

1 Select a straight-line feature on the photo such as a highway, section line, or field edge and determine its bearing. Draw this reference line on the photograph, extend it as necessary, and record the bearing.

2 Pick a point of beginning from which the line of approach to a field location will be run. This should be some feature visible on both photo and ground, such as a fence corner, road intersection, or stream fork. Draw a line on the photograph from the beginning point to location, and extend until it intersects the reference line. Measure the angle between the two lines with a protractor and determine the bearing of the line of approach (Fig. 11-3).

3 Measure the distance between the point of beginning and the field location to the nearest 0.01 inch and convert to feet or chains at the calculated photo scale.

11-8 Measuring heights by parallax. To determine heights of objects on stereopairs of photographs, it is necessary to measure or estimate (1) absolute stereoscopic parallax and (2) differential parallax. Absolute stereoscopic parallax, measured parallel to the line of flight, is the algebraic difference of the distances of the two images from their respective principal points. Except in mountainous terrain, the average photo base length is ordinarily used as an approximation of absolute stereoscopic parallax. It is measured as the mean distance between the PP and CPP for an overlapping pair of photographs.

FIG. 11-3   Inventory forester using a protractor to establish a compass bearing on a contact print.
U.S. Forest Service photograph.

Differential parallax is the difference in the absolute stereoscopic
parallax at the top and the base of the object, measured parallel to
the flight line. The basic formula for conversion of parallax measurements on aerial photographs is

$$h = \frac{H \times dP}{P + dP}$$

where h = height of measured object
   H = height of aircraft above ground datum
   P = absolute stereoscopic parallax at base of object being measured
   dP = differential parallax

If object heights are to be determined in feet, the height of the aircraft
must also be in feet. Absolute stereoscopic parallax and differential parallax must be expressed in the same units; ordinarily, these units will
be in thousandths of inches or hundredths of millimeters.

11-9 Parallax measuring devices. Differential parallax dP is usually
measured stereoscopically with a parallax wedge or stereometer employing the "floating mark" principle; use of the wedge is detailed here.

This device, usually printed on transparent film, consists of two graduated lines that converge from about 2.5 to 1.8 in. apart. Numbers printed on the right-hand side indicate distance between the lines (dP) at intervals of 0.002 in.

In use, the parallax wedge is placed over the stereoscopic image with the converging lines perpendicular to the line of flight and adjusted

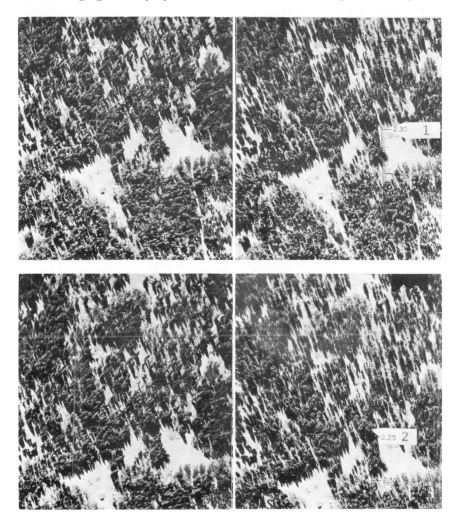

FIG. 11-4 Parallax wedge superimposed over a stereogram for determining tree height. The wedge is positioned for a ground reading in the upper view; in the lower stereogram, it has been shifted for a reading at treetop level. *U.S. Forest Service photograph.*

until a single fused line of graduations is seen sloping downward through the stereoscopic image. Differential parallax is obtained by counting the number of intervals between the point where a graduation appears to rest on the ground and the point where a graduation appears to "float" in the air at the same height as the top of the object.

In Fig. 11-4, for example, the graduation that corresponds to ground level (upper view) is read as **2.300** in. When the tree top reading of **2.242** in. (2.25 in. in the lower view) is subtracted, dP is recorded as 0.058 in. Assuming a flight altitude H of 4,000 ft and a photo base length P of 2.55 in., the values may be substituted in the parallax formula:

$$\text{Tree height } h = \frac{4,000 \times .058}{2.550 + .058} = \frac{232.00}{2.608} = 89 \text{ ft}$$

Stereometers or parallax bars are more sophisticated instruments for measuring differential parallax, and many interpreters perfer such devices because the floating mark is movable for easy placement on the ground and at crown levels (Fig. 11-5). However, the precision of height

FIG. 11-5 With a mirror stereoscope, the entire overlap of 9 × 9-in. prints can be viewed. This model includes magnifying binoculars and a stereometer (positioned over the photographs) for measuring heights of objects. *Courtesy of Zeiss-Aerotopograph.*

determination is about the same as for the wedge, depending on the stereoscopic perception of individual interpreters. At photo scales of 1:12,000 to 1:15,840, skilled interpreters can often measure the heights of clearly defined objects within ±10 ft.

SPECIES IDENTIFICATION AND TYPE MAPPING

11-10   Type recognition by elimination. The degree to which forest types and species-groups can be recognized depends on the quality, scale, and season of photography, the type of film used, and the interpreter's training. A general knowledge of forest ecology is helpful, and field experience in the specific area to be mapped is even more valuable.

A generalized forest cover map, when available, provides the first step in the identification process, i.e., the elimination of those cover types not likely to occur in a given locality. The second step, heavily dependent on a knowledge of local vegetation, is to establish which forest types can logically be encountered in the area to be mapped.

Recognition of an individual species, often feasible only on large-scale photography, is normally the culmination of intensive study. It is obvious that the forest interpreter must be familiar with branching patterns and crown shapes of all important species in this particular region. Mature conifers in sparsely stocked stands can often be recognized by the configuration of their crowns or from shadows that fall in open areas of the stand (Figs. 11-6 and 11-7).

Aside from shadows, crown shapes, and branching patterns, the chief diagnostic features to be considered in recognizing tree species are photographic texture (smoothness or coarseness of images), tonal contrast, relative sizes of tree images at a given photo scale, and topographic location or site. Most of these characteristics constitute rather weak clues when observed singly, yet together they may be the final link in the chain of identification by elimination.

11-11   Vegetation keys. For some parts of the United States and Canada, vegetation "keys" are available as aids in the recognition of tree species. Keys are useful for training neophyte interpreters and as reference material for more experienced personnel. Depending on the method of presenting diagnostic features, photo interpretation keys may be grouped into two general classes: *selective* keys and *elimination* keys. Selective keys are usually made up of typical illustrations and descriptions of trees in a specific region, e.g., pines of Florida. They are organized for comparative use; the interpreter merely selects the key example that most nearly coincides with the forest stand he must identify. By contrast, elimination keys require the user to follow a step-by-step procedure, working from the general to the specific. One of the more common forms of elimination keys is the dichotomous type. With this type the interpreter must continually select one of two contrasting alternatives until he progressively eliminates all but one item—the one being sought.

As a rule, vegetation keys are most easily constructed in northern

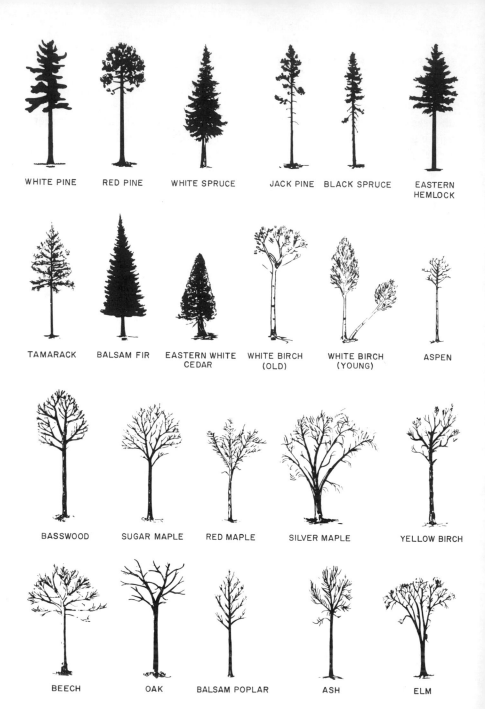

FIG. 11-6 Silhouettes of selected forest trees. Individual species can often be identified when distinctive tree shadows fall on snow or level ground. *Courtesy of L. Sayn-Wittgenstein, Forest Research Branch, Canada Department of Forestry.*

and western forests where conifers predominate, because there are relatively few species to be considered and crown patterns are rather distinctive for each important group. By contrast, few, if any, reliable keys are available for the highly variable hardwood forests of Southern and Eastern United States.

Three important forest types occurring along the Kantishna River in central Alaska are pictured in Fig. 11-8. As an aid in identifying

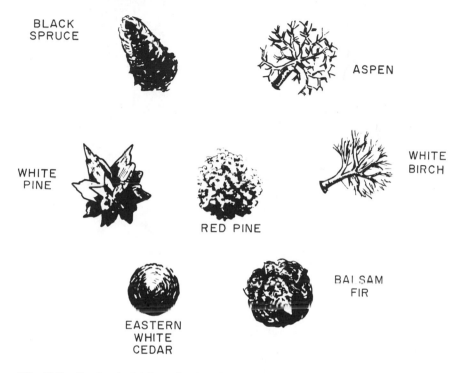

FIG. 11-7 Overhead sketches of selected tree crowns. Compare with Figs. 11-6 and 11-8. *Courtesy of L. Sayn-Wittgenstein, Forest Research Branch, Canada Department of Forestry.*

these types, the following descriptions were developed as part of a selective vegetation key:

QUAKING ASPEN: Gray-toned, rounded, and thin crowns whose images appear fuzzy on large-scale prints (due to continual leaf movement). Usually found on drier, upland sites.

WHITE SPRUCE: Straight, vertical boles with spire-shaped or conical crowns that cast black and narrowly triangular shadows. Occurs on moist, well-drained sites, occasionally in mixture with paper birch.

PAPER BIRCH: Whitish crowns having a star-shaped or palmlike appearance, particularly for immature trees or when foliage is not fully developed. Mature crowns

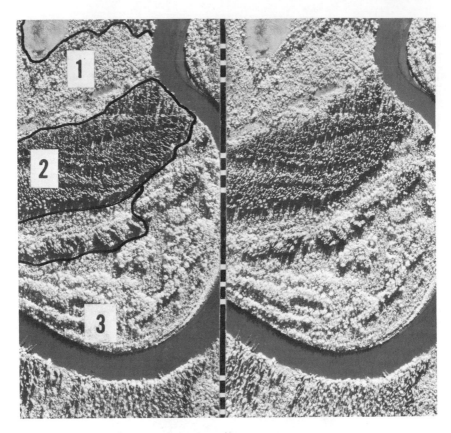

FIG. 11-8 Infrared stereogram illustrating three forest
associations in central Alaska. Types are
(1) quaking aspen, (2) white spruce, and
(3) paper birch. Scale is about 420 ft per
in.; land elevation is approximately 300 ft.
U.S. Forest Service photograph.

are broad and rounded. Occurs on moist, well-drained sites, sometimes in association with white spruce.

11-12 Timber type maps. Type maps are no longer considered essential by all foresters, but at times their cost may be justified. A general ownership map showing principal roads, streams, and forest types may be desired for management planning and illustrative purposes. Also, in making a photo-controlled ground cruise where precise forest-area estimates are required, it may be necessary to measure stand areas on controlled maps of known scale rather than directly on contact prints; this is particularly important when topography causes wide variation in photo scales.

The wise interpreter will delineate only those forest types that he can consistently recognize. For maximum accuracy, type lines should be drawn under the stereoscope. Wherever feasible, it is recommended that forest cover types be coded according to the numerical system devised by the Society of American Foresters (1954). In the past, timber type maps have assumed a wide variety of forms from one locale to another, but it is advantageous to employ uniform symbols for designating tree species and stand-size classes.

After all forest types have been delineated, the desired detail can be transferred to a base map by using a vertical sketchmaster. By moving this instrument up or down on its adjustable legs, differences between photo and map scales can be reconciled. The sketchmaster accommodates a single annotated print which is placed face up under a large mirror. Photo images are reflected from the mirror to a semisilvered mirror in the eyepiece housing. The semitransparent eyepiece mirror thus provides a monocular view of the reflected photo image superimposed on the base map. When control points on photo and map have been matched, the transfer of detail becomes a simple tracing procedure (Fig. 11-9).

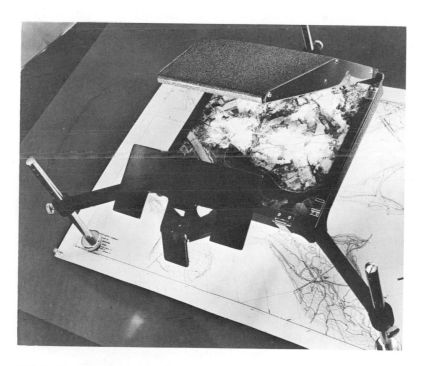

FIG. 11-9 Vertical sketchmaster for transferring detail from single contact prints to a base map. A semisilvered eyepiece mirror enables the operator to view photograph and map simultaneously. *Courtesy of Aero Service Division of Litton Industries.*

PHOTO ESTIMATES OF STAND VOLUME

11-13 Individual tree volumes. Ordinary tree volume tables can be easily converted to aerial volume tables when correlations can be established between tree crown diameters and stem diameters. When this technique is applied, photo determinations of crown diameter and total tree height are merely substituted for the usual field measures of dbh and merchantable height, respectively. Photographic measurements are usually limited to well-defined, open-grown trees, and crown counts are required to obtain total volume for a given stand of timber.

Tree crowns are rarely circular, but because individual limbs are often invisible on aerial photos, crowns usually appear roughly circular or elliptical. As only the portions visible from above can be evaluated, photo measures of crown diameter are often lower than ground checks of the same trees. Nevertheless, most interpreters can determine average crown diameter with reasonable precision if they take several readings and avoid bias in measurement.

When an aerial cruise is being made, photo measurements may include all trees on 0.2- to 1-acre circular plots, or stands may be delineated according to height classes for determination of the average tree per unit area. In the latter instance, a tree count must be made for obtaining the total stand volume. As a rule, the individual-tree approach to aerial cruising is of limited value unless large-scale photographs are available. When scales are smaller than 1:12,000 (1,000 ft per in.) images are usually too small to permit accurate assessment of individual trees.

11-14 Aerial stand volume tables. If recent photographs and reliable aerial stand volume tables can be obtained, average stand volume per acre can be estimated with a minimum of fieldwork. Estimates are made in terms of gross volume, as amount of cull or defect cannot be adequately evaluated. Even-aged stands of simple species structure are best suited for this type of estimating, especially if gross and net volumes are essentially identical. All-aged stands of mixed hardwoods are more difficult to assess, but satisfactory results can be obtained where field checks are made to adjust the photo estimate of stand volume per acre and to determine allowance for defect. Though photo volumes cannot be expressed by species and diameter classes, total gross volumes for areas as small as 40 acres can be estimated within 10 to 15 per cent of volumes derived from conventional ground cruises.

Most aerial stand volume tables for mixed species are constructed in terms of cubic feet per acre. Tables for species occurring naturally in pure stands, such as Douglas fir, may be expressed either in board feet or cubic feet per acre. Three photographic measurements of the dominant stand are generally required for entering an aerial stand volume table: average total height, crown diameter, and crown closure per cent. In Table 11-1, crown diameter has been eliminated as a variable, and only measurements of stand height and crown closure are required. Similar tables have been published for other important timber types in the United States and Canada.

TABLE 11-1 Aerial-photo Stand Volume Table for Even-aged Douglas Fir in the Pacific Northwest (In 100 Cu Ft Per Acre)*

Stand height, ft†	Crown closure, %‡								
	15	25	35	45	55	65	75	85	95
40	5	8	11	13	14	15	15	14	13
50	7	11	15	18	20	21	22	21	20
60	9	15	20	24	27	29	30	29	28
70	12	19	25	31	34	37	39	39	38
80	14	24	31	38	43	46	48	49	49
90	17	28	38	45	52	56	59	61	61
100	21	33	45	54	61	67	72	74	75
110	24	39	52	63	72	79	85	88	90
120	28	45	60	73	83	92	99	103	106
130	31	51	68	83	95	106	114	120	124
140	35	57	77	94	108	121	130	138	143
150	40	64	86	105	122	136	148	157	163
160	44	71	96	118	136	153	166	177	185
170	49	79	106	130	152	170	185	198	208
180	54	87	117	144	168	188	206	220	232
190	59	95	128	158	184	208	227	244	257
200	64	104	140	173	202	228	250	269	284
210	70	113	152	188	220	249	274	295	313
220	75	122	165	204	239	271	298	322	342
230	81	132	178	220	259	293	324	351	373
240	87	142	192	238	280	317	351	380	406
250	94	152	206	256	301	342	379	411	439
260	100	163	221	274	323	367	408	443	474

* Gross volume, in trees 5.0 in. and larger, from stump to top limit of 4.0 in. d.i.b. (Reprinted from Pope, 1962.)
† Average height of dominants and codominants, as measured in the field.
‡ Includes all trees in the major canopy; average photo estimate of several experienced interpreters. Table based on 282 one-fifth-acre plots, largely in western Oregon.

Crown closure per cent, also referred to as *crown density*, is the proportion of the forest canopy occupied by the trees. The term may refer to all crowns in the stand regardless of canopy level or only to the dominants. Estimates are purely ocular, and stands are commonly grouped into 10 per cent density classes. Evaluation of crown closure is much more subjective than the determination of tree height or crown diameter. Actual measurement is virtually impossible on small-scale photographs, and accuracy is thus largely dependent on the interpreter's judgment. Crown closure is useful because of its relation to stand volume per acre. It is applied in lieu of BA or number of trees per acre, because these variables cannot often be determined directly from available photography.

11-15 Stand volume estimates. One of several procedures for making aerial volume estimates is as follows:

1 Outline tract boundaries on the photographs, utilizing the effective area of every other print in each flight line. This assures stereoscopic coverage of the area on a minimum number of photographs and avoids duplication of measurements by the interpreter.
2 Delineate important forest types. Except where type lines define stands of relatively uniform stocking and total height, they should be further broken down into homogeneous units so that measures of height, density, and crown diameter will apply to the entire unit. Generally, it is unnecessary to recognize stands smaller than 5 to 10 acres.
3 Determine the acreage of each condition class with dot grids. This determination can often be made on contact prints.
4 By stereoscopic examination, measure the variables for entering the aerial stand volume table. From the table, obtain the average volume per acre for each condition class.
5 Multiply gross volumes per acre from the table by condition class areas to determine gross volume.
6 Add class volumes for the total gross volume on the tract.

11-16 Adjusting photo volumes by field checks. When aerial volume tables are not sufficiently reliable for pure photo estimates and allowance must be made for defective trees, some of the plots interpreted should be selected for field measurement. For example, if 350 plots were interpreted and every tenth plot selected, 35 plots would be visited in the field. If the field volumes averaged 600 cu ft per acre as opposed to 800 cu ft per acre for the photo plots, the adjustment ratio would be $600 \div 800$ or 0.75. If the 35 field plots are representative of the total, the ratio can be applied to the average photo volume per acre to determine the adjusted volume. It is desirable to compute ratios by forest types, because hardwoods are likely to require larger adjustments than conifers.

The accuracy of aerial cruises depends not only upon the volume tables but upon the availability of recent photographs and the interpreter's ability to make photo measurements correctly. This last item may be the greatest single source of error. It is advisable to measure each photo variable twice for an average or to have two interpreters assess each plot.

PHOTO STRATIFICATIONS FOR GROUND CRUISING

11-17 Advantages of stratification. A photo-controlled ground cruise combines the features of aerial and ground estimating, offering a means of obtaining timber volumes with high efficiency. Photographs are used for area determination, for allocation of field samples by forest types or stand-size classes, and for designing the pattern of fieldwork. For each stratum, tree volume, growth, cull per cents, form class, or other data are obtained on the ground by conventional methods. The resulting inventory will often prove more efficient than a nonstratified random sample employing the same total number of field plots.

If the variation among units within strata is less than the variation among units that are not in the same stratum, the population estimate will be more precise than if sampling had been at random over the entire population. From a practical standpoint, the application of stratified random sampling requires that the forester be able to recognize the strata on aerial photographs, determine their areas, and measure a number of ground samples within each stratum.

11-18 A sample problem. As a consulting forester, it may be assumed that you have been asked to cruise a 300-acre tract of timber. Your client wants a simple forest type map and estimates of mean board-foot volumes per acre. Although you haven't actually seen the tract, it is located in an area where you have previous cruising experience. At first, you consider using "the old reliable," viz., a 10 per cent cruise utilizing ⅕-acre circular plots. Thus a total of 150 sample units would be measured during the conduct of the inventory.

Later, you discover that stereoscopic study of recent aerial photographs enables you to delineate the five principal forest types within the project area. Your type map and acreage summary derived from the photographs appear as in Fig. 11-10. Assuming that a total of 150 sample plots will actually be measured, the next question that arises is, How should they be distributed among the five strata or forest type classifications? Two common procedures for handling this problem are known as proportional allocation and optimum allocation.

11-19 Proportional allocation of field plots. This approach calls for distribution of the 150 field plots in proportion to the *area* of each

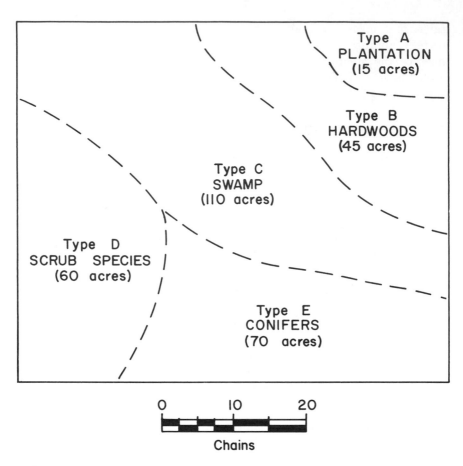

FIG. 11-10 Forested tract of 300 acres stratified according to five type classifications.

type. For the five forest types in Fig. 11-10, the number of plots in each stratum would be computed as follows:

$$\text{Type A—Plantation} \quad \frac{15 \text{ acres}}{300 \text{ acres}} (150) = 7 \text{ plots}$$

$$\text{Type B—Hardwoods} \quad \frac{45 \text{ acres}}{300 \text{ acres}} (150) = 23 \text{ plots}$$

$$\text{Type C—Swamp} \quad \frac{110 \text{ acres}}{300 \text{ acres}} (150) = 55 \text{ plots}$$

$$\text{Type D—Scrub species} \frac{60 \text{ acres}}{300 \text{ acres}} (150) = 30 \text{ plots}$$

$$\text{Type E—Conifers} \quad \frac{70 \text{ acres}}{300 \text{ acres}} (150) = 35 \text{ plots}$$

$$\text{Total} \qquad\qquad\qquad\qquad 150 \text{ plots}$$

One disadvantage of proportional allocation is that large areas receive more sample plots than small ones, irrespective of variation in volume per acre. Of course, the same limitation applies to simple random sampling. When the various strata can be reliably recognized and their areas determined, proportional allocation will generally be superior to a non-stratified sample of the same intensity.

11-20   Estimation of type variances.   To base an allocation of field plots on both area and variation in volume per acre requires estimates of the variance for each type in terms of the desired units. In this example, we are interested in board-foot volumes per acre; hence the *variances must be expressed accordingly.* Three possible ways of deriving these statistics are:

1   Measure a "preliminary" set of field samples in each stratum and compute variances. Although this is the preferred approach, the method can be costly for small tracts, for the follow-up cruise is still ordinarily required.
2   Measure several plots within each stratum on aerial photographs, determine the volume per acre of each plot, and compute variances therefrom. This technique presumes the use of recent, large-scale photographs in the hands of skilled interpreters; furthermore, it implies that photo-derived volumes will accurately predict variances of field samples to be measured subsequently. The latter assumption can be hazardous.
3   Rely on previous cruising experience and stereoscopic study of available aerial photographs to estimate the *range of volume* expected within each forest type or stratum. In this particular example, it is presumed that the standard deviation (i.e., the square root of the variance) may be estimated as being equal to one-fourth of the range (Freese, 1962, op. cit.). The reader is cautioned, however, that this approximation procedure should be used only when more reliable estimates of the standard deviation are not available.

For the five forest types or strata previously defined, the ranges, the standard deviations, and the variances have been computed as indicated in Table 11-2. With these data and the type acreages, field plots may now be distributed by the method referred to as optimum allocation.

TABLE 11-2 Estimates of Variances from Ranges of Board-foot Volume Per Acre

Forest type	Volume range, bd ft per acre	Standard deviation (range ÷ 4),* bd ft per acre	Variance (standard deviation)², bd ft per acre
A. Plantation	1,800	450	202,500
B. Hardwoods	10,800	2,700	7,290,000
C. Swamp	4,800	1,200	1,440,000
D. Scrub species	3,000	750	562,500
E. Conifers	5,400	1,350	1,822,500

* The standard deviation is best determined from a preliminary set of field observations. However, this method of calculation sometimes provides a good approximation.

11-21 Optimum allocation of field plots. With this procedure, the 150 sample plots are allocated to the various strata by a plan that results in the smallest standard error possible with a fixed number of observations. Determining the number of plots to be assigned to each stratum requires first a product of the area and standard deviation for each type. Referring back to Fig. 11-10 and Table 11-2, these products would be derived as follows:

Type A—Plantation	15(450)	= 6,750
Type B—Hardwoods	45(2,700)	= 121,500
Type C—Swamp	110(1,200)	= 132,000
Type D—Scrub species	60(750)	= 45,000
Type E—Conifers	70(1,350)	= 94,500
Sum of five products		399,750

The number of plots to be allocated to each stratum is computed by expressing each product of "area times standard deviation" as a proportion of the product sum (399,750 in this example). Thus the 150 field plots would be distributed in the following manner:

Type A—Plantation $\dfrac{6,750}{399,750}(150) = 0.0169(150) =$ 3 plots

Type B—Hardwoods $\dfrac{121,500}{399,750}(150) = 0.3039(150) =$ 46 plots

Type C—Swamp $\dfrac{132,000}{399,750}(150) = 0.3302(150) =$ 49 plots

Type D—Scrub species $\dfrac{45,000}{399,750}(150) = 0.1126(150) =$ 17 plots

Type E—Conifers $\dfrac{94,500}{399,750}(150) = 0.2364(150) =$ 35 plots

Total 150 plots

By this method of plot allocation, only three plots are assigned to the homogeneous plantation (instead of the seven plots dictated by proportional allocation). On the other hand, the number in the hardwood type is doubled (from 23 to 46 plots), and the number assigned to the scrub species Type D is reduced from 30 to 17 plots. In this instance, the number assigned to swamp and conifer types remained relatively unchanged. When both stratum areas and variances can be reliably determined, optimum allocation is the preferred method for distributing a fixed number of inventory plots.

Following the field measurement of all sample plots, mean volumes and variances should be computed for each stratum recognized in sampling. Sample means and standard errors for each stratum may be pooled for an estimate of the population mean (Freese, 1962), or total volume for each stratum may be derived as outlined in the next section.

11-22 Expansion of volume per acre estimates. When independent estimates of area and volume per acre are made for each stratum, total volume for each type should be computed by using the formula for the standard error of a product (Sec. 8-18). This is necessary because standard errors logically accompany estimates of both area and volume.

As an example, it might be assumed that the mean volume for Type B (hardwoods) is estimated as $4{,}000 \pm 400$ bd ft per acre and that the area of this type is 45 ± 2.5 acres. Total volume for this stratum is therefore computed as

$$4{,}000(45) \pm \sqrt{(4{,}000 \times 2.5)^2 + (45 \times 400)^2}$$
$$= 180{,}000 \pm \sqrt{424{,}000{,}000} = 180{,}000 \pm 20{,}591 \text{ bd ft}$$

The same procedure would be repeated for each of the other four strata if standard errors accompanied estimates of type areas.

11-23 Arrangement of sample plots. Statistical formulas used here were developed for *random* sampling designs, and it is presumed that all field plots within each stratum will be located by random selection. Although systematic plot arrangements may often provide equally reliable results, variances and standard errors of such designs can only be approximated. Even when a systematic grid method is deemed essential from the standpoint of field travel, the initial sample should be chosen at random.

PROBLEMS

11-1 Using a set of aerial photographs from your own locality, determine the average scale (*a*) as a representative fraction, (*b*) in feet or chains per inch, and (*c*) in acres per square inch. Then establish a line of known compass bearing on the photographs.

11-2 Determine the heights of 10 trees, buildings, or other objects from parallax measurements. After completion of photographic estimates, obtain ground measurements of the same objects with an Abney level or other hypsometer. Compare results, and explain reasons for differences noted.

11-3 Delineate the principal forest types found on photographs in your locality; code types by the Society of American Foresters designations, and verify by ground reconnaissance. Which types are easily recognized? Which types are particularly difficult to identify?

11-4 Obtain 100 or more paired ground measurements of dbh and crown diameter for a coniferous species in your region. On standard cross-section paper, plot stem diameters (*y* axis) over crown diameters (*x* axis). If a logical trend is indicated, fit a balanced curve to the plotted points. Tabulate results by reading the predicted dbh for each 2-ft increment in average crown diameter. Then use these data to convert a standard tree volume table into an aerial tree volume table.

11-5 Using local photographs, stratify a forest area by three to five volume or type categories. Design ground cruises based on (a) stratified random sampling and (b) simple random sampling. Use the same number of field plots for both cruises. Compare results and relative efficiencies of the two systems.

REFERENCES

American Society of Photogrammetry
1952. Manual of photogrammetry, 2d ed. George Banta Company, Inc., Menasha, Wisc. 876 pp., illus.

——— 1960. Manual of photographic interpretation. George Banta Company, Inc., Menasha, Wisc., 868 pp., illus.

Avery, T. Eugene
1958. Composite aerial volume table for southern pines and hardwoods. *J. Forestry* **56**:741–745. illus.

——— 1962. Interpretation of aerial photographs. Burgess Publishing Company, Minneapolis. 192 pp., illus.

——— 1964. To stratify or not to stratify? *J. Forestry* **62**:106–108. illus.

——— **and Meyer, Merle P.**
1959. Volume tables for aerial timber estimating in northern Minnesota. *U.S. Forest Serv., Lake States Forest Expt. Sta. Sta. Paper* 78. 21 pp., illus.

Bernstein, David A.
1962. Guide to two-story forest type mapping in the Douglas-fir subregion. U.S. Forest Service, Region 6. 15 pp., illus.

Heller, R. C., Doverspike, G. E., and Aldrich, R. C.
1964. Identification of tree species on large-scale panchromatic and color aerial photographs. U.S. Forest Service, Government Printing Office, Washington, D.C. 17 pp., illus.

Johnson, Evert W.
1952. Timber volume determinations using aerial photographs. Alabama Polytechnic Institute. 43 pp., illus.

——— 1954. Ground control for planimetric base maps. *J. Forestry* **52**:89–95. illus.

——— 1954. "Shadow-height" computations made easier. *J. Forestry* **52**:438–442. illus.

Kramer, P. R., and Sturgeon, E. E.
1942. Transect method of estimating forest area from aerial photo index sheets. *J. Forestry* **40**:693–696. illus.

Lutz, H. J., and Caporaso, A. P.
1958. Indicators of forest land classes in air-photo interpretation of the Alaska Interior. *U.S. Forest Serv., Alaska Forest Res. Center Sta. Paper* 10. 31 pp., illus.

Minor, C. O.

1951. Stem-crown diameter relations in southern pine. *J. Forestry* **49**:490–493. illus.

Moessner, Karl E.

1957. Preliminary aerial volume tables for conifer stands in the Rocky Mountains. *U.S. Forest Serv., Intermt. Forest and Range Expt. Sta. Res. Paper* 41, 17 pp., illus.

1957. How important is relief in area estimates from dot sampling on aerial photos? *U.S. Forest Serv., Intermt. Forest and Range Expt. Sta. Res. Paper* 42. 16 pp., illus.

———— and Jensen, C. E.

1951. Timber cruising on aerial photos. *U.S. Forest Serv., Central States Forest Expt. Sta. Tech. Paper* 126. 27 pp., illus.

————, Brunson, D. F., and Jensen, C. E.

1951. Aerial volume tables for hardwood stands in the Central States. *U.S. Forest Serv., Central States Forest Expt. Sta. Tech. Paper* 122. 15 pp., illus.

Pope, Robert B.

1962. Constructing aerial photo volume tables. *U.S. Forest Serv., Pacific Northwest Forest and Range Expt. Sta. Res. Paper* 49. 25 pp., illus.

Sayn-Wittgenstein, Leo

1961. Recognition of tree species on air photographs by crown characteristics. *Photogrammetric Eng.* **27**:792–809. illus.

Society of American Foresters

1954. Forest cover types of North America, exclusive of Mexico. Committee on forest types, Washington, D.C. 68 pp., illus.

Wilson, R. C.

1949. The relief displacement factor in forest area estimates by dot templets on aerial photographs. *Photogrammetric Eng.* **15**:225–236. illus.

Zsilincsky, Victor G.

1963. Photographic interpretation of tree species in Ontario. Ontario Department of Lands and Forests. 80 pp., illus.

CHAPTER **12**

SITE, STOCKING, DENSITY, AND TREE GROWTH

EVALUATION OF SITE QUALITY

12-1 Factors affecting site. As defined by the Society of American Foresters (1958), the term *site* refers to "an area, considered as to its ecological factors with reference to capacity to produce forests or other vegetation; the combination of biotic, climatic, and soil conditions of an area." Stated more briefly, site is the aggregate of all environmental conditions affecting the survival and growth of a plant community. Accurate measures of site quality are important to foresters because of the need for evaluating the wood-producing potential of various areas in terms of a particular species or species group.

A logical approach to site evaluation might require analysis of such factors as available soil nutrients and moisture, depth of the "A" horizon, available light, temperature regimes, and topography (Heiberg and White, 1956). However, the average forester often has difficulty in making consistent and objective measurements of these items; furthermore, the translation of such data into a meaningful index of site quality often requires the services of a skilled soil scientist.

Among other factors that have been considered are plant indicators, i.e., use of lesser vegetation as an indication of site quality. In many forest regions, there are certain key species comprising the ground cover that are especially useful in extensive site classifications (Haddock and Smith, 1956). This is particularly true in relatively undisturbed stands of simple species structure. The principal drawbacks to the use of plant indicators are that (1) the method permits site evaluation only in relative or qualitative terms, and (2) a sound background in plant ecology is a prerequisite for reliable classifications.

12-2   Site index. An ideal index of site quality would be simple to measure in quantitative terms, directly related to growth or volume per unit area, free from the effects of stand density, sensitive to periodic site changes, and applicable in open as well as in forested lands. Site index based on tree height at a specified age is a simple numerical value, but there is some question as to its usefulness in terms of the other stipulations cited (Sammi, 1965). Nevertheless, tree height growth is the most widely accepted quantitative measure of site in North America.

As generally applied, site index is measured by determining the average total height of dominant and codominant trees in pure, even-aged stands at an index age such as 25, 50, or 100 years. When these two variables have been ascertained for a given species, they are used as coordinates for interpolating site index from a specially prepared set of curves. As an example, if the average height of a stand of eastern white pine is 70 ft at an age of 35 years, the site index would be read as 95 from Fig. 12-1. This means that the expected stand height for this site is 95 ft at the index age of 50 years.

In preparing site index curves for various tree species, either age at breast height or total age may be used as the independent variable. Age at breast height is preferable, because this is a standard point of tree measurement and a convenient height for making increment borings. When total age is used, it is necessary to estimate the number of years required for the tree to grow from seed to the height where an increment boring is made; this number is then added to the annual ring count to arrive at total age. Use of age at breast height in lieu of total age eliminates the need for such arbitrary correction factors (Husch, 1956).

12-3   Field measures of height and age. Because site index curves for major commercial timber species are readily available, field determina-

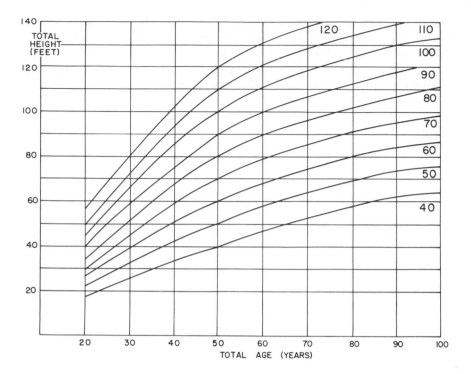

FIG. 12-1 Site index relationships for eastern white
pine at age 50. *From Hampf*, 1964, *and*
Gevorkiantz, 1957.

tions are essentially made up of total height and age measurements
for 10 to 20 dominant and codominant trees in even-aged stands. The
estimated number of trees to be sampled may also be calculated by
this rule-of-thumb formula suggested by Gevorkiantz (1957):

$$\text{No. of sample trees} = 5 + \frac{R^2}{30}$$

where R is the estimated *range* of total heights in the stand.

Total heights are commonly measured with an Abney level or clinometer. In climates where tree growth is characterized by annual rings,
ages of standing trees are usually determined by extracting a radial
core of wood with an increment borer. The auger of the increment borer
is normally pressed against the tree at dbh and turned until the screw
bit reaches the pith. The extractor is inserted through the center of
the auger, and the borer is given a reverse turn to snap the core loose
and permit its removal (Fig. 12-2). The resulting annual ring count
gives the age of the tree from the point of the increment boring upward.

For the site index potential to be expressed on a standard basis, a definite stand age must be presumed. For most regions, the period in the life of the stand that approximates the culmination of mean annual growth (Sec. 12-15) in well-stocked stands has been selected as the proper indexing age. Accordingly, 100 years has been used for most western species and 50 years for eastern species. Special site curves based

FIG. 12-2   Extraction of a core of wood with an increment borer. *U.S. Forest Service photograph.*

on an index age of 25 years are available for plantations that are managed on rotations shorter than 50 years.

12-4   Limitations of site index.   The main drawbacks that have been cited regarding the continued use of site index as a measure of site quality are as follows:

1   Exact stand age is difficult to determine, and small errors can cause relatively large changes in the site index value.
2   The concept of site index is not well suited for uneven-aged stands, areas of mixed species composition, or open lands.
3   Effects of stand density are not considered except by arbitrary selection of measured trees in well-stocked stands that have been unaffected by past suppression. Other variables associated with stand volume (that is, dbh and

stem form) are not directly taken into account. As a result, an index based on height and age alone may not provide a valid estimate of the growing capacity for a particular site.

4 Site index is not a constant; instead, it may change periodically due to environmental and climatic variations.

5 Except in limited instances, the site index value for one species cannot be translated into a usable index for a different species on the same site (Doolittle, 1958).

In spite of the foregoing limitations, site index remains at a high level of popularity because it provides a simple numerical value that is easily measured and understood by the practicing forester. Its use will apparently be continued until the day when the varied factors affecting soil productivity can be reduced to an equally simple and quantitative measurement.

12-5 Even-aged versus uneven-aged stands. The terms *even-aged stands* and *dominant-codominant trees* have been used in the preceding discussions of site index. Therefore, it is appropriate to define these expressions. Even-aged stands are those in which tree ages do not differ by more than 10 to 20 years. In stands where the harvesting or rotation age is as long as 100 to 200 years, however, age differences up to 25 per cent of the rotation age may be allowed (Society of American Foresters, 1958).

Uneven-aged stands are those where age differences exceed the stated limits or where three or more age classes are represented. *All-aged stands* are rarities that are virtually nonexistent. In theory, they include trees of all ages from minute seedlings to the harvest or rotation age.

12-6 Tree crown classes. As a descriptive aid in distinguishing various crown levels in even-aged stands, four crown classes are defined by the Society of American Foresters (1958) as follows:

1 *Dominant*—Trees with crowns extending above the general level of the crown cover and receiving full light from above and partly from the side; larger than the average trees in the stand, and with crowns well-developed but possibly somewhat crowded on the sides.

2 *Codominant*—Trees with crowns forming the general level of the crown cover and receiving full light from above, but comparatively little from the sides; usually with medium-sized crowns more or less crowded on the sides.

3 *Intermediate*—Trees shorter than those in the two preceding classes, but with crowns either below or extending into the crown cover formed by co-dominant and dominant trees, receiving little direct light from above, and none from the sides; usually with small crowns considerably crowded on the sides.

4 *Overtopped*—Trees with crowns entirely below the general level of the crown cover receiving no direct light either from above or from the sides.

STOCKING AND STAND DENSITY

12-7 The concept of stocking. Although stocking and stand density are terms that are often applied interchangeably, stocking is a qualitative expression that compares the existing number of trees in a stand to the number desired for optimum growth and volume. Accordingly, stands may be referred to as understocked, fully stocked (the theoretical ideal), or overstocked. Stands that deviate from the arbitrary norm of full stocking may also be described in relative terms, such as 30 per cent stocked or 110 per cent stocked.

In contrast to the comparative nature of stocking, stand density is a quantitative term describing the extent of stem crowding within a stocked area. Density is usually expressed as some combination of stem diameter, BA, height, form, or number of trees per acre.

The main difficulty arising from the application of stocking concepts is that of deciding just what should constitute optimum stocking for a particular species on a given site. As outlined by Bickford (1957), "the stocking that results in maximum yield is the ideal that every forest manager would like to have if he only knew what it was and could recognize it if he saw it." Although stocking can also be specified in terms of the capacity of an area to support trees, most foresters think of stocking in terms of "best growth" rather than as a measure of site occupation.

Stocking levels are of prime concern to the forest manager, because controlled changes in these levels may allow the forester to shorten or lengthen his rotation, favor desired species, and maximize the yield of selected timber products. Although the extremes of stocking can be easily recognized, full or optimum stocking can only be defined as a closed canopy stand that represents the "average best" to be found. Understocked stands are characterized by trees of rough form, excessive taper, and a high live-crown ratio. Overstocked stands may represent a stagnated condition when there is a low live-crown ratio and numerous dead stems. In both instances, the result is a reduction in net volume increment from the "fully stocked" ideal.

12-8 The question of normality. As a holdover from European forestry practices, stands that are fully stocked have also been referred to as *normal* stands. The theory was developed that maximum volume increment would be obtained with full or normal stocking. Thus an ideal and regulated normal forest would be comprised of a normal distribution of age classes, normal growing stock, and consequently a normal increment. In such a hypothetical forest, tree crowns are fitted together so that no sunlight is wasted, and each crown is matched with a root system that fully utilizes the soil (Bickford, 1957).

As a follow-up to the foregoing concept, normal yield tables were compiled to describe the expected production of normal forests. Such tables were based on the "average best," pure, even-aged stands that could be located for various species and site conditions; normality was maintained by restriction of cutting to light thinnings (Table 12-1).

TABLE 12-1 "Normal" Yield Table for Even-aged Upland Oak Forests*

Total age, years	Yield per acre by site index (age 50), cu ft				
	40	50	60	70	80
10	0	0	0	10	20
15	0	20	40	80	190
20	20	70	170	360	620
25	100	250	510	820	1,170
30	270	540	880	1,260	1,690
35	480	820	1,240	1,690	2,160
40	680	1,090	1,580	2,090	2,610
45	870	1,350	1,910	2,470	3,040
50	1,060	1,600	2,230	2,830	3,450
55	1,240	1,840	2,520	3,180	3,820
60	1,420	2,080	2,800	3,480	4,160
65	1,590	2,290	3,050	3,770	4,480
70	1,750	2,510	3,290	4,030	4,770
75	1,900	2,710	3,510	4,280	5,060
80	2,050	2,900	3,730	4,510	5,340
85	2,200	3,070	3,920	4,740	5,600
90	2,330	3,230	4,120	4,960	5,870
95	2,460	3,380	4,300	5,180	6,130
100	2,590	3,520	4,480	5,400	6,380

* Merchantable cubic volumes per acre are outside bark to a 4-in. top diameter. From Schnur, 1937.

In brief, the normal forest represented a paradox—a goal to be sought by forest managers but one that was both unrealistic and unattainable, if not undesirable.

Fortunately, the elusive concept of normality is gradually being erased from American forest management. Even under the hazardous assumption that a normal forest can be attained (and recognized when existent), it has become increasingly apparent that so-called full stocking does not necessarily imply maximum volume growth. Furthermore, the utility of normal yield tables is severely handicapped by the fact that no reliable methods are available for predicting yields of nonnormal or understocked natural stands. Normal yield tables are additionally limited in value because of their failure to account for variations in stand structure, i.e., stem distribution in size and space.

As a realistic alternative to the normality concept, Nelson and Bennett (1965) have suggested "that response surfaces be developed over a variety of stocking levels, thus changing the idea of stocking from a constant to a variable. We have then utilized a tool which allows us to solve, for a series of optimum stocking levels, each optimum representing the biological considerations of the forest manager. Sufficient examples of this approach, using multiple-regression techniques in the form of variable-density tables, are now available for both yield and growth to make normality a historical artifact rather than a dynamic theory." This viewpoint is endorsed and followed in succeeding discussions of growth and yield.

12-9 Basal area per acre. Because of its direct correlation with cubic volume, BA per acre provides a logical expression of stand density, particularly for even-aged plantations having a limited range of stem diameters. BA is simple to measure by point-sampling techniques, objective, and easily understood.

In the preparation of empirical yield tables (i.e., yield tables based on measurements of "average" existing stands) BA per acre has often been used as a measure of relative stocking by comparing actual BA with some arbitrary standard. However, as density *percentages* derived from BA tend to promote the concept of normality, it appears desirable to merely express this variable in terms of square feet per acre—with no implication as to stocking percentages. Empirical yield tables can thus be derived by multiple-regression analysis using the variables of BA per acre, site index, and stand age for a given species.

12-10 Number of trees per acre. As an expression of stand density, number of trees per acre has little value unless coupled with some measure of tree size, spacing, or distribution, i.e., stand structure. Number of trees per acre in relation to original tree spacing is an important variable for use in the derivation of empirical yield tables for plantations. As an example, Table 12-2 shows a plantation yield table based on tree spacing, total age, and site index at age 25. Use of such tables in stand growth prediction is discussed in Chap. 13.

Variations of this density expression include the number of trees per acre in relation to diameter, height, or tree form. Use of all three factors together leads to a measure of density based on volume. When qualified

TABLE 12-2 Empirical Yield Table (Abridged) for Slash Pine
Plantations in the Middle Coastal Plain of
Georgia and the Carolina Sandhills*

Total age, years	Original spacing, ft	Site index (age 25)			
		40	50	60	70
		Cubic feet per acre			
10	6 × 6	25	118	280	464
	6 × 8	23	106	250	413
	8 × 8	20	94	222	368
	10 × 10	17	79	187	310
	15 × 15	13	59	139	231
15	6 × 6	122	570	1,346	2,228
	6 × 8	109	507	1,197	1,981
	8 × 8	97	451	1,068	1,766
	10 × 10	82	380	897	1,484
	15 × 15	61	283	669	1,106
20	6 × 6	268	1,243	2,938	4,700
	6 × 8	238	1,106	2,613	4,200
	8 × 8	212	985	2,328	3,718
	10 × 10	179	828	1,958	3,173
	15 × 15	133	619	1,439	2,360

* Includes all trees 4.6 in. in diameter and larger. Volumes are
inside bark to a top diameter of 4.0 in. From Bennett, McGee,
and Clutter, 1959.

by number of trees and average size, volume may provide a useful indication of density to the forest manager; however, volume is not generally
recommended in lieu of other stand density evaluations (Bickford, 1957).

12-11   Stand-density index.   As proposed by Reineke (1933) for even-
aged stands, stand-density index is the number of trees per acre expressed
as a per cent of the number representing full stocking for the same
average diameter in unmanaged stands. Although empirical yield tables
have been prepared by using stand-density index (Langdon, 1961), there
are indications that the technique produces inconsistent results for some
species. Thus BA per acre, which appears to be an equally reliable index,
is preferred because it is easily derived without constructing the special
charts required for stand-density index.

12-12   Crown closure.   The percentage of a forest area covered by tree
crowns is referred to as *crown closure* or *crown density*. Strictly speaking,
this is a measure of area occupation rather than stand density, and

reliable crown closure estimates from aerial photographs are generally confined to even-aged stands of trees having an excurrent branching habit.

Although crown closure is used in lieu of the number of trees per acre for constructing aerial stand volume tables, it is not a particularly reliable measure of density, especially in uneven-aged stands comprised of tolerant species. As a rule, ocular photo estimates are made by 10 per cent density classes, and such estimates can vary widely with individual interpreters and the quality of photographs available.

TREE GROWTH

12-13 Increases in diameter. Tree growth is an intermittent process characterized by changes in stem form and dimension over a period of time. In temperate forests, a growing tree adds a yearly layer of wood just under the bark, from ground level to tip and all around the stem. In cross section, these layers appear as annual rings. Accordingly, tree age can be determined by counting the rings, and the volume of each ring is a measure of the wood added to the central stem that particular year.

Annual rings tend to be wider during the early life of a tree; as age increases, the ring width gradually decreases, resulting in a reduction of annual diameter increment. Even though the *width* of each ring normally decreases as the tree becomes older, this thinner wood layer is added over a larger stem diameter or bole surface. Therefore, the *volume* of wood added annually may be equal to or greater than that of previous years (Geneel et al., 1960). In addition to age, the rate of diameter growth is dependent on the soil moisture availability and the amount of leaf surface functioning in the photosynthetic process. Wider spacing among trees results in more root growing space and larger crowns which, in turn, lead to faster diameter growth.

12-14 Increases in height. Changes in tree height are of prime concern for predicting future stand composition and for selecting the ideal crop trees in pure stands. The typical course of height growth is illustrated by the sigmoid curve in Fig. 12-3. Height growth proceeds slowly until the seedling is well established; this is followed by a period of rapid growth during the next 20 to 30 years, depending on the species and site involved. As a tree begins to attain maturity, height growth gradually tapers off but never completely ceases as long as the tree is living and healthy.

The cumulative growth curve in Fig. 12-3 follows the same general configuration for most functions of tree growth—whether this be height, diameter, BA, or cubic volume. Although the exact form of the cumulative growth curve will differ with the variable used and climatic fluctuations, the elongated S-shaped pattern is a characteristic that can be invariably expected. From the foregoing, it can be seen that wood production in the central stem of a tree can be predicted by measuring past rates of diameter and height growth. Indeed, the primary objective

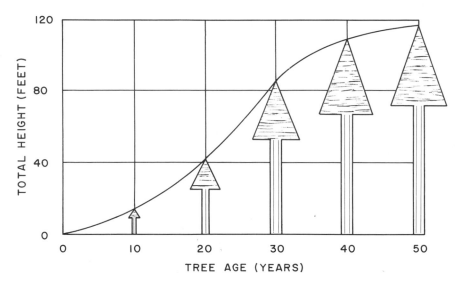

FIG. 12-3   Cumulative height growth pattern followed by
many coniferous species.

of most tree growth studies is the reliable prediction of future wood yields.

12-15   Periodic and mean annual growth.   The increase in tree or stand volume for 1 year is referred to as the *current annual growth.* Because current growth is difficult to measure for a single year, the average annual growth over a period of 5 to 10 years is commonly substituted instead. The differences in tree size or volume between the start and the end of a growth period, divided by the number of years involved, is properly termed *periodic annual growth.* By contrast, the *average* or *mean annual growth* is derived by dividing total tree volume at any point in time by total age.

Current or periodic annual growth, whether based on volume or tree size characteristics, increases rapidly, reaches a crest, and then drops off rapidly. In comparison, mean annual growth increases more slowly, attains a maximum at a later age, and falls more gradually. When curves

of current and mean annual growth are plotted over tree age, they inter-
sect at the peak of the latter (Fig. 12-4). This "culmination point"
for mean annual growth is regarded as the ideal harvesting or rotation
age in terms of most efficient volume production. The rotation age actually selected, however, is also dependent on trends in stumpage values,

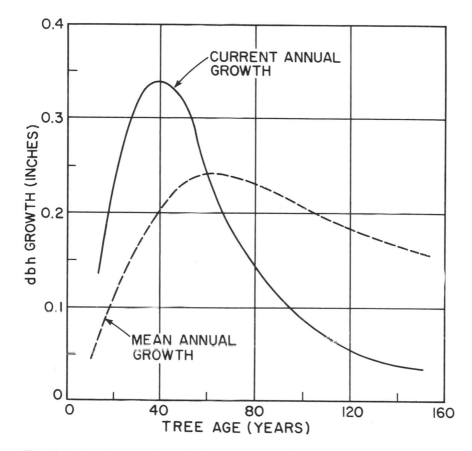

FIG. 12-4 Graphic comparison of the current annual
and mean annual growth curves of a tree.
From Bruce and Schumacher, 1950.

tree size specifications for various products, and other management
considerations.

12-16 Past growth from complete stem analysis. The most accurate
method of gauging accumulated tree volume growth is by complete stem
analysis. Although it is possible to obtain needed measurements and

annual ring counts by climbing and boring standing trees, the usual technique requires that sample trees be felled and cut into sections at the end of a designated growth period. D.i.b. at the beginning of the growth period is derived by counting annual rings back to the desired year. The total starting volume of all tree sections is subtracted from current volume to obtain cubic-foot growth.

The exact method followed in making a complete stem analysis, including points of stem measurement and intervals between sections, varies according to tree form and desired precision. Therefore, the procedures outlined in Table 12-3 are intended merely to serve as an illustration of the computations involved. In this example, an 8-year growth period is presumed for a coniferous tree having a total height of 50 ft at the time of felling.

The tree is severed 1 ft above ground to minimize effects of butt swell; it is cut into uniform 10-ft lengths, excepting the final 9-ft top section. Present d.i.b. is obtained at each cutting point; for elliptical cross sections, this is derived by averaging minimum and maximum diameters. Next, average cross-section diameters are converted to BA in square feet, followed by computations of present cubic volume for each section.

In Table 12-3, stump content is computed as the volume of a cylinder; i.e., taper in the first 1-ft section is ignored. *Present* volumes of the four 10-ft sections are derived from Smalian's formula, and content of the top 9-ft section is computed as the volume of a conoid (Sec. 3-11).

To obtain *previous* stem volume, diameters are measured by counting back eight annual rings from the present. Cubic volumes for stump and lower stem sections are calculated as before. For the top section, however, previous length must be determined by making several trial-and-error cuts from the tip downward—until the first ring preceding the growth period is located. Once the previous top length has been measured, its cubic content is again computed as the volume of a conoid (or other suitable geometric solid).

The difference in stem volume between the beginning and end of the specified time period represents gross growth. When this value is divided by the number of years in the period (8 in this example), the result is a measure of periodic annual growth.

Some stem analyses require that sectional cuts be made at both stump and dbh levels, depending on the objectives. In such cases, the stem section below dbh is usually regarded as a cylinder for purposes of deriving cubic volume. Cutting intervals above dbh may also be shortened to 4 ft or less when greater precision is desired. During inclement weather, stem sections about 1 in. thick can be extracted at desired intervals and the actual analysis performed indoors.

TABLE 12-3 Simplified Stem-analysis Computations for a Tree-growth Period of 8 Years

Section height above ground, ft	Average diameter, in.	Basal area, sq ft	Average basal area, sq ft	Section length, ft	Section volume, cu ft
1	14.6	1.163	(Stump) 1.163	1	1.163
11	12.8	0.894	(Section 1) 1.028	10	10.280
21	10.5	0.601	(Section 2) 0.748	10	7.480
31	8.7	0.413	(Section 3) 0.507	10	5.070
41	5.2	0.147	(Section 4) 0.280	10	2.800
50	0.0	(Conoid)	(Top) 0.049	9	0.441

Present total height: 50 ft   Present cubic volume: 27.234

Section height above ground, ft.	Average diameter, in.	Basal area, sq ft	Average basal area, sq ft	Section length, ft	Section volume, cu ft
1	12.1	0.799	(Stump) 0.799	1	0.799
11	10.7	0.624	(Section 1) 0.712	10	7.120
21	9.0	0.442	(Section 2) 0.533	10	5.330
31	7.5	0.307	(Section 3) 0.374	10	3.740
41	4.3	0.101	(Section 4) 0.204	10	2.040
43	0.0	(Conoid)	(Top) 0.034	2	0.068

Previous total height: 43 ft   Previous cubic volume: 19.097
Gross volume increase: 8.137 cu ft
Periodic annual growth: 8.137/8 = 1.017 cu ft per year

12-17 Tree growth as a percentage value. The calculation of tree growth in percentage terms is an expression of the average rate of change in size or volume over a given time period (Belyea, 1959). Because each year's annual ring is added over the cumulative size of the tree stem, tree growth has been most frequently regarded as a compound interest relationship. Despite the apparent logic of the compound interest theory, however, observations of actual volumes in uncut timber stands at three or more points in time indicate that tree growth is sometimes best described by *simple interest rates* (Grosenbaugh, 1958).

Actually, the argument of compound versus simple interest is largely an academic question, because growth per cent alone has little practical value in management decision making. A large number of growth per cent formulas have been proposed in previous years, many of which are misleading because of the inherent nature of tree growth itself. Because the base dimensions of a tree are constantly increasing, a uniform annual ring width results in a progressively lower and lower annual interest rate as the tree gets larger. Thus when the absolute increment remains constant, interest rates can appear astounding for small trees but strictly mediocre for larger ones.

Compound interest formulas are readily available in standard texts on forest finance and valuation. In terms of simple interest, the growth percentage in volume at any age is the current (periodic) annual growth divided by the "base volume" at the beginning of the growth period. Expressed as a formula, annual simple interest rates may be computed by

$$\text{Growth per cent} = \frac{V_2 - V_1}{n \times V_1}(100)$$

where V_2 = volume or tree size at end of growth period
V_1 = volume or tree size at start of growth period
n = number of years in growth period

Substituting growth values from Table 12-3, the annual simple interest rate would be

$$\text{Growth per cent} = \frac{27.234 - 19.097}{8(19.097)}(100) = 5.3 \text{ per cent}$$

12-18 Predictions of tree growth. As stated earlier, the principal reason for analyzing the past growth of trees is to establish a pattern for predicting future growth. From the standpoint of practical forest management, growth prediction is usually approached from a *stand* basis rather than in terms of individual trees. However, because tree growth is the integral component of stand growth, the trends of tree size increases are appropriately considered first. Stand growth prediction is discussed in Chap. 13.

Because the rate of tree growth in diameter, height, form, or volume is heavily dependent on relative age, prediction of future yields from past growth should be limited to short periods of time—usually not more than 5 to 10 years. Otherwise, large errors will result from the assumption that future growth will be equivalent or similar to past growth. As a rule, growth predictions are most reliable during the midlife of a tree, i.e., when size increases can be characterized by the central (near-linear) portion of the cumulative growth curve (Fig. 12-3). When cumulative growth curves are available for the desired species, future growth for short time periods can be approximated by ocular extension of such trends. Curves of periodic or mean annual growth can be utilized in like fashion, but the hazards of this procedure for extended time periods are readily apparent.

12-19 Future yields from growth percentage. This approach is analogous to the foregoing technique, for it presumes that future growth will proceed at the same *rate* as past growth. Even though this may be a reasonable postulation for a 3 to 5 year span, it is not recommended for longer periods. The annual growth rate of 5.3 per cent derived in Sec. 12-17 may be used as a simple example. Projecting the present tree volume of 27.234 cu ft ahead by 3 years would result in a theoretical increase of 15.9 per cent. Thus future tree volume would be computed as (1.159) (27.234) or 31.564 cu ft.

12-20 Growth prediction from diameter and height increases. Assume that a tree 14 in. in diameter and 65 ft tall had a dbh of 12 in. and a height of 55 ft 10 years ago. An obvious conclusion is that trees *now* 12 in. in diameter and 55 ft tall (on the same site) will grow 2 in. in diameter and 10 ft in height during the next 10 years. Actual rates of diameter and height increases may be obtained from complete stem analyses, from increment borings of standing trees, or from periodic remeasurement of permanent sample plots.

One simple method of short-term growth prediction for individual trees accommodates changes in height growth by use of a local volume table or height-dbh curve for the desired species.[1] Rates of diameter increase are obtained from increment borings at dbh. In the example that follows, the annual cubic volume growth per tree (outside bark) is based on the number of annual rings in the last $\frac{1}{2}$ in. of tree radius.

Assume that a tree with a dbh of 12.8 in. has a present merchantable

[1] This procedure may not be suited to long-term growth prediction. Over long periods of time, significant changes may occur in the height-dbh relationship for even-aged stands.

volume of 20.4 cu ft, outside bark, as read from a local volume table. An increment boring at dbh shows four annual rings in the last ½ in. of tree radius; i.e., the tree required 4 years to produce the last full inch of diameter growth. When this tree was exactly 1 in. smaller in diameter or 11.8 in. dbh, its merchantable volume was 17.2 cu ft—as read from the same local volume table. The difference in volume of 3.2 cu ft was thus produced in 4 years, for a periodic annual growth of 3.2/4 or 0.8 cu ft.

For the next 3 to 5 years, it is reasonably safe to assume that cubic volume will continue to increase at the rate of past growth, yielding a merchantable tree volume of 22.8 cu ft within 3 years or 24.4 cu ft after 5 years. As emphasized in Sec. 12–18, tree growth is a near-linear function of age during the middle years of stem development, particularly if the stand is relatively undisturbed by fire, heavy cutting, or unusual changes in density and competition.

Because the relationship of bark thickness to d.o.b. changes as a tree grows, predictions more than 5 years ahead should properly be based on wood growth alone, i.e., inside bark measurements. In such instances, future dbh values are developed by computing inside-outside bark ratios for each diameter class involved.

Where CFI systems are established, the most reliable method of obtaining growth information is by repeated measurements of the same trees on permanent sample plots. The technique of complete stem analysis is also recommended, especially for research studies dealing with patterns and fluctuations in growth cycles. Although the increment borer is a useful inventory tool, this method of growth determination probably ranks below the other two in terms of reliability. Some species exhibit widely divergent patterns of radial growth from one side of the tree to another as viewed on an increment core, depending on live-crown configuration. Many ring-porous hardwoods are extremely difficult to bore with conventional equipment, and certain diffuse-porous species have inconspicuous annual ring delineations. Even though these factors are often beyond the control of the inventory forester, they can nevertheless contribute to erroneous growth estimates.

PROBLEMS

12-1   Prepare a brief report on (*a*) the possibilities of using plant indicators as a measure of site in your locality or (*b*) the factors affecting site that can be measured or deduced from stereoscopic study of aerial photographs.

12-2   Determine two site index values for the same area by height-age measurements of different species growing in mixture. What would be the expected difference in cubic volume *per acre* for the two species at the index age, assuming that average stem diameter is about the same for both species?

12-3 On recent aerial photographs of your locality, locate 10 to 30 circular sample plots that represent a wide density range in terms of crown closure estimates. Visit each plot and obtain ground estimates of BA per acre for the dominant-codominant stems that were visible on the photographs. On cross-section paper, plot BA per acre values (y axis) over crown closure per cents (x axis). If a definite trend is evident, fit a balanced curve to the plotted points. Explain possible reasons for the pattern of plotted points obtained.

12-4 Prepare curves of periodic and mean annual increment for an important timber species. Does the culmination of mean annual growth roughly coincide with the accepted rotation age for that species? Give reasons for differences.

12-5 Make a complete stem analysis of a tree that is 20 to 40 years old. Using a growth period of 5 to 10 years, compute (a) present cubic volume, (b) periodic annual growth in cubic feet, (c) growth per cent by simple interest rates, and (d) predicted future volume 5 to 10 years hence.

REFERENCES

Baker, Frederick S.
1960. A simple formula for gross current annual increment. *J. Forestry* **58**:488–489.

Barnes, G. H.
1962. Yield of even-aged stands of western hemlock. *U.S. Dept. Agr. Tech. Bull.* 1273. 52 pp.

Belyea, Harold Cahill
1959. Two new formulae for predicting growth per cent. *J. Forestry* **57**:104–107.

Bennett, Frank A.
1963. Growth and yield of slash pine plantations. *U.S. Forest Serv., Southeast. Forest Expt. Sta. Res. Paper* SE-1. 23 pp., illus.

1962. Growth and yield of planted conifers in relation to initial spacing and stocking. *Proc. Soc. Am. Foresters*, Atlanta, Ga., pp. 22–26. illus.

————, McGee, C. E., and Clutter, J. L.
1959. Yield of old field slash pine plantations. *U.S. Forest Serv., Southeast. Forest Expt. Sta. Paper* 107. 19 pp.

Bickford, C. Allen, et al.
1957. Stocking, normality, and measurement of stand density. *J. Forestry* **55**:99–104.

Bruce, Donald, and Schumacher, Francis X.
1950. "Forest mensuration," 3d ed. McGraw-Hill Book Company, New York. 483 pp., illus.

Dick, James
1963. Forest stocking determined by sequential stocked-quadrat tally. *J. Forestry* **61**:290–294. illus.

Doolittle, Warren T.
1958. Forest soil-site relationships and species comparisons in the Southern Appalachians. *Soil Sci. Soc. Am. Proc.* **22**:455–458.

Gessel, Stanley P., Turnbull, Kenneth J., and Tremblay, F. Todd
1960. How to fertilize trees and measure response. National Plant Food Institute, Washington, D.C. 67 pp., illus.

Gevorkiantz, S. R.
1957. Site index curves for white pine in the Lake States. *U.S. Forest Serv., Lake States Forest Expt. Sta. Tech. Note* 483. 2 pp.

Gingrich, Samuel F.
1964. Criteria for measuring stocking in forest stands. *Proc. Soc. Am. Foresters,* Denver, Colo., pp. 198–201. illus.

Grosenbaugh, L. R.
1958. Allowable cut as a new function of growth and diagnostic tallies. *J. Forestry* 56:727–730.

Haddock, P. G., and Smith, J. H.
1956. Comments on "A site evaluation concept." *J. Forestry* 54:404–405.

Hampf, Frederick E.
1964. Site index curves for some forest species in the Eastern United States. U.S. Forest Service, Eastern Region. 34 pp., illus.

Heiberg, Svend O., and White, Donald P.
1956. A site evaluation concept. *J. Forestry* 54:7–10.

Husch, B.
1956. Use of age at d.b.h. as a variable in the site index concept. *J. Forestry* 54:340.

Johnson, Floyd A., and Worthington, Norman P.
1963. Procedure for developing a site index estimating system from stem analysis data. *U.S. Forest Serv., Res. Paper* PNW-7. 10 pp., illus.

Kozlowski, Theodore T.
1963. Growth characteristics of forest trees. *J. Forestry* 61:655–662. illus.

Langdon, O. Gordon
1961. Yield of unmanaged slash pine stands in South Florida. *U.S. Forest Serv., Southeast. Forest Expt. Sta. Sta. Paper* 123. 13 pp., illus.

Mader, Donald L.
1963. Volume growth measurement—an analysis of function and characteristics in site evaluation. *J. Forestry* 61:191–193.

Nelson, Thomas C., and Bennett, Frank A.
1965. A critical look at the normality concept. *J. Forestry* 63:107–109.

————, **Lotti, T., Brender, E. V., and Trousdell, K. B.**
1961. Merchantable cubic-foot volume growth in natural loblolly pine stands. *U.S. Forest Serv., Southeast. Forest Expt. Sta. Sta. Paper* 127. 12 pp., illus.

Putnam, John A., Furnival, George M., and McKnight, J. S.
1960. Management and inventory of southern hardwoods. *U.S. Dept. Agr. Handbook* 181, Washington, D.C. 102 pp., illus.

Reineke, L. H.
1933. Perfecting a stand-density index for even-aged forests. *J. Agr. Res.* 46:627–638.

Sammi, John C.
1965. An appeal for a better index of site. *J. Forestry* 63:174–176.

Schnur, G. Luther
1937. Yield, stand, and volume tables for even-aged upland oak forests. *U.S. Dept. Agr. Tech. Bull.* 560. 88 pp.

Seip, Hans Kristian
1963. Scandinavian mensuration. *Proc. Soc. Am. Foresters,* Boston, Mass. pp. 34–36.

Society of American Foresters
1958. Forest terminology, 3d ed., rev. Washington, D.C. 97 pp.

Staebler, George R.
1955. Gross yields and mortality for fully stocked stands of Douglas-fir. *U.S. Forest Serv., Pacific Northwest Forest and Range Expt. Sta. Res. Paper* 14. 20 pp.

Watt, Richard F.
1960. Second-growth western white pine stands—site index and species changes, normality percentage trends, mortality. *U.S. Dept. Agr. Tech. Bull.* 1226. 60 pp.

CHAPTER 13

STAND GROWTH AND PREDICTION

GROWTH TERMINOLOGY

13-1   Components of stand growth.   As defined by Gilbert (1954), the basic elements of stand growth are accretion, mortality, and ingrowth. *Accretion* is the growth on all trees that were measured at the beginning of the period. It includes the growth on trees that were cut during the period, plus those trees that died and were utilized. *Mortality* is the volume of trees initially measured that died during a specified growth period and were not utilized. The volume of those trees that grew into the lower inventoried diameter class during the growth period is termed *ingrowth*.

The growth elements of accretion, mortality, and ingrowth ·may be conveniently designated by the letters A, M, and I, respectively. Expressions of gross growth GG, net growth NG, and volume increase or production P for a given area may then be derived as follows:

Gross growth $GG = A + I$
Net growth $NG = A - M$ (ingrowth excluded)
Production $P = A - M + I$

Gross growth is a measure of the change in total volume for a given stand. In any given diameter class, it is the change in volume, plus mortality, during the growth period.

Net growth represents the stand volume increment based on the initial trees after mortality has been deducted. When ingrowth is added to net growth, the result is volume increase or *production*, i.e., a measure of the net change in volume during a specified growth period. If certain trees were harvested between the two successive inventories, yield volume Y must also be considered in computing production values. The preceding formula thus becomes

$$P = A - M + I - Y$$

13-2 Applications of growth terms. For purposes of illustration, it may be assumed that the volume of a given stand 10 years ago was 1,350 cu ft per acre (V_1). The present stand volume is 1,630 cu ft per acre (V_2). During the growth period, an intermediate cutting produced a yield Y of 280 cu ft per acre. Ingrowth I amounted to 65 cu ft per acre, and mortality M was measured as 25 cu ft per acre. Stand accretion or the volume increase attributed to the initial trees may therefore be computed as

$$A = V_2 - V_1 + Y + M - I$$
$$A = 1,630 - 1,350 + 280 + 25 - 65$$
$$A = 520 \text{ cu ft per acre}$$

The initial stand volume of 1,350 cu ft (V_1) included mortality and yield volumes; hence they were added to the present stand volume of 1,630 cu ft (V_2) in this calculation. Applying the other growth formulas, gross growth (which includes ingrowth) is $520 + 65$ or 585 cu ft per acre; net growth (excluding ingrowth) is $520 - 25$ or 495 cu ft per acre, and production is calculated as $520 - 25 + 65 - 280$ or 280 cu ft per acre.

For those foresters who wish to determine how much timber they can cut during a period, volume increase or production P provides the best estimate. However, it should be remembered that ingrowth is often a large and variable component of production. When ingrowth volume fluctuates widely from one growth period to another, it may be difficult to maintain production at preconceived levels.

Accretion is regarded as the best measure for comparing volume yields from two or more different methods of management or cutting. Because some cutting methods make more efficient use of the growing stock than others, accretion provides a useful index to the effects of a given treatment on the growth of trees initially present in the stand (Gilbert, 1954). Net growth estimates are primarily valuable in large areas where mortality rates can be reliably determined. Net growth values for small tracts may be unreliable, because the loss of one large tree can offset the growth on several acres of land.

To evaluate growth trends by dbh classes, average annual diameter increments should be used. Such increments are the basis for the stand table projection method of predicting growth.

GROWTH PREDICTION FROM YIELD TABLES

13-3 Use of empirical tables.   As outlined in Chap. 12, variable-density yield tables based on stand age, site index, and BA per acre (or tree spacing) are rapidly replacing the outmoded concept of normal yield tables (Vuokila, 1965). Prediction of the volume growth of even-aged stands is one of the primary reasons for developing empirical yield tables.

Once reliable yield tables have been compiled for the desired species, their application is simple. For a given site index and spacing (or BA level), future volume is read directly from the yield table at the desired stand age. Referring back to Table 12-2, for example, it may be assumed that a stand of slash pine has been planted at a spacing of 8×8 ft on an area where the site index (at age 25) is 50. The expected yield at age 15 is read from the table as 451 cu ft per acre; at age 20, the expected yield is 985 cu ft per acre. The predicted periodic annual growth is therefore $(985 - 451)/5$ or 107 cu ft per acre for this particular stand.

Even though the variables of site index, spacing, and age are carefully determined, there are likely to be some errors resulting from this method of growth prediction. The effect of unusual climatic cycles during a short prediction period may result in erratic growth patterns that cannot be accommodated by the "average conditions" implicit in a yield table. Another factor that may contribute to growth prediction errors is the actual amount of mortality occurring in stands under consideration. Although yield tables are customarily constructed in terms of *net* growth or volume, a specific mortality rate has been necessarily presumed. When the actual mortality differs appreciably from the assumed "standard," adjustments of tabular yields are required before reliable growth predictions can be expected.

Referring again to Table 12-2, this particular yield table requires a 3 per cent adjustment in tabulated values for each five-point (5 per cent) variation in survival from the presumed standard. To illustrate the adjustment, assume that the preceding 8×8-ft planting at age **15** had a survival of only **63** per cent. Values in Table **12-2** for 15-year-old plantations spaced 8×8 ft presumed a **73** per cent survival, however. The required adjustment is computed as

$$\frac{63\% - 73\%}{5\%} \times 3\% = -6\%$$

Thus for this particular species, age, and tree spacing, the yield table values would be decreased **6** per cent to account for the "nonaverage" mortality rate (Bennett, McGee, and Clutter, *op. cit.*). The reader must remember, however, that the foregoing method of adjustment applies only to the specific stand conditions described; the required correction varies with tree spacing, age, and the yield table selected.

13-4 Growth prediction equations. Most variable-density yield tables are now developed by multiple-regression techniques from the independent variables of stand age, site index, and BA per acre. For plantation yields, tree spacing may be substituted in lieu of BA as previously described. The details of multiple-regression analysis are beyond the scope of this volume, but several reliable references to this method of yield table construction are cited following Chap. 12. The works of Vuokila (1965) and Clutter (1963) also provide a review of variable-density yield tables and their applications.

A study by Brender (1960) dealing with growth predictions for natural stands of loblolly pine illustrates another approach commonly used in growth predictions. The following multiple-regression equation was developed for predicting annual cubic-foot volume growth per acre from the independent variables of BA, stand age, and site index:

$$\text{Net cubic-foot growth} = -20.748 + 6.4535(\text{BA}) - 0.02529(\text{BA})^2$$
$$+ 5.02606 \frac{(10,000)}{(AS)} - 235.034 \frac{(\text{BA})}{(S)}$$

where BA = basal area per acre of trees 5.6 in. dbh and larger
 A = stand age
 S = average site index, age 50

13-5 Tabulation of predicted growth. The foregoing equation, accounting for **68** per cent of the variation in cubic foot growth, is based on **1,552** acres of loblolly pine divided into **202** stands by age, stocking, and site index. The dependent variable of net growth was obtained from **100** per cent repeated inventories at **5**- to **12**-year intervals.

The cubic foot growth equation, solved for a variety of BA levels, sites, and age classes, was used to compile Table **13-1**. This tabulation differs from the usual variable-density yield table in that net *annual* cubic foot growth is shown in lieu of predicted *accumulative yields* at

TABLE 13-1 Predicted Annual Cubic-foot Growth Per Acre for Natural Loblolly Pine Stands in the Lower Piedmont*

Basal area stocking, sq ft	Predicted growth at ages—					
	20	30	40	50	60	70
Site index 60						
20	61.7	48.1	41.0	36.5	34.0	32.0
30	74.3	60.7	53.7	49.2	46.7	44.6
40	81.9	68.3	61.3	56.7	54.2	52.2
50	84.6	71.1	64.0	59.5	57.0	55.0
60	82.1	68.5	61.5	57.0	54.5	52.4
70		60.9	53.9	49.4	46.9	44.9
80			41.5	37.0	34.5	32.4
Site index 70						
20	66.7	55.1	49.1	45.6	43.0	41.0
30	85.0	73.4	67.4	63.8	61.3	59.3
40	98.4	86.9	80.8	77.3	74.8	72.8
50	106.6	95.0	89.0	85.5	83.0	80.9
60	109.7	98.1	92.1	88.6	86.1	84.0
70	107.7	96.2	90.1	86.6	84.1	82.1
80		89.2	83.1	79.6	77.1	75.1
90			71.1	67.5	65.0	63.0
100			53.9	50.4	47.9	45.9
Site index 80						
20	71.1	60.6	55.0	52.0	50.0	48.5
30	93.6	83.1	77.5	74.5	72.5	71.0
40	111.1	100.5	95.0	92.0	90.0	88.5
50	123.5	112.9	107.4	104.4	102.4	100.9
60	130.8	120.3	114.7	111.7	109.7	108.2
70	133.1	122.5	117.0	114.0	112.0	110.5
80	130.3	119.8	114.2	111.2	109.2	107.7
90	122.5	111.9	106.4	103.4	101.4	99.9
100		99.0	93.5	90.5	88.5	87.0

* The original table also included cubic-foot growth for site index 90 and 100. Volumes are based on trees 5.6 in. dbh and larger to a top diameter of 4.0 in. inside bark. From Brender, 1960.

various ages. However, it serves the same general purpose as a conventional yield table. In addition to their utility for estimating growth, such tables can be used for deciding on thinning needs and what BA levels provide the best growth in stands of a given age and site index. As seen in Table 13-1, for example, maximum cubic foot growth on site index 80 is attained with a BA of 70 sq ft per acre. When this BA level is reduced by one-third, however, growth is lessened by only 8 to 10 per cent (Brender, 1960).

The use of growth prediction equations is a popular technique for even-aged stands, because it is rapid and permits immediate estimates of stand growth without the necessity of predicting future tree sizes. As previously cited, however, large errors may result unless careful consideration is given to the effects of climatic cycles and unusual mortality rates. Also, multiple-regression equations do not include all the complex interactions of growth and site quality; thus such equations provide only approximate yields. In general, growth prediction periods should be limited to a maximum of 10 years for fast-growing species and 20 years for slower-growing stands.

STAND TABLE PROJECTION

13-6 Characteristics of stand projection. This method of growth prediction recognizes the structure of a stand, and growth projections are made according to dbh classes. The method is best suited to uneven-aged, low-density, and immature timber stands. In dense or overmature forests where mortality rates are high, stand table projection may be of questionable value for providing reliable information on net stand growth.

The procedure ordinarily followed in the stand table projection method of growth prediction may be briefly summarized as follows:

1 A present stand table showing the number of trees in each dbh class is developed from a conventional inventory. (See Sec. 9-19.)
2 Past periodic growth, by dbh classes, is determined from increment borings or from remeasurements of permanent sample plots. When increment borings are used, growth values must be converted from an inside-bark basis to outside-bark readings.
3 Past diameter growth rates are applied to the present stand table to derive a future stand table showing the predicted number of trees in each dbh class at the end of the growth period. Numbers of trees in each class must then be corrected for expected mortality and predicted ingrowth.
4 Both present and future stand tables are converted to stock tables (Sec. 9-19) by use of an appropriate local volume table. Thus for short growth periods, the expected changes in tree height during the growth period are inherently accommodated by diameter increases.
5 Periodic stand growth is obtained as the difference between the total volume of the present stand and that of the future stand.

13-7 Diameter growth. Rates of diameter growth outside bark are best obtained from repeated measurements of permanent sample plots (Fig. 13-1). Consecutive inventories of the same trees provide a direct evaluation of combined wood and bark increment at dbh. As a result, many of the problems encountered in estimating stem growth from increment borings can be avoided.

FIG. 13-1 Dendrometer or growth band for measuring small changes in tree diameter on a permanent sample plot. *U.S. Forest Service photograph.*

As an example, Table 13-2 was compiled from remeasurements of dbh outside bark for southern pines and hardwoods distributed throughout the state of Alabama. Tree species and diameters were sampled in proportion to occurrence. All the major southern pines were represented; the principal hardwoods sampled were red and white oaks, hickories, yellowpoplar, sweetgum, and tupelos. The lack of a definite differentiation in growth by diameter classes was attributed to the moderate stand-density levels common in that state (Judson, 1965). Tabulations

TABLE 13-2 Annual Diameter Growth by Diameter Class in Alabama*

Dbh class, in.	Pine species			Hardwood species		
	No. of sample trees	Mean growth, in.	Standard deviation, in.	No. of sample trees	Mean growth, in.	Standard deviation, in.
6	522	0.22	0.13	733	0.13	0.10
8	352	0.23	0.13	416	0.13	0.11
10	179	0.24	0.12	255	0.13	0.10
12	88	0.22	0.12	122	0.14	0.10
14	40	0.24	0.14	66	0.14	0.10
16	11	0.26	0.19	40	0.13	0.09
18	10	0.21	0.09	18	0.16	0.10
20+	8	0.18	0.09	12	0.15	0.13
All diameters	1,210	0.22	0.13	1,662	0.13	0.10

* Diameter growth (outside bark) based on remeasurements of 2,872 trees by the U.S. Forest Survey. Reprinted from Judson, 1965.

of this nature, however, are ideally suited to efficient stand table projections.

When diameter growth is not available in the foregoing form, it is customary to rely on increment borings at dbh instead. Assuming we wish to estimate diameter growth (outside bark) for the last 10 years, estimates for each dbh class might be handled according to the following step-by-step procedure:

1 Measure present dbh to the nearest 0.1 in. and subtract diameter bark thickness to obtain present d.i.b. at breast height.
2 From an increment boring, obtain the 10-year wood growth in diameter and subtract from present d.i.b. to derive d.i.b. at breast height 10 years ago.
3 For each diameter class recognized, plot present diameter bark thickness over present d.i.b. at breast height. Draw a smooth, balanced curve through the plotted points. Read off appropriate bark thicknesses for each d.i.b. 10 years ago (step 2) and add these values together to arrive at an estimate of dbh (outside bark) 10 years ago.
4 Subtract dbh (outside bark) 10 years ago from present d.o.b. to derive the estimated growth in diameter during the stated time period. If future growth is presumed to equal past growth, this information may be applied directly in a stand table projection.

13-8 Stand mortality and ingrowth. The reliability of stand table projections leans heavily on the derivation of realistic estimates of mortality and ingrowth. As with diameter increment, such information is preferably obtained from consecutive reinventories of permanent sample plots; in reality, there is no other sound procedure for making these predictions. Mortality rates are desired for each dbh recognized in the stand table, because the natural demise of smaller stems is usually much greater than for larger diameters. Only when growth predictions are made for very short time periods (perhaps 3 years or less) can mortality be regarded as a negligible factor.

For growth predictions of 5 to 10 years, ingrowth is usually accounted for by having the present stand table include several diameter classes below the minimum dbh desired in the future stand table. As an illustration, if 10-year growth predictions are planned for trees 10 in. dbh and larger, the initial stand table might include all stems that might logically grow into the 10-in.-dbh class during the interim, e.g., those stems presently 6 in. or more in diameter.

13-9 A sample stand projection. For purposes of illustration, it will be assumed that the information on pine species in Table 13-2 represents a 20-acre stand for which a 10-year volume growth prediction is desired for stems in the 10-in.-dbh class and larger. Present and future board-foot volumes are to be derived from a local volume table based on the Scribner log rule. The present stand table, including adjustments for mortality and applicable decadal growth rates, appears as shown in Table 13-3. The 6-in. and 8-in. trees are included in the present stand table to accommodate ingrowth into larger diameter classes.

Because mortality has been deducted from the present stand in Table 13-3, the next step is the application of diameter growth rates in deriving

TABLE 13-3 Present Stand Table, Mortality, and Expected 10-year
Diameter Growth for a 20-acre Pine Stand
in Alabama

Dbh class, in.	Present stand, no. of stems	Expected mortality, per cent	Expected survival, no. of stems	10-year dbh growth, in.
6	522	40	313	2.2
8	352	35	229	2.3
10	179	25	134	2.4
12	88	20	70	2.2
14	40	15	34	2.4
16	11	10	10	2.6
18	10	10	9	2.1
20+	8	20	6	1.8
Totals	1,210		805	

a future stand table. The method used here was proposed by Chapman and Meyer (*op. cit.*) The upward movement of trees into larger dbh classes is proportional to the ratio of growth to the chosen diameter class interval:

$$\text{Growth index ratio} = \frac{g}{i}$$

where g is the diameter growth in inches and i is the diameter class interval in inches.

Using the 6-in.-dbh class from Table 13-3 as an example:

$$\text{Growth index ratio} = \frac{2.2}{2.0} = 1.10$$

The interpretation of a growth index ratio of 1.10 is that 100 per cent of the trees move up one dbh class, and 0.10 or 10 per cent of these advance two classes. Thus, of the 313 trees expected to survive in the 6-in. class, 90 per cent (282 trees) move up to the 8-in. class, and 10 per cent (31 trees) move all the way to the 10-in. class. None will remain in the 6-in. class in this instance. If the growth index ratio had been less than unity, for example, 0.80, 80 per cent of the trees would move up one class interval, and 20 per cent would remain in the present dbh class. For the dbh classes in Table 13-3, growth index ratios and the future stand table is shown in Table 13-4.

TABLE 13-4 Application of Growth-Index Ratios in Deriving a Future Stand Table for a 20-acre Pine Stand in Alabama

Dbh class, in.	Present stand surviving, no. of stems	Growth-index ratio, g/i	No. of stems moving up, by dbh classes			Future stand table, no. of stems
			No change	1 class	2 classes	
6	313	1.10	0	282	31	0
8	229	1.15	0	195	34	282
10	134	1.20	0	107	27	226
12	70	1.10	0	63	7	141
14	34	1.20	0	27	7	90
16	10	1.30	0	7	3	34
18	9	1.05	0	8	1	14
20	6	0.90	1	5	0	12
22	0		0	0	0	6
Totals	805		1	694	110	805

Once the future stand table has been derived, present and future volumes (stock tables) can be obtained from an appropriate local volume table (Table 13-5). Volume production is computed for each dbh class as the difference between present and future volumes. For this hypothetical stand, the predicted net volume growth for the 10-year period is

TABLE 13-5 Predicted 10-year Volume Production of a 20-acre Pine Stand in Alabama

Dbh class, in.	Present stand table, no. of stems	Future stand table, no. of stems	Scribner volume per tree, bd ft	Present stock table, bd ft	Future stock table, bd ft	Volume production, bd ft
6	313	0				
8	229	282				
10	134	226	42	5,628	9,492	3,864
12	70	141	86	6,020	12,126	6,106
14	34	90	136	4,624	12,240	7,616
16	10	34	201	2,010	6,834	4,824
18	9	14	280	2,520	3,920	1,400
20	6	12	369	2,214	4,428	2,214
22	0	6	481	0	2,886	2,886
Totals	805	805		23,016	51,926	28,910

28,910 bd ft or 1,445 bd ft per acre. On an *annual* basis, the predicted growth per acre is estimated as 144.5 bd ft.

PROBLEMS

13-1 If data are available from measured permanent sample plots in your locality, compute stand accretion, gross growth, net growth, and production for several plots representing similar stand conditions.

13-2 Develop a future stand table for trees 10 in. and larger for the hardwood species listed in Table 13-2. Assume a 5-year growth prediction period and mortality rates that are one-half those shown in Table 13-3. Arrange final data as in Table 13-4.

13-3 Construct a homemade dendrometer of the type shown in Fig. 13-1 and described by Liming (1957). Use it to measure diurnal changes in dbh over a 6- to 10-week period.

REFERENCES

Barrett, James P., and Allen, Peter H.
1966. Predicting yield of extensively managed white pine stands. *Univ. New Hampshire Agr. Expt. Sta. Tech. Bull.* 108. 15 pp., illus.

Brender, E. V.
1960. Growth prediction for natural stands of loblolly pine in the lower Piedmont. *Georgia Forest Res. Council Rept.* 6. 7 pp., illus.

Buell, Jesse H.
1945. The prediction of growth in uneven-aged timber stands on the basis of diameter distributions. *Duke Univ. School of Forestry Bull.* 11. 70 pp.

Clutter, Jerome L.
1963. Compatible growth and yield models for loblolly pine. *Forest Sci.* **9**:354–371. illus.

———— and **Bennett, Frank A.**
1965. Diameter distributions in old-field slash pine plantations. *Georgia Forest Res. Council Rept.* 13. 9 pp., illus.

Cooper, Charles F.
1961. Equations for the description of past growth in even-aged stands of ponderosa pine. *Forest Sci.* **7**:72–80.

Davis, Kenneth P.
1964. The importance and uses of growth information in timber management. *J. Forestry* **62**:490–492.

Evert, F.
1964. Components of stand volume and its increment. *J. Forestry* **62**:810–813.

Ffolliott, Peter F.
1965. Determining growth of ponderosa pine in Arizona by stand projection. *U.S. Forest Serv., Res. Note* RM-52. 4 pp.

Gilbert, Adrian M.
1954. What is this thing called growth? *U.S. Forest Serv., Northeast. Forest Expt. Sta. Paper* 71. 5 pp.

Gruschow, G. F., and Evans, T. C.
1959. The relation of cubic-foot volume growth to stand density in young slash pine stands. *Forest Sci.* 5·49–55

Judson, George M.
1965. Tree diameter growth in Alabama. *U.S. Forest Serv., Res. Note* SO-17. 3 pp.

Kirby, C. L.
1962. The growth and yield of white spruce—aspen stands in Saskatchewan. *Forestry Branch Dept. Nat. Resources Prov. Saskatchewan Tech. Bull.* 4. 58 pp., illus.

Lemmon, Paul E., and Schumacher, F. X.
1963. Theoretical growth and yield of hypothetical ponderosa pine stands under different thinning regimes. *Forest Sci.* **9**:33–43.

Liming, Franklin G.
1957. Homemade dendrometers. *J. Forestry* **55**:575–577. illus.

Meyer, H. Arthur
1952. Structure, growth, and drain in balanced, uneven-aged forests. *J. Forestry* **50**:85–92.

Nelson, Thomas C.
1964. Growth models for stands of mixed species composition. *Proc. Soc. Am. Foresters,* Denver, Colo., pp. 229–231.

Roe, A. L.
1952. Growth of selectively cut ponderosa pine stands in the Upper Columbia Basin. *U.S. Dept. Agr. Handbook* 39.

Vuokila, Yrjo
1965. Functions for variable density yield tables of pine based on temporary sample plots. Forest Research Institute, Helsinki, Finland. 86 pp., illus.

Winkenwerder, Hugo, and Clark, Elias T.
1922. Handbook of field and office problems in forest mensuration. John Wiley & Sons, Inc., New York. 133 pp.

CHAPTER **14**

CONTINUOUS FOREST INVENTORY AND DATA PROCESSING

CONTINUOUS FOREST INVENTORY

14-1 The continuous forest inventory concept. CFI is basically an extensive system of permanent sample plots that are established, maintained, and periodically remeasured for purposes of deriving representative forest management data for large tracts. Volume, growth, and mortality are obtained from frequent inventories of systematically arranged plots that are presumably treated in exactly the same manner as the surrounding forest. Under current practices, the wealth of information resulting from these oft-repeated inventories is collated, sorted, and summarized by use of machine-sort cards and electronic data processing equipment.

In the words of Stott (1959),

CFI provides top management with the facts from which sound, workable, high-level policy decisions are made. It is industry's application of automation to the woods, and from the woods it brings an endless flow of advice on long-range timber resource planning. CFI goes beyond the limited confines of special research studies to measure and record changes in trees and forest cover on a representative, forest-wide basis.

It should be noted here that there is some disagreement among practicing foresters about the relative merits of CFI systems. Although it is often conceded that reliable information on tree growth and mortality can best be obtained by some scheme of permanent plot remeasurement (Hall, 1959), a number of organizations have found that a full-fledged CFI system is an expensive luxury that can present problems as well as solutions. Because of the low sampling intensity of most industrial CFI systems (e.g., about two sample plots per square mile), such systems supplement rather than replace conventional cruises. Special inventories are still likely to be required for cutting compartments or logging units during the season prior to harvesting operations.

14-2 Historical aspects. The basic concepts of CFI were developed in Europe in the late 1800s. The European foresters generally credited with this development were Gurnaud and Biolley, who originated a management system known as the "method of control." In the United States, CFI had its beginning in 1937 when several growth plots were established on industrial lands in northern Wisconsin (Barton, 1960). The recent impetus given to CFI systems in this country is thus not due to the discovery of a new innovation but to the adaptation of CFI procedures to automatic data processing equipment. Estimates indicate that there are more than 50,000 permanent plots on 25 million acres of industrial and public forest lands in the United States (Stott and Semmons, 1960).

CFI has been used by both private and public foresters in the United States for the development of management plans, cutting budgets, silvicultural work improvement programs, and broad timber-operating schedules. By using this system, the forester is able to keep abreast of changes in the forest and its condition and to have forest data available quickly before they become outdated. Fact finding and organizing are expedited, with results available while they are still applicable. CFI plots have encouraged soil, insect, and disease studies, have provided the incentive for the development of comprehensive road plans, and have increased the utilization of inferior species and defective individuals.

14-3 Characteristics of continuous forest inventory systems. Some of the factors that distinguish CFI systems from conventional inventories are as follows:

1 Permanent sample plots are systematically located over the entire forest property, often arranged on a square grid pattern. As a rule, fixed-radius,

circular plots of 0.1 to 0.25 acre are spaced at intervals of 25 to 80 chains.

2 Every living tree above a selected minimum dbh is numbered and conspicuously marked—or its exact bearing and distance from plot center is noted on a special map of the plot.

3 For every "tally" tree, a detailed record of stem measurements is obtained. These data are coded on the field tally form or entered directly on a machine-sort data card.

4 All original tally trees on each plot are remeasured at intervals of 3 to 10 years.

5 Following each remeasurement, summary reports show the present forest conditions, areas in various cover types, and number, size, volume, and quality of the different species of trees present. Difference reports (developed by contrasting current tree measurements with previous ones) show, in relation to time, the changes in cover type, the addition or loss of volume and quality, and the addition or loss of trees in various categories (Barton, 1960).

6 It is hoped that sample plots are subjected to exactly the same conditions or treatments as the surrounding forest, whether this be stand improvement, harvesting, fires, floods, or insect and disease infestations. Only under these conditions can it be assumed that the sample plots are truly representative in nature.

14-4 Planning a continuous forest inventory. The first step in organizing a CFI system on a given forest is a planning conference with a forester proficient in continuous inventory methods (Stott, 1959). Objectives of the planning conference are as follows:

1 The primary aims and goals of forest management in the chosen area should be reviewed.

2 A working plan of specific field instructions and sampling design should be prepared.

3 Procedures should be outlined for supervising and checking fieldwork and data processing.

4 Flow charts or diagrams covering each inventory phase should be prepared.

5 Expected results should be critically examined to make certain that summary reports will be in the format desired by top management.

For determining the number of sample plots to be established, a conventional statistical approach has rarely been used in the past. Inappropriate as it may appear, sampling intensity has commonly been determined by trial-and-error schemes based on experience from active CFI systems. The following rule-of-thumb formula has been proposed by Barton (1960):

No. of plots $= 100 + 0.0025 \times$ acres in tract

Founded on the premise that any CFI system requires a minimum of 100 plots, this empirical formula reputedly applies to all tracts from 100 to 3.5 million acres in size. As a general rule, CFI systems have not been encouraged for tracts smaller than 25,000 acres, but workable schemes have been devised for forests as small as 2,500 acres (Baker and Hunt, 1960).

Proponents of CFI systems have commonly assumed that stratified random sampling is unsuited to permanent plot inventories because of continually changing conditions in forest stands. In fact, however, some form of stratified sampling (possibly based on forest types or topographic sites) is probably the most desirable method to use for permanent plot allocation. Furthermore, the statistical determination of sampling intensities in accordance with desired levels of precision is highly recommended in lieu of the rule-of-thumb approach.

14-5 Plot establishment and measurement. Although CFI plots are occasionally located at random, they have been more commonly arranged in a systematic fashion, often on a square grid basis. A 1:1 grid arrangement of 250 plots throughout a tract of 60,000 acres would result in a spacing of approximately 49×49 chains, i.e., one plot for each 2,400 square chains. The most common circular plot sizes employed in the past have been $\frac{1}{5}$ or $\frac{1}{7}$ acre. Point samples have been used in lieu of fixed-radius plots in a few instances.

Each plot center is permanently marked on forest maps and on the ground. The center may also be referenced from a known landmark several chains distant, and by recording the bearing and distance to two or more "witness trees" on the plot. There is disagreement as to whether permanent plots should be marked (1) conspicuously, so that they can be easily relocated, or (2) inconspicuously, to ensure that they are accorded the same treatment as nonsampled portions of the forest. There are obvious drawbacks to either method. All tally trees may also be numbered with paint or metal tags and marked at the point of dbh measurement.

Each tree is measured for diameter, pulpwood and sawlog height, crown class, vigor, grade, and operability. When machine-sort data cards are used, such information is recorded on "tree detail cards." The plot is also described as to site, topography, forest cover type, density, stand size, and stand condition; these items are entered on "plot description cards." At each reinventory, trees that have attained the minimum diameter during the measurement interval are tallied as ingrowth. Also, felling records are kept to correct yields for these plots cut during the measurement interval.

Plot inventories are preferably made immediately after a growing season and prior to heavy snowfall. For tracts smaller than 100,000 acres, it is often possible to establish all plots in a single season and remeasure them within similar time limitations. On larger areas, field-work may be conducted each fall on a rotation system that reinventories about one-fifth of the forest each year.

14-6 Advantages and limitations. Among the principal advantages that have been cited by advocates of CFI are the following:

1 Large amounts of field data are processed quickly and efficiently, and woods accounting reports become more businesslike and intelligible to top management. The data obtained are flexible, and they can be quickly sorted and compiled for any factor or variable for which information has been collected.

2 Differences between periodic remeasurements of permanent sample plots yield accurate growth data. In addition, trees initially sampled but absent at a later tally can be classified as either dead or cut. Through this system, valuable information is available to the forest manager for the development of future forest policy.

3 Because each plot is representative of a particular area of the forest, any plot change provides a measure of habitat change within the forest.

4 With the mechanically arranged samples, plot volumes and plot areas are directly related; thus there is a constant volume expansion factor for the whole forest or for any part of it (Stott, 1959).

5 CFI could be an ideal method for providing needed yield table data and for volume regulation of all-aged hardwood forests (Furnival, 1962).

Detractors of CFI systems point out that much of the information collected is unnecessary and never used in applied management. Such systems are expensive to establish and maintain, and remeasurements often have to be financed by funds critically needed for other management operations. Other disadvantages that have been specified are:

1 CFI does not replace cruises for timber sales, because there are never enough permanent plots within a cutting compartment to yield reliable volume estimates.

2 The forest manager can rarely be certain that CFI plots, especially if conspicuously marked, will be treated exactly the same as the surrounding forest area.

3 Continuity of inventory is a virtue only in growth assessment, and precise estimates of growth are not vital until the property approaches the desired levels of growing stock (Grosenbaugh, 1959).

4 Temporary point samples without punched-card compilation for individual trees may be much more efficient than conventional CFI plots.

In summary, forest management objectives may not be efficiently served by any one method of sampling or data collection. Techniques requiring permanent sample plots are well suited to growth estimates, but they may be unduly expensive or inefficient means of obtaining timber volumes and other inventory facts. CFI appears to have an established position in managing certain types of industrial forest holdings, but it is not a panacea for all inventory problems.

MACHINE-SORT CARDS FOR DATA PROCESSING

14-7 Field recording of inventory data. The magnitude of measurement information collected on large-scale forest inventories makes it almost mandatory that some method of automatic data processing be adopted. The use of standardized machine-sort cards for handling unit records therefore represents one logical solution to the problem of summarizing large volumes of inventory data into usable bits of information. Today, most CFI systems and large-scale forest surveys make full use of mark-sensed or punched cards in lieu of conventional field tally sheets.

In those instances where hand-written tally sheets are still employed, tree measurement data (including species and other qualitative descriptions) are recorded in numerical "codes" so that they can be efficiently transferred to standard punched cards in the office. Foresters have also adapted portable tape recorders for automating the process of tallying inventory data (Sundahl, 1965).

14-8 The unit record card. The use of machine-sort cards for data processing in the United States dates back to 1890 when an engineer named Herman Hollerith perfected a punched card to handle United States census statistics. In those days, holes were punched one by one, and it was not until 1916 that a device was developed to punch as many as nine holes in a card at one time. Early card-handling devices were extremely slow by today's standards, because they operated on mechanical rather than electrical principles. It was not until the mid-1940s that vacuum tubes (transistors came even later) were adapted for development of electronic computers and high-speed data processing equipment. The widespread use of such equipment has been largely responsible for increased interest in CFI systems in North America.

The three basic types of unit record cards in common use are (1) the standard machine-punched card, (2) the prescored or port-a-punch card, and (3) the mark-sensed card. These cards accommodate 80, 40, and 27 vertical columns of numbers, respectively. The standard 80-column card is designed for office punching of data from numerically coded source documents, e.g., cruise tally sheets, although a portable key punch can be used in the field as described by Rudolph and Sherrill (1957).

When the port-a-punch card is used, numerical data are entered directly in the field by hand punching of prescored holes with a special stylus. Cards are placed in a special port-a-punch holder during the punching process (Fig. 14-1). Mark-sensed cards are also designed for direct field tallying; graphite pencil marks are drawn through the desired column numbers in lieu of punched holes. If port-a-punch cards and mark-sensed cards are carefully handled in the field, tabulations can be later transferred automatically to standard 80-column punched cards.

On all three types of cards, each column is numbered from 0 to 9, and there are spaces for two additional unmarked "position punches" in the margin above each column. These latter spaces are referred to as the "11" and "12" punch positions, and they are used for alphanumeric punching, i.e., when it is desired to code alphabetical characters in the numbered columns.

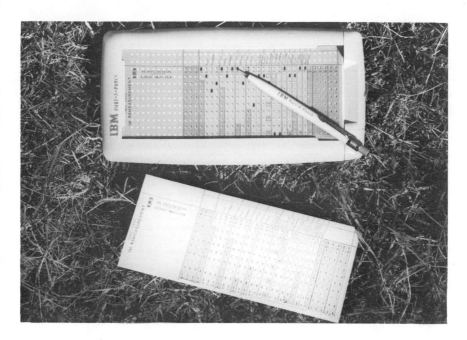

FIG. 14-1 Port-a-punch holder, stylus, and prescored
card used for CFI. *Courtesy of Southeast
Timber Division, Rayonier Incorporated.*

14-9 Alphanumeric card punching. Coding for alphabetical characters
is normally the only reason for double punching in a given column of
numbers, i.e., having two punches in the same vertical column. Alphanumeric punching is accomplished by using a "0," "11," or "12" punch
position *in addition to* one of the regular 1 to 9 punches. Codes are
as follows:

12-1	A	11-1	J	0-2	S
12-2	B	11-2	K	0-3	T
12-3	C	11-3	L	0-4	U
12-4	D	11-4	M	0-5	V
12-5	E	11-5	N	0-6	W
12-6	F	11-6	O	0-7	X
12-7	G	11-7	P	0-8	Y
12-8	H	11-8	Q	0-9	Z
12-9	I	11-9	R		

In processing, a machine known as an alphabetic interpreter can
"read" the holes punched in the preceding fashion and print letters or
numerals directly back on the same card. Student registration cards
at many universities are handled by alphabetic interpreters. Examples

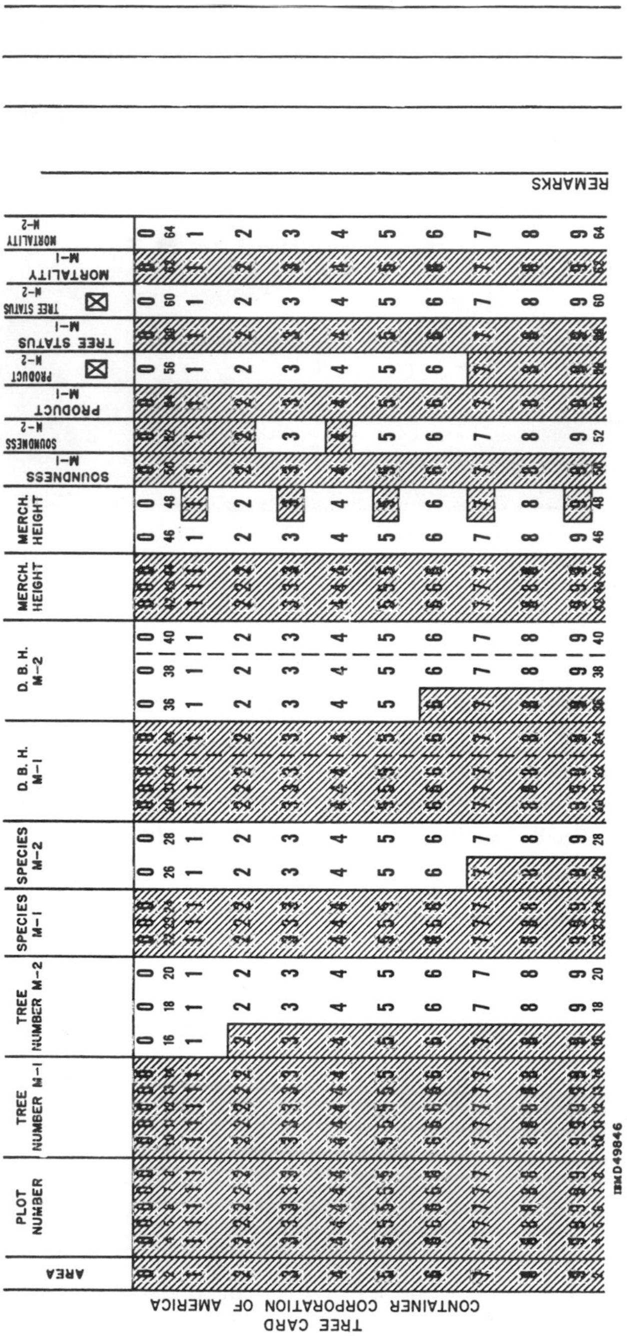

FIG. 14-2 Sample port-a-punch tree-detail card for use in CFI. *Courtesy of Container Corporation of America.*

of other semiautomatic and automatic data processing machines that are familiar to inventory specialists include the key punch, card verifier, card sorter, collator, and accounting machine or tabulator. Specific functions of these and related machines have been detailed by Honer (1964).

14-10 Port-a-punch tallies for CFI. Two distinct types of port-a-punch cards are used for tallying; these are known as tree cards and plot cards. As these titles imply, a different tree card is used to record the measurements of each stem tallied; therefore, there may be 30 or more tree cards required for each plot. Conversely, only one plot card is needed per location to describe such items as cover type, site, topography, and general stand conditions. On both types of cards, "M–1 measurements" based on the previous inventory will have been entered prior to the current field tally. Therefore, present measurements will be punched exclusively in columns designated as "M–2." This procedure provides an opportunity for visual card checks during the field tally to assure that coded measurements are logical and correctly punched.

14-11 Tree card tallies. A simplified port-a-punch tree card is pictured in Fig. 14-2. Coded tree data to be punched in each column or group of columns are identified by printed headings and separated by vertical lines. These block designations are referred to as *fields*. In general, shaded areas on the card represent previous measurements, and nonshaded columns are reserved for the current field tally. Following is a hypothetical series of tree measurements or codes that might be punched in such a tally card:

AREA. Any one of 10 different districts, counties, regions, or states might be coded here by punching a digit from 0 to 9.

PLOT NUMBER: The three-digit field printed on the card accommodates up to 1,000 plots, that is, 000 through 999.

TREE NUMBER: The M–2 nonshaded field can accommodate any tree number up to 199.

SPECIES: Tree species are usually coded in two digits, as from 01 to 99. Standardized codes adopted by the Society of American Foresters or the U.S. Forest Survey are suggested here.

DBH: Stem diameters are recorded to the nearest 0.1 in., with the vertical dashed line serving as the decimal point. In the M–2 field, trees up to 69.9 in. dbh may be punched.

MERCHANTABLE HEIGHT: In the nonshaded field, heights of 02 to 98 ft may be punched, by 2-ft intervals. Unless tops are broken or previous errors occurred, M–2 heights should always be equal to or greater than M–1 heights.

SOUNDNESS: With a one-digit code, tree soundness might be recorded in 10 per cent classes: that is, 0 = 100 per cent sound; 3 = 30 per cent, and so on. Some of the soundness (freedom from defect) digits have been shaded out on this particular tree card. As a rule, the soundness per cent in M-2 should not show an increase over the M-1 value.

PRODUCT: Based on expected utilization, trees might be coded as 0 = culls and nonmerchantable; 1 = nonpulping species; 2 = pulpwood; 3 = poles or piling; 4 = sawtimber; 5 = veneer logs, and so on. The code applied should be based on the highest value class for any given tree.

TREE STATUS: This field serves as a check on the logic of M-2 data as compared with M-1 information. Code examples are:

No error; M-2 appears logical	= 0
Wrong species on M-1	= 1
Wrong dbh on M-1	= 2
Wrong height on M-1	= 3
Wrong soundness on M-1	= 4
New tree—ingrowth	= 5
Wrong tree number on M-1	= 6
Tree missed on M-1 (not ingrowth)	= 7
Tree outside plot included on M-1	= 8
Legitimate height reduction on M-2	= 9

MORTALITY: A suggested coding system for tree mortality based on the primary causal agent is as follows:

Living tree: either old or ingrowth	= 0
Harvested or felled tree	= 1
Fire	= 2
Lightning	= 3
Disease	= 4
Insects	= 5
Wind or ice breakage	= 6
Logging or mechanical damage	= 7
Timber stand improvement	= 8
Cause of death unknown	= 9

14-12 Plot card tallies. A sample port-a-punch plot card, designed to accompany the tree card previously described, is shown in Fig. 14-3. Columns reserved for "area" and "plot no." are the same as on the tree card. Other fields on the plot card may be briefly summarized as follows:

OWNERSHIP: A two-digit code indicating the class of ownership (e.g., fee simple or leased land) is punched here.

CROWN CLOSURE: This refers to per cent of overstory density, recorded to nearest 10 per cent class (for example, 30 per cent = 3).

AGE: Average stand age, coded to the nearest 5 or 10 years, may be punched in this one-digit field.

CHIEF SPECIES: Any one of 10 predominant species or forest cover types may be registered here.

UNDERSTORY: A record of the predominant type of understory vegetation on the plot.

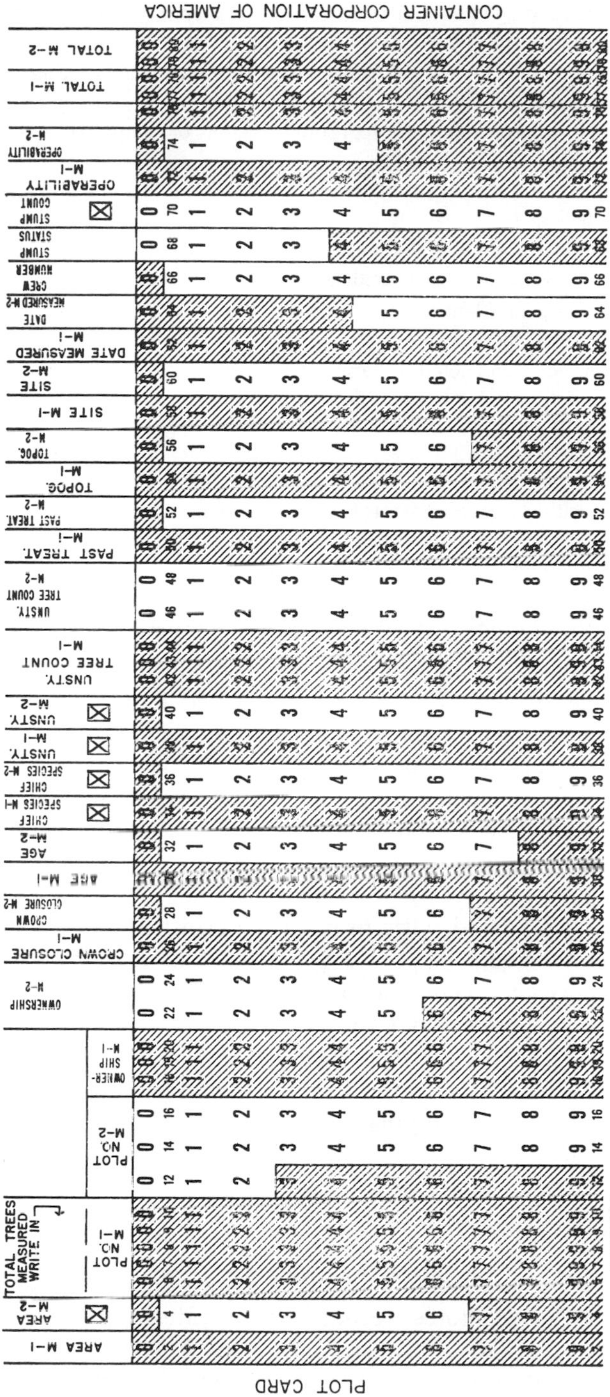

FIG. 14-3 Sample port-a-punch plot-description card for use in CFI. *Courtesy of Container Corporation of America.*

UNDERSTORY TREE COUNT: This field is reserved for a count of desirable reproduction on the plot, e.g., number of Douglas fir seedlings present.

PAST TREATMENT: A code describing types of stand treatments during the past 5 years; e.g., thinning = 1; seed-tree cut = 2, and so on.

TOPOGRAPHY: The appropriate physiographic region or slope is coded in this column.

SITE: Ordinarily, this refers to site index at a specified index age and is coded by 10-ft height classes.

DATE MEASURED: The month of the year that the plot was measured is punched here. On this card, only months 5 through 9 (May to September) are assignable.

CREW NUMBER: This code identifies the inventory crew for purposes of work assignments, supervisory plot checks, etc.

STUMP STATUS: A code restricted to areas where pine stumps are utilized in the wood naval-stores industry. Code examples are no stumps = 0; nonaccessible stumps = 1; operable stumps = 2, and so on. A stump *count* can be code-punched in the following column of the card.

OPERABILITY: This may be a measure of merchantability or value per unit area, anticipated difficulties in logging and timber removal, or accessibility. Code examples are high-density sawtimber stand within 20 chains of a graded road = 1; medium-density sawtimber = 2, and so on.

TOTAL: Although shaded on the card illustrated, this field may be used to indicate the total number of stems measured on the current plot inventory.

14-13 Card handling and error checks. Port-a-punch cards must be kept free of blemishes or folds and not allowed to become wet in the field. Wet cards cannot be handled with automatic data processing equipment even after they have become thoroughly dry. Thus field tallies are customarily suspended during rainy days or periods of excessive dampness and humidity. Cards should be transported and kept in moistureproof boxes, except during the actual tally.

Before the forester leaves a measured plot, all punched data should be checked and compared with previously recorded information. Each designated column should be punched, but no columns should have more than one hole except where "postion punches" are specified. A check should be made to assure that a card has been punched for each measurable tree; then tree cards are preferably arranged in order according to tree number. Errors detected in punching should be corrected by punching a new card or by applying special patches available from card suppliers.

THE U.S. FOREST SURVEY

14-14 Inventory organization. The U.S. Forest Survey is a periodic re-inventory of the nation's forest resources on a state-by-state basis. Originally authorized by the McSweeney-McNary Forest Research Act of 1928, this nationwide inventory encompasses all ownerships of commercial forest land in each of the 50 states. Since the inception of the Forest

Survey around 1930, all the 759 million acres of forest land in the United States has been inventoried at least once. Reinventories, normally planned at intervals of 8 to 15 years, have been completed on much of this land.

Fieldwork, data analysis, and published results are the responsibility of Forest Survey projects located at Regional Experiment Stations of the Forest Service, U.S.D.A. At the conclusion of fieldwork in each state, data are collated and summarized by electronic data processing equipment; results are publicized by Forest Survey reports describing the current supply and demand for timber in that state. The general pattern of permanent plot relocation, field data collection, and office compilation is illustrated by Fig. 14-4.

14-15 Survey objectives. As stated in the official handbook of field instructions, the primary objectives of the Forest Survey are to provide the resource data needed to develop economically and silviculturally sound timber management plans and to provide the action programs to meet present and anticipated demands for timber. This requires information on the national forest situation as well as periodic reports appraising the timber resources of each state or geographic region covered by the survey.

Procedures for collecting and recording field data are aimed at providing answers to these general questions:

1 What is the area and productive capacity of the land available to grow timber?
2 What is the current annual growth on this area?
3 What is the present condition of this land, and how are these conditions associated with current net growth, particularly in terms of action required to increase or adjust net growth by species, age class, or tree quality?
4 How will the current net growth respond to changes in these conditions, either in the absence of disturbances or as a result of natural or man-made disturbances?

14-16 The national outlook for timber. At irregular intervals, usually about every 10 years, Forest Survey information from the individual states is summarized and incorporated into a national appraisal of the timber situation in the United States. The most recent of these nationwide reports, "Timber Trends in the United States" (*U.S. Dept. Agr., Forest Resource Rept* 17), was officially released in 1965. Quoting from this forest resource publication,

Reports on the nation's timber situation are required from time to time to provide a basis for judging the general effectiveness of forestry programs. Forests in different regions show highly divergent trends in timber growth, inventories, and availability of wood products for industrial use. Continuing changes are evident in timber markets and utilization practices. And changing forestry policies and programs significantly affect the outlook for production of timber crops. . . .

FIG. 14-4   *The U.S. Forest Survey in Brief*

Permanent plot locations are transferred from aerial photographs used on the previous survey to current prints by proportional dividers. Field crews use the new photos to locate the exact sample point on the ground.

A specially graduated steel tape is used to define the limits of point samples upon which tree tallies are taken. Field data are entered on plot sheets by numerical codes.

After field plot sheets have been double-checked for errors, coded entries are key-punched into standard machine-sort cards for automatic data processing equipment.

When all punched cards have been verified for accuracy, they may be arranged in desired numerical sekuence by running them through a sorter. Subsequent calculations and summaries are developed on electronic computers.

Timber-based economic activities employ more than 3 million workers. In many parts of the country, timber industries constitute the primary economic base for income and employment. Values added attributable to timber harvesting, timber processing, manufacture of wood products, construction, transportation, and marketing of wood products in recent years have annually accounted for about 5 per cent of the gross national product.

FUNCTIONS OF ELECTRONIC COMPUTERS

14-17 Analog computers. Analog computers can be typified by an ordinary slide rule, a device that utilizes parallel rulers to make linear measurements which are *analogous* to numerical values. Because the parallel rulers are graduated on a logarithmic scale, multiplication and division are accomplished by adding or subtracting logarithms.

A clock or watch may also be regarded as an elemental analog computer, because the *relative positions* of two rotating hands are used to determine the time of day. Here, the physical measurement of the degree of rotation is translated into a quantitative and meaningful time estimate by use of fixed numerals on the clock face. Modern analog computers are often characterized by linear position, degree of rotation, or measurement of some physical quantity, in keeping with these principles. Such values might be represented by electrical voltages or mechanical motion within the computer, and resulting answers may likewise be represented by a physical position or by voltages displayed on a dial (Savory, 1962).

Analog computers are designed for making fast *relational* computations rather than for solving problems that require accuracy to the last digit. On a slide rule, for example, accuracy is governed by the precision to which the physical parts are machined and graduated. Electronic analog computers, although lacking flexibility and adaptation to diverse uses, are ideally suited to problems requiring instantaneous control changes, as in antiaircraft fire control or missile guidance and tracking (Nett and Hetzler, 1959). When antiaircraft fire is being directed, for example, constant changes may occur in wind velocity and in the range, direction, and speed of a moving target. A highly specialized analog computer can continuously digest these and other pertinent data and produce recommended tracking guides within a sufficient time to be effectively used.

14-18 Digital computers. In contrast to the analog computer, a digital computer may be regarded as a counting device that works only with numbers. Digital computers are designed to perform the basic arithmetic functions of addition, subtraction, multiplication, and division. Computing accuracy is not based directly on precise machining of physical parts, and such devices are adaptable to a wide variety of mathematical problem situations. As a result, digital computers are the type most likely to be utilized by the inventory forester.

Examples of digital computers range from the simple abacus, which dates back to 3000 B.C., to today's automobile mileage recorders (odometers) and electric desk calculators. All these and similar computers are based on the simple concept of counting digits. The principal feature that distinguishes a complex electronic digital computer from these less sophisticated devices is *computing speed*. Limited only by the speed with which electrical impulses can travel through myriads of circuits, transistors, and relays, some digital computers are capable of performing more than 1 million additions or subtractions *per second*. Unfortunately, the preparation of data for electronic computation requires a considerably longer period of time. Thus as will be described later, *all* problems are not readily suited to computerized solutions.

14-19   Steps in computer operation.   The procedural process by which many digital computers operate may be divided into five nominal steps: input, storage, programmed control, processing or computation, and output.

Input is the process by which the problem or raw data are fed into the computer. Because few digital computers react to verbal orders, data are commonly reduced to numerical codes and supplied to the computer in the form of punched cards, paper tape, or magnetic tape. Some computers also accept printed or magnetic characters produced on a special typewriter. In any event, input data are automatically "read" into the computer and stored in accessible *memory units* for subsequent retrieval and calculations.

The *control* section of a computer directs and coordinates the entire arithmetic process according to precise directions supplied by human operators. These step-by-step instructions, supplied to the computer in a special code or "language," are referred to as a *program*. A program instructs the computer to perform such tasks as add two numbers and store the answer in a third location, divide a number by another, multiply two numbers and sum the results, or compare two numbers to determine if one is higher, equal to, or lower than the other. Then it may branch to different areas of the program based upon the results of the comparison, read a card or a section of magnetic tape, print a line, or punch a card. There are many others, depending upon the complexity of the computer (Davis, 1962).

Although *processing* or arithmetical computations proceed according to programmed control, answers or problem solutions may be simultaneously produced as *output* in the form of punched cards, magnetic tape, or typed characters. In some instances, summary tables may be printed out in a format entirely suitable for direct photocopying and immediate publication. As pointed out by Hall (1962),

The computer has made the standard volume table obsolete in much inventory work. Instead, volume equations are used, and these may be as complicated as one may wish to make them, for the computer takes practically no more time to solve an 8-variable formula than a 2-variable formula. In fact, this possibility of using the computer has raised a whole new concept of tree volume calculation—to calculate the exact volume of each tree from its individual measurements, rather than applying averages from many trees.

14-20 When to use a computer. First, it should be emphasized that digital computers are not capable of solving problems that human programmers themselves cannot solve. The very necessity of step-by-step machine instructions should make this point clear, because a correct program cannot be written unless a solution is available for the problem at hand. Furthermore, the problem must usually be a mathematical one, for digital computers are tacitly unsuited for handling nonmathematical data. On the other hand, the high speed of computer operation makes it feasible to process much larger quantities of data than ever before. Thus it may be possible to accommodate problems that were previously *impractical* to solve because of the computational load involved.

In brief, the identifying characteristics of electronic computation are carefully organized data collection and deliberate, painstaking programming, followed by extremely fast data processing and calculation of results. As Freese (1958) has outlined,

> The combination of low-speed programming and high-speed computing pretty well suggests the type of problems for which the use of electronic computers can be considered. The problem must be one involving a large mass of computation, so that the advantage of fast computing will offset the time-consuming job of program writing. This situation may exist because of the amount of data to be handled, the number or size of computations to be performed, the frequency with which the problem arises, or a combination of these.

14-21 Research applications of computers. The use of computers for determining exact tree volumes has been outlined previously. Other diversified applications include scientific literature retrieval systems, evaluation of aerodynamic design equations, automatic language translation, and programmed composition of poetry or music. For industrial forestry enterprises, computers are now being used to select optimum management programs by predicting the different outcomes that would result from various planning decisions.

Clutter and Bamping (1965) have programmed a large, high-speed digital computer to *simulate* the operation of a forestry enterprise. The series of computer programs that carry out this simulation are identified as the "Foresty Operations Simulator" or simply "FOPS." Reliable predictions for forest management planning are complicated by the uncertainty associated with future biological and economic conditions and the magnitude of changing variables that must be kept under surveillance during a future planning period. This latter item involves (1) defining appropriate mathematical models to describe the enterprise, (2) providing input information required for calculation with the models, and (3) actually carrying out the arithmetic involved in projecting the models forward through time. In spite of the apparent simplicity of the problem, it is only recently that computing equipment capable of dealing with it in detail has become available.

PROBLEMS

14-1 Prepare a written report on an existing industrial CFI system, with special emphasis on plot establishment, measurement techniques, and field tally methods.

14-2 For oral presentation, prepare a 20-min review of the most recent U.S. Forest Survey release dealing with the timber resources of your state.

14-3 For oral presentation, prepare a 20-min report on the operation of either (a) the slide rule or (b) the abacus.

14-4 Visit a computer center or data-processing installation in your vicinity, and prepare a written report on the types of data being analyzed or processed.

REFERENCES

Baker, Robert D., and Hunt, Ellis V., Jr.
1960. Continuous forest inventory with punched cards for a small property. *Stephen F. Austin State Coll. Bull.* 5. 51 pp., illus.

Barton, W. W.
1960. A method of continuous forest inventory for management. U.S. Forest Service, Eastern Region, Upper Darby, Pa. 4 pp.

Clutter, Jerome L., and Bamping, James H.
1965. Computer simulation of an industrial forestry enterprise. *Proc. Soc. Am. Foresters,* Detroit, Mich. pp. 180–185. illus.

Davis, H. O.
1962. Computers and you. Minutes of southwestern technical committee, American Pulpwood Association, Shreveport, La. 6 pp.

Edenfield, J. C.
1962. Computers and reliability. Minutes of southwestern technical committee, American Pulpwood Association, Shreveport, La. 12 pp., illus.

Freese, Frank
1958. Desk calculator or electronic computer? Paper presented at conference on methods and techniques of measuring understory vegetation, Southern and Southeastern Forest Experiment Stations, Tifton, Ga. 8 pp.

Furnival, George M.
1962. Continuous forest inventory in bottomland hardwoods. *Proc. Soc. Am. Foresters,* Atlanta, Ga., pp. 124–126.

Grosenbaugh, L. R.
1959. Should continuity dominate forest inventories? Paper presented at short course on continuous inventory control in forest management held at University of Georgia, Athens. 13 pp.

Guttenberg, Sam
1962. Computer programs of interest for the pulp industry. Minutes of southwestern technical committee, American Pulpwood Association, Shreveport, La. 6 pp.

Hall, O. F.
1962. Computers in forest management. Minutes of southwestern technical committee, American Pulpwood Association, Shreveport, La. 10 pp.

——————
1959. The contribution of remeasured sample plots to the precision of growth estimates. *J. Forestry* **57**:807–811.

Honer, T. G.
1964. Machines and principles in unit record data processing for forestry purposes. *Forest Res. Branch Can. Dept. Forestry Publ.* 1082. 35 pp., illus.

International Business Machines
1957. Machine functions. IBM, New York. 31 pp., illus.

Nett, Roger, and Hetzler, Stanley A.
1959. An introduction to electronic data processing. The Free Press of Glencoe, New York. 287 pp., illus.

Nyyssonen, Aarne
1963. Analysis of two alternative methods for national forest inventories in Northern Europe. *Acta Forestalia Fennica* 76, Helsinki. 18 pp., illus.

Rudolph, Victor J., and Sherrill, B. C.
1957. Field key–punching of forestry data. *J. Forestry* **55**:377–378. illus.

Savory, L. E.
1962. Research and computers. Minutes of southwestern technical committee, American Pulpwood Association, Shreveport, La. 5 pp.

Stott, Calvin B.
1959. Industrial CFI: What it is, what it does, and how it does. Paper presented at Washington, D.C. section, Society of American Foresters (February). 6 pp.

———— **and Semmons, George**
1960. Our changing inventory methods and the CFI system in North America. Paper presented at Fifth World Forestry Congress, Seattle, Wash. 6 pp.

Sundahl, William E.
1965. Cruising timber with portable tape recorder cuts costs. *J. Forestry* **63**:284–285.

U.S. Department of Agriculture
1965. Timber trends in the United States. *U.S. Forest Serv., Forest Resource Rept.* 17, Washington, D.C. 235 pp., illus.

Wheeler, P. R.
1935. The punched card method in colleges and universities; applications in agricultural research: Forestry. Columbia University Press, New York, pp. 369–376.

Wright, John P.
1961. Computation of height growth on continuous forest inventory plots. *J. Forestry* **59**:772–773.

Young, Harold E., and Altenberger, Russell A.
1963. Electronic computers and non-research forestry applications. *The Consultant* (July). 4 pp.

APPENDIX TABLES

APPENDIX TABLE 1 Areas of Circles in Square Feet for Diameters of 1 to 240 in.*

	.0	.1	.2	.3	.4	.5	.6	.7	.8	.9
1	.0055	.0066	.0079	.0092	.0107	.0123	.0140	.0158	.0177	.0197
2	.0218	.0241	.0264	.0289	.0314	.0341	.0369	.0398	.0428	.0459
3	.0491	.0524	.0559	.0594	.0631	.0668	.0707	.0747	.0788	.0830
4	.0873	.0917	.0962	.1008	.1056	.1104	.1154	.1205	.1257	.1310
5	.1364	.1419	.1475	.1532	.1590	.1650	.1710	.1772	.1835	.1899
6	.1963	.2029	.2097	.2165	.2234	.2304	.2376	.2448	.2522	.2597
7	.2673	.2749	.2827	.2907	.2987	.3068	.3150	.3234	.3318	.3404
8	.3491	.3578	.3667	.3757	.3848	.3941	.4034	.4128	.4224	.4320
9	.4418	.4517	.4616	.4717	.4819	.4922	.5027	.5132	.5238	.5346
10	.5454	.5564	.5675	.5786	.5899	.6013	.6128	.6244	.6362	.6480
11	.6600	.6720	.6842	.6964	.7088	.7213	.7339	.7466	.7594	.7724
12	.7854	.7985	.8118	.8252	.8386	.8522	.8659	.8797	.8936	.9076
13	.9218	.9360	.9503	.9648	.9793	.9940	1.0088	1.0237	1.0387	1.0538
14	1.0690	1.0843	1.0998	1.1153	1.1310	1.1467	1.1626	1.1786	1.1947	1.2109
15	1.2272	1.2436	1.2601	1.2768	1.2935	1.3104	1.3273	1.3444	1.3616	1.3789
16	1.3963	1.4138	1.4314	1.4491	1.4669	1.4849	1.5029	1.5211	1.5394	1.5578
17	1.5763	1.5948	1.6136	1.6324	1.6513	1.6703	1.6895	1.7087	1.7281	1.7476
18	1.7671	1.7868	1.8066	1.8265	1.8466	1.8667	1.8869	1.9073	1.9277	1.9483
19	1.9689	1.9897	2.0106	2.0316	2.0527	2.0739	2.0953	2.1167	2.1382	2.1599
20	2.1817	2.2035	2.2255	2.2476	2.2698	2.2921	2.3145	2.3371	2.3597	2.3824
21	2.4053	2.4282	2.4513	2.4745	2.4978	2.5212	2.5447	2.5683	2.5920	2.6159
22	2.6398	2.6639	2.6880	2.7123	2.7367	2.7612	2.7858	2.8105	2.8353	2.8602
23	2.8852	2.9104	2.9356	2.9610	2.9865	3.0121	3.0377	3.0635	3.0895	3.1155
24	3.1416	3.1678	3.1942	3.2206	3.2472	3.2739	3.3006	3.3275	3.3545	3.3816
25	3.4088	3.4362	3.4636	3.4911	3.5188	3.5466	3.5744	3.6024	3.6305	3.6587

*Reprinted from U.S. Forest Serv., Pacific Southwest Forest and Range Expt. Sta. Misc. Paper 72, 1962.

	.0	.1	.2	.3	.4	.5	.6	.7	.8	.9
26	3.6870	3.7154	3.7439	3.7726	3.8013	3.8302	3.8591	3.8882	3.9174	3.9467
27	3.9761	4.0056	4.0352	4.0649	4.0948	4.1247	4.1548	4.1849	4.2152	4.2456
28	4.2761	4.3067	4.3374	4.3682	4.3991	4.4301	4.4613	4.4925	4.5239	4.5554
29	4.5869	4.6186	4.6504	4.6823	4.7144	4.7465	4.7787	4.8111	4.8435	4.8761
30	4.9087	4.9415	4.9744	5.0074	5.0405	5.0737	5.1071	5.1405	5.1740	5.2077
31	5.2414	5.2753	5.3093	5.3434	5.3776	5.4119	5.4463	5.4808	5.5155	5.5502
32	5.5851	5.6200	5.6551	5.6903	5.7256	5.7610	5.7965	5.8321	5.8678	5.9036
33	5.9396	5.9756	6.0118	6.0481	6.0844	6.1209	6.1575	6.1942	6.2310	6.2680
34	6.3050	6.3421	6.3794	6.4168	6.4542	6.4918	6.5295	6.5673	6.6052	6.6432
35	6.6813	6.7196	6.7579	6.7964	6.8349	6.8736	6.9124	6.9513	6.9903	7.0294
36	7.0686	7.1079	7.1473	7.1869	7.2265	7.2653	7.3062	7.3461	7.3862	7.4264
37	7.4667	7.5072	7.5477	7.5883	7.6291	7.6699	7.7109	7.7519	7.7931	7.8344
38	7.8758	7.9173	7.9589	8.0006	8.0425	8.0844	8.1265	8.1686	8.2109	8.2533
39	8.2958	8.3384	8.3811	8.4239	8.4668	8.5098	8.5530	8.5962	8.6396	8.6831
40	8.7266	8.7703	8.8141	8.8580	8.9021	8.9462	8.9904	9.0348	9.0792	9.1238
41	9.1684	9.2132	9.2581	9.3031	9.3482	9.3934	9.4387	9.4842	9.5297	9.5754
42	9.6211	9.6670	9.7130	9.7591	9.8053	9.8516	9.8980	9.9445	9.9911	10.0379
43	10.0847	10.1317	10.1788	10.2259	10.2732	10.3206	10.3681	10.4157	10.4635	10.5113
44	10.5592	10.6073	10.6555	10.7037	10.7521	10.8006	10.8492	10.8979	10.9467	10.9956
45	11.0447	11.0938	11.1431	11.1924	11.2419	11.2915	11.3412	11.3909	11.4409	11.4909
46	11.5410	11.5912	11.6416	11.6920	11.7426	11.7932	11.8440	11.8949	11.9459	11.9970
47	12.0482	12.0996	12.1510	12.2025	12.2542	12.3059	12.3578	12.4098	12.4619	12.5141
48	12.5664	12.6188	12.6713	12.7239	12.7767	12.8295	12.8825	12.9356	12.9887	13.0420
49	13.0954	13.1489	13.2025	13.2563	13.3101	13.3640	13.4181	13.4723	13.5265	13.5809
50	13.6354	13.6900	13.7447	13.7995	13.8544	13.9095	13.9646	14.0198	14.0752	14.1307

APPENDIX TABLE 1 Areas of Circles in Square Feet for Diameters of 1 to 240 in. *(Continued)*

	.0	.1	.2	.3	.4	.5	.6	.7	.8	.9
51	14.1863	14.2419	14.2977	14.3536	14.4097	14.4658	14.5220	14.5784	14.6348	14.6914
52	14.7480	14.8048	14.8617	14.9187	14.9758	15.0330	15.0903	15.1478	15.2053	15.2630
53	15.3207	15.3786	15.4366	15.4947	15.5528	15.6112	15.6696	15.7281	15.7867	15.8455
54	15.9043	15.9633	16.0223	16.0815	16.1408	16.2002	16.2597	16.3193	16.3790	16.4389
55	16.4988	16.5589	16.6190	16.6793	16.7397	16.8002	16.8608	16.9215	16.9823	17.0432
56	17.1042	17.1654	17.2266	17.2880	17.3494	17.4110	17.4727	17.5345	17.5964	17.6584
57	17.7205	17.7828	17.8451	17.9076	17.9701	18.0328	18.0956	18.1585	18.2215	18.2846
58	18.3478	18.4111	18.4745	18.5381	18.6017	18.6655	18.7293	18.7933	18.8574	18.9216
59	18.9859	19.0503	19.1148	19.1795	19.2442	19.3091	19.3740	19.4391	19.5043	19.5696
60	19.6350	19.7005	19.7661	19.8318	19.8976	19.9636	20.0296	20.0958	20.1620	20.2284
61	20.2949	20.3615	20.4282	20.4950	20.5619	20.6290	20.6961	20.7634	20.8307	20.8982
62	20.9658	21.0335	21.1012	21.1692	21.2372	21.3053	21.3735	21.4419	21.5103	21.5789
63	21.6475	21.7163	21.7852	21.8542	21.9233	21.9925	22.0618	22.1313	22.2008	22.2705
64	22.3402	22.4101	22.4801	22.5501	22.6203	22.6906	22.7611	22.8316	22.9022	22.9730
65	23.0438	23.1148	23.1858	23.2570	23.3283	23.3997	23.4712	23.5428	23.6145	23.6864
66	23.7583	23.8303	23.9025	23.9748	24.0471	24.1196	24.1922	24.2649	24.3377	24.4107
67	24.4837	24.5568	24.6301	24.7034	24.7769	24.8505	24.9242	24.9980	25.0719	25.1459
68	25.2200	25.2942	25.3686	25.4430	25.5176	25.5923	25.6670	25.7419	25.8169	25.8920
69	25.9672	26.0425	26.1180	26.1935	26.2692	26.3449	26.4208	26.4968	26.5729	26.6491
70	26.7254	26.8018	26.8783	26.9549	27.0317	27.1085	27.1855	27.2625	27.3397	27.4170
71	27.4944	27.5719	27.6495	27.7272	27.8051	27.8830	27.9610	28.0392	28.1175	28.1958
72	28.2743	28.3529	28.4316	28.5104	28.5894	28.6684	28.7475	28.8268	28.9061	28.9856
73	29.0652	29.1449	29.2247	29.3046	29.3846	29.4647	29.5449	29.6253	29.7057	29.7863
74	29.8669	29.9477	30.0286	30.1096	30.1907	30.2719	30.3532	30.4347	30.5162	30.5979
75	30.6796	30.7615	30.8435	30.9255	31.0077	31.0900	31.1725	31.2550	31.3376	31.4203

	.0	.1	.2	.3	.4	.5	.6	.7	.8	.9
76	31.5032	31.5862	31.6692	31.7524	31.8357	31.9191	32.0026	32.0862	32.1699	32.2537
77	32.3377	32.4217	32.5059	32.5902	32.6745	32.7590	32.8436	32.9283	33.0131	33.0980
78	33.1831	33.2682	33.3535	33.4388	33.5243	33.6099	33.6955	33.7813	33.8672	33.9533
79	34.0394	34.1256	34.2119	34.2984	34.3850	34.4716	34.5584	34.6453	34.7323	34.8194
80	34.9066	34.9939	35.0813	35.1689	35.2565	35.3443	35.4321	35.5201	35.6082	35.6964
81	35.7847	35.8731	35.9616	36.0503	36.1390	36.2279	36.3168	36.4059	36.4951	36.5843
82	36.6737	36.7632	36.8528	36.9426	37.0324	37.1223	37.2124	37.3025	37.3928	37.4832
83	37.5737	37.6643	37.7550	37.8458	37.9367	38.0277	38.1189	38.2101	38.3015	38.3929
84	38.4845	38.5762	38.6680	38.7599	38.8519	38.9440	39.0363	39.1286	39.2210	39.3136
85	39.4063	39.4990	39.5919	39.6849	39.7780	39.8712	39.9646	40.0580	40.1515	40.2452
86	40.3389	40.4328	40.5268	40.6208	40.7150	40.8093	40.9038	40.9983	41.0929	41.1876
87	41.2825	41.3774	41.4725	41.5677	41.6630	41.7584	41.8539	41.9495	42.0452	42.1410
88	42.2370	42.3330	42.4292	42.5254	42.6218	42.7183	42.8149	42.9116	43.0084	43.1053
89	43.2024	43.2995	43.3967	43.4941	43.5916	43.6891	43.7868	43.8846	43.9825	44.0805
90	44.1786	44.2769	44.3752	44.4737	44.5722	44.6709	44.7697	44.8685	44.9675	45.0666
91	45.1658	45.2652	45.3646	45.4641	45.5638	45.6635	45.7634	45.8634	45.9635	46.0637
92	46.1640	46.2644	46.3649	46.4655	46.5663	46.6671	46.7681	46.8691	46.9703	47.0716
93	47.1730	47.2745	47.3761	47.4778	47.5796	47.6816	47.7836	47.8858	47.9880	48.0904
94	48.1929	48.2955	48.3982	48.5010	48.6039	48.7070	48.8101	48.9133	49.0167	49.1202
95	49.2237	49.3274	49.4312	49.5351	49.6391	49.7432	49.8475	49.9518	50.0563	50.1608
96	50.2655	50.3703	50.4751	50.5801	50.6852	50.7904	50.8958	51.0012	51.1067	51.2124
97	51.3181	51.4240	51.5300	51.6361	51.7423	51.8486	51.9550	52.0615	52.1681	52.2748
98	52.3817	52.4887	52.5957	52.7029	52.8102	52.9176	53.0251	53.1327	53.2404	53.3482
99	53.4562	53.5642	53.6724	53.7806	53.8890	53.9975	54.1061	54.2148	54.3236	54.4325
100	54.5415	54.6507	54.7599	54.8693	54.9787	55.0883	55.1980	55.3078	55.4177	55.5277

	.0	.1	.2	.3	.4	.5	.6	.7	.8	.9
101	55.6378	55.7481	55.8584	55.9688	56.0794	56.1901	56.3008	56.4117	56.5227	56.6338
102	56.7450	56.8563	56.9678	57.0793	57.1910	57.3027	57.4146	57.5265	57.6386	57.7508
103	57.8631	57.9755	58.0880	58.2007	58.3134	58.4263	58.5392	58.6523	58.7655	58.8787
104	58.9921	59.1056	59.2192	59.3330	59.4468	59.5607	59.6748	59.7889	59.9032	60.0176
105	60.1320	60.2466	60.3613	60.4762	60.5911	60.7061	60.8212	60.9365	61.0518	61.1673
106	61.2829	61.3986	61.5143	61.6302	61.7463	61.8624	61.9786	62.0949	62.2114	62.3279
107	62.4446	62.5614	62.6783	62.7953	62.9124	63.0296	63.1469	63.2643	63.3819	63.4995
108	63.6173	63.7351	63.8531	63.9712	64.0894	64.2077	64.3261	64.4446	64.5632	64.6820
109	64.8008	64.9198	65.0388	65.1580	65.2773	65.3967	65.5162	65.6358	65.7555	65.8753
110	65.9953	66.1153	66.2355	66.3557	66.4761	66.5966	66.7172	66.8379	66.9587	67.0796
111	67.2006	67.3218	67.4430	67.5644	67.6858	67.8074	67.9291	68.0509	68.1728	68.2948
112	68.4169	68.5391	68.6615	68.7839	68.9065	69.0291	69.1519	69.2748	69.3978	69.5209
113	69.6441	69.7674	69.8908	70.0144	70.1380	70.2618	70.3856	70.5096	70.6337	70.7579
114	70.8822	71.0066	71.1311	71.2557	71.3805	71.5053	71.6303	71.7553	71.8805	72.0058
115	72.1312	72.2567	72.3823	72.5080	72.6338	72.7598	72.8858	73.0120	73.1382	73.2646
116	73.3911	73.5177	73.6444	73.7712	73.8981	74.0251	74.1523	74.2795	74.4069	74.5343
117	74.6619	74.7896	74.9174	75.0453	75.1733	75.3014	75.4296	75.5580	75.6864	75.8150
118	75.9436	76.0724	76.2013	76.3303	76.4594	76.5886	76.7179	76.8473	76.9769	77.1065
119	77.2363	77.3661	77.4961	77.6262	77.7564	77.8867	78.0171	78.1476	78.2782	78.4090
120	78.5398	78.6708	78.8018	78.9330	79.0643	79.1957	79.3272	79.4588	79.5905	79.7223
121	79.8543	79.9863	80.1185	80.2507	80.3831	80.5156	80.6482	80.7809	80.9137	81.0466
122	81.1796	81.3128	81.4460	81.5794	81.7128	81.8464	81.9801	82.1139	82.2478	82.3818
123	82.5159	82.6501	82.7845	82.9189	83.0535	83.1881	83.3229	83.4578	83.5928	83.7279
124	83.8631	83.9984	84.1338	84.2694	84.4050	84.5408	84.6766	84.8126	84.9487	85.0849
125	85.2212	85.3576	85.4941	85.6307	85.7674	85.9043	86.0412	86.1783	86.3155	86.4528

	.0	.1	.2	.3	.4	.5	.6	.7	.8	.9
126	86.5901	86.7276	86.8653	87.0030	87.1408	87.2787	87.4168	87.5549	87.6932	87.8316
127	87.9701	88.1086	88.2473	88.3861	88.5251	88.6641	88.8032	88.9425	89.0818	89.2213
128	89.3609	89.5005	89.6403	89.7802	89.9202	90.0604	90.2006	90.3409	90.4814	90.6219
129	90.7626	90.9033	91.0442	91.1852	91.3263	91.4675	91.6088	91.7503	91.8918	92.0334
130	92.1752	92.3171	92.4590	92.6011	92.7433	92.8856	93.0280	93.1705	93.3132	93.4559
131	93.5987	93.7417	93.8848	94.0279	94.1712	94.3146	94.4581	94.6017	94.7454	94.8892
132	95.0332	95.1772	95.3214	95.4656	95.6100	95.7545	95.8991	96.0438	96.1886	96.3335
133	96.4785	96.6237	96.7689	96.9143	97.0597	97.2053	97.3510	97.4968	97.6427	97.7887
134	97.9348	98.0810	98.2274	98.3738	98.5203	98.6670	98.8138	98.9607	99.1077	99.2547
135	99.4020	99.5493	99.6967	99.8442	99.9919	100.1396	100.2875	100.4355	100.5835	100.7317
136	100.8800	101.0284	101.1770	101.3256	101.4743	101.6232	101.7721	101.9212	102.0704	102.2196
137	102.3590	102.5185	102.6681	102.8178	102.9677	103.1176	103.2676	103.4178	103.5681	103.7184
138	103.8589	104.0195	104.1702	104.3210	104.4719	104.6230	104.7741	104.9253	105.0767	105.2281
139	105.3797	105.5314	105.6832	105.8351	105.9871	106.1392	106.2914	106.4438	106.5962	106.7488
140	106.9014	107.0542	107.2071	107.3601	107.5132	107.6664	107.8197	107.9731	108.1266	108.2803
141	108.4340	108.5879	108.7419	108.8960	109.0501	109.2044	109.3588	109.5134	109.6680	109.8227
142	109.9776	110.1325	110.2876	110.4428	110.5980	110.7534	110.9089	111.0645	111.2202	111.3761
143	111.5320	111.6880	111.8442	112.0005	112.1568	112.3133	112.4699	112.6266	112.7834	112.9403
144	113.0973	113.2545	113.4117	113.5691	113.7265	113.8841	114.0418	114.1996	114.3575	114.5155
145	114.6736	114.8318	114.9902	115.1486	115.3071	115.4658	115.6246	115.7835	115.9424	116.1015
146	116.2608	116.4201	116.5795	116.7390	116.8987	117.0584	117.2183	117.3783	117.5383	117.6985
147	117.8588	118.0192	118.1797	118.3404	118.5011	118.6619	118.8229	118.9840	119.1451	119.3064
148	119.4678	119.6293	119.7909	119.9526	120.1144	120.2764	120.4384	120.6006	120.7628	120.9252
149	121.0877	121.2503	121.4130	121.5758	121.7387	121.9017	122.0648	122.2281	122.3914	122.5549
150	122.7185	122.8821	123.0459	123.2098	123.3738	123.5380	123.7022	123.8665	124.0310	124.1955

APPENDIX TABLE 1   Areas of Circles in Square Feet for Diameters of 1 to 240 in. (*Continued*)

	.0	.1	.2	.3	.4	.5	.6	.7	.8	.9
151	124.3602	124.5249	124.6898	124.8548	125.0199	125.1851	125.3504	125.5159	125.6814	125.8470
152	126.0128	126.1786	126.3446	126.5107	126.6769	126.8432	127.0096	127.1761	127.3427	127.5095
153	127.6763	127.8432	128.0103	128.1775	128.3448	128.5121	128.6796	128.8472	129.0150	129.1828
154	129.3507	129.5188	129.6869	129.8552	130.0235	130.1920	130.3606	130.5293	130.6981	130.8670
155	131.0361	131.2052	131.3744	131.5438	131.7132	131.8828	132.0525	132.2223	132.3922	132.5622
156	132.7323	132.9025	133.0729	133.2433	133.4138	133.5845	133.7553	133.9262	134.0971	134.2682
157	134.4394	134.6108	134.7822	134.9537	135.1254	135.2971	135.4690	135.6409	135.8130	135.9852
158	136.1575	136.3299	136.5024	136.6751	136.8478	137.0206	137.1936	137.3666	137.5398	137.7131
159	137.8865	138.0600	138.2336	138.4073	138.5811	138.7550	138.9291	139.1032	139.2775	139.4519
160	139.6263	139.8009	139.9756	140.1504	140.3254	140.5004	140.6755	140.8508	141.0261	141.2016
161	141.3771	141.5528	141.7286	141.9045	142.0805	142.2566	142.4328	142.6092	142.7856	142.9622
162	143.1388	143.3156	143.4925	143.6695	143.8466	144.0238	144.2011	144.3785	144.5560	144.7337
163	144.9114	145.0893	145.2673	145.4453	145.6235	145.8018	145.9802	146.1587	146.3374	146.5161
164	146.6949	146.8739	147.0529	147.2321	147.4114	147.5908	147.7703	147.9499	148.1296	148.3094
165	148.4893	148.6694	148.8495	149.0298	149.2102	149.3906	149.5712	149.7519	149.9327	150.1136
166	150.2947	150.4758	150.6570	150.8384	151.0199	151.2014	151.3831	151.5649	151.7468	151.9288
167	152.1109	152.2931	152.4755	152.6579	152.8405	153.0231	153.2059	153.3888	153.5717	153.7548
168	153.9380	154.1214	154.3048	154.4883	154.6720	154.8557	155.0396	155.2235	155.4076	155.5918
169	155.7761	155.9605	156.1450	156.3296	156.5144	156.6992	156.8842	157.0692	157.2544	157.4397
170	157.6251	157.8106	157.9962	158.1819	158.3677	158.5536	158.7397	158.9258	159.1121	159.2984
171	159.4849	159.6715	159.8582	160.0450	160.2319	160.4189	160.6061	160.7933	160.9807	161.1681
172	161.3557	161.5434	161.7312	161.9191	162.1071	162.2952	162.4834	162.6717	162.8602	163.0487
173	163.2374	163.4261	163.6150	163.8040	163.9931	164.1823	164.3716	164.5610	164.7506	164.9402
174	165.1300	165.3198	165.5098	165.6999	165.8901	166.0804	166.2708	166.4613	166.6519	166.8426
175	167.0335	167.2244	167.4155	167.6066	167.7979	167.9893	168.1808	168.3724	168.5641	168.7559

	.0	.1	.2	.3	.4	.5	.6	.7	.8	.9
176	168.9479	169.1399	169.3321	169.5243	169.7167	169.9092	170.1018	170.2945	170.4873	170.6802
177	170.8732	171.0663	171.2596	171.4529	171.6464	171.8399	172.0336	172.2274	172.4213	172.6153
178	172.8094	173.0036	173.1980	173.3924	173.5870	173.7816	173.9764	174.1713	174.3663	174.5613
179	174.7566	174.9519	175.1473	175.3428	175.5385	175.7342	175.9301	176.1260	176.3221	176.5183
180	176.7146	176.9110	177.1075	177.3041	177.5009	177.6977	177.8947	178.0917	178.2889	178.4862
181	178.6835	178.8810	179.0786	179.2764	179.4742	179.6721	179.8701	180.0683	180.2666	180.4649
182	180.6634	180.8620	181.0607	181.2595	181.4584	181.6574	181.8566	182.0558	182.2551	182.4546
183	182.6542	182.8538	183.0536	183.2535	183.4535	183.6536	183.8539	184.0542	184.2546	184.4552
184	184.6558	184.8566	185.0575	185.2535	185.4596	185.6608	185.8621	186.0635	186.2650	186.4667
185	186.6684	186.8703	187.0723	187.2143	187.4765	187.6788	187.8812	188.0837	188.2863	188.4891
186	188.6919	188.8949	189.0979	189.3011	189.5044	189.7078	189.9112	190.1149	190.3186	190.5224
187	190.7263	190.9304	191.1345	191.3388	191.5431	191.7476	191.9522	192.1569	192.3617	192.5666
188	192.7716	192.9768	193.1820	193.3873	193.5928	193.7984	194.0040	194.2098	194.4157	194.6217
189	194.8278	195.0341	195.2404	195.4468	195.6534	195.8600	196.0668	196.2737	196.4807	196.6878
190	196.8950	197.1023	197.3097	197.5172	197.7249	197.9326	198.1405	198.3484	198.5565	198.7647
191	198.9730	199.1814	199.3899	199.5995	199.8073	200.0161	200.2251	200.4341	200.6433	200.8526
192	201.0619	201.2714	201.4810	201.6937	201.9006	202.1105	202.3205	202.5307	202.7409	202.9513
193	203.1618	203.3724	203.5831	203.7939	204.0048	204.2158	204.4269	204.6382	204.8495	205.0610
194	205.2725	205.4842	205.6960	205.9079	206.1199	206.3320	206.5442	206.7566	206.9690	207.1816
195	207.3942	207.6070	207.8199	208.0328	208.2459	208.4591	208.6724	208.8859	209.0994	209.3130
196	209.5268	209.7406	209.9546	210.1687	210.3829	210.5972	210.8116	211.0261	211.2407	211.4554
197	211.6703	211.8852	212.1003	212.3154	212.5307	212.7461	212.9616	213.1772	213.3929	213.6087
198	213.8247	214.0407	214.2568	214.4731	214.6895	214.9059	215.1225	215.3392	215.5560	215.7729
199	215.9900	216.2071	216.4243	216.6417	216.8591	217.0767	217.2944	217.5122	217.7301	217.9481
200	218.1662	218.3844	218.6027	218.8212	219.0397	219.2584	219.4771	219.6960	219.9150	220.1341

APPENDIX TABLE 1   Areas of Circles in Square Feet for Diameters of 1 to 240 in. *(Continued)*

	.0	.1	.2	.3	.4	.5	.6	.7	.8	.9
201	220.3533	220.5726	220.7920	221.0115	221.2312	221.4509	221.6708	221.8908	222.1108	222.3310
202	222.5513	222.7717	222.9922	223.2128	223.4336	223.6544	223.8754	224.0964	224.3176	224.5389
203	224.7602	224.9817	225.2033	225.4250	225.6469	225.8688	226.0908	226.3130	226.5352	226.7576
204	226.9801	227.2027	227.4254	227.6482	227.8711	228.0941	228.3172	228.5405	228.7638	228.9873
205	229.2108	229.4345	229.6583	229.8822	230.1062	230.3303	230.5545	230.7788	231.0033	231.2278
206	231.4525	231.6772	231.9021	232.1271	232.3522	232.5774	232.8027	233.0281	233.2537	233.4793
207	233.7050	233.9309	234.1569	234.3829	234.6091	234.8354	235.0618	235.2883	235.5150	235.7417
208	235.9685	236.1955	236.4225	236.6497	236.8770	237.1044	237.3318	237.5594	237.7872	238.0150
209	238.2429	238.4709	238.6991	238.9273	239.1557	239.3842	239.6128	239.8415	240.0703	240.2992
210	240.5282	240.7573	240.9866	241.2159	241.4454	241.6749	241.9046	242.1344	242.3643	242.5943
211	242.8244	243.0546	243.2849	243.5154	243.7459	243.9766	244.2074	244.4382	244.6692	244.9003
212	245.1315	245.3628	245.5942	245.8258	246.0574	246.2891	246.5210	246.7530	246.9850	247.2172
213	247.4495	247.6819	247.9144	248.1470	248.3798	248.6126	248.8456	249.0786	249.3118	249.5451
214	249.7784	250.0119	250.2455	250.4792	250.7131	250.9470	251.1810	251.4152	251.6494	251.8838
215	252.1183	252.3529	252.5875	252.8224	253.0573	253.2923	253.5274	253.7626	253.9980	254.2334
216	254.4690	254.7047	254.9405	255.1764	255.4124	255.6485	255.8847	256.1210	256.3575	256.5940
217	256.8307	257.0674	257.3043	257.5413	257.7784	258.0156	258.2529	258.4903	258.7278	258.9655
218	259.2032	259.4411	259.6790	259.9171	260.1553	260.3936	260.6320	260.8705	261.1091	261.3478
219	261.5867	261.8256	262.0647	262.3039	262.5431	262.7825	263.0220	263.2616	263.5013	263.7411
220	263.9811	264.2211	264.4612	264.7015	264.9419	265.1823	265.4229	265.6636	265.9044	266.1453
221	266.3863	266.6275	266.8687	267.1101	267.3515	267.5931	267.8347	268.0765	268.3184	268.5604
222	268.8025	269.0447	269.2871	269.5295	269.7721	270.0147	270.2575	270.5004	270.7433	270.9864
223	271.2296	271.4729	271.7164	271.9599	272.2035	272.4473	272.6911	272.9351	273.1792	273.4233
224	273.6676	273.9120	274.1565	274.4012	274.6459	274.8907	275.1357	275.3807	275.6259	275.8712
225	276.1166	276.3620	276.6076	276.8534	277.0992	277.3451	277.5911	277.8373	278.0835	278.3299

	.0	.1	.2	.3	.4	.5	.6	.7	.8	.9
226	278.5764	278.8230	279.0696	279.3164	279.5634	279.8104	280.0575	280.3047	280.5521	280.7995
227	281.0471	281.2948	281.5426	281.7905	282.0385	282.2866	282.5348	282.7831	283.0315	283.2801
228	283.5287	283.7775	284.0264	284.2754	284.5245	284.7737	285.0230	285.2724	285.5219	285.7715
229	286.0213	286.2711	286.5211	286.7712	287.0214	287.2717	287.5221	287.7726	288.0232	288.2739
230	288.5248	288.7757	289.0268	289.2779	289.5292	289.7806	290.0321	290.2837	290.5354	290.7872
231	291.0391	291.2912	291.5433	291.7956	292.0479	292.3004	292.5530	292.8057	293.0585	293.3114
232	293.5644	293.8175	294.0708	294.3241	294.5776	294.8311	295.0848	295.3386	295.5925	295.8465
233	296.1006	296.3548	296.6091	296.8636	297.1181	297.3728	297.6275	297.8824	298.1374	298.3925
234	298.6477	298.9030	299.1584	299.4139	299.6696	299.9253	300.1812	300.4371	300.6932	300.9494
235	301.2057	301.4621	301.7186	301.9752	302.2319	302.4887	302.7457	303.0027	303.2599	303.5172
236	303.7746	304.0321	304.2897	304.5474	304.8052	305.0631	305.3211	305.5793	305.8375	306.0959
237	306.3544	306.6130	306.8717	307.1305	307.3894	307.6484	307.9075	308.1667	308.4261	308.6855
238	308.9451	309.2048	309.4646	309.7244	309.9844	310.2446	310.5048	310.7651	311.0255	311.2861
239	311.5467	311.8075	312.0684	312.3294	312.5904	312.8516	313.1130	313.3744	313.6359	313.8975
240	314.1593	314.4211	314.6831	314.9452	315.2073	315.4696	315.7320	315.9945	316.2572	316.5199

OPERATION: Clear-return control towards operator; Carriage in seventh position; Number 7 Tab Key depressed.

N = Number whose root is desired.

1. Beginning at extreme left of Keyboard Dial, enter N and touch Add Bar.

2. Beginning at extreme left of Keyboard Dial, enter Column B number and touch Add Bar.

3. Beginning at extreme left of Keyboard Dial, enter Column C number and touch Division Key.

The square root of N appears in Upper Dials, accurate to five digits.

A	B	C	A	B	C	A	B	C	A	B	C
1.00			2.06			3.96			7.1		
	102	202 00		21	289 834		402	401 006		72	536 66
1.04			2.14			4.09			7.3		
	106	205 92		218	295 3		416	407 93		74	544 065
1.08			2.22			4.23			7.5		
	11	209 77		226	300 67		43	414 736		76	551 37
1.12			2.30			4.37			7.7		
	114	213 55		234	305 95		444	421 43		78	558 575
1.16			2.38			4.51			7.9		
	118	217 26		242	311 13		458	428 025		8	565 69
1.20			2.46			4.65			8.1		
	122	220 91		25	316 236		472	434 52		82	572 72
1.24			2.55			4.80			8.3		
	126	224 507		26	322 5		488	441 82		84	579 66
1.29			2.65			4.96			8.5		
	132	229 79		27	328 64		504	449 006		86	586 52
1.35			2.75			5.12			8.7		
	138	234 954		28	334 67		52	456 08		88	593 3
1.41			2.85			5.28			8.9		
	144	240 01		29	340 594		536	463 04		9	600 00
1.47			2.95			5.44			9.1		
	15	244 956		3	346 42		552	469 9		92	606 63
1.53			3.05			5.61			9.3		
	156	249 806		31	352 14		57	477 5		94	613 19
1.59			3.15			5.79			9.5		
	162	254 56		32	357 78		588	484 98		96	619 68
1.65			3.25			5.97			9.7		
	168	259 235		33	363 326		606	492 35		98	626 1
1.71			3.36			6.15			9.9*		
	174	263 82		342	369 87		624	499 606		1	632 46
1.77			3.48			6.33			10.1		
	18	268 33		354	376 305		642	506 76		102	638 75
1.83			3.60			6.51			10.3		
	186	272 77		366	382 63		66	513 817		104	644 98
1.90			3.72			6.7			10.5		
	194	278 575		378	388 85		68	521 543		106	651 16
1.98			3.84			6.9			10.7		
	202	284 26		39	394 974		7	529 16		108	657 27
2.06			3.96			7.1			10.9		

*For square roots of numbers from 9.9 to but not including 10 enter N in step 1 beginning in *next to leftmost keyboard* dial instead of in leftmost dial.

Group 1

A	B	C
10.9		
	11	663 33
11.1		
	112	669 33
11.3		
	114	675 28
11.5		
	116	681 18
11.7		
	118	687 03
11.9		
	12	692 82
12.1		
	122	698 57
12.3		
	124	704 28
12.5		
	126	709 93
12.7		
	128	715 54
12.9		
	13	721 11
13.1		
	132	726 64
13.3		
	134	732 12
13.5		
	136	737 57
13.7		
	138	742 97
13.9		
	14	748 33
14.1		
	142	753 66
14.3		
	144	758 95
14.5		
	146	764 2
14.7		
	148	769 42
14.9		
	15	774 6
15.1		
	152	779 75
15.3		
	154	784 86
15.5		
	156	789 94
15.7		

Group 2

A	B	C
15.7		
	158	794 99
15.9		
	16	800 01
16.2		
	164	809 946
16.6		
	168	819 763
17.0		
	172	829 465
17.4		
	176	839 054
17.8		
	18	848 535
18.2		
	184	857 91
18.6		
	188	867 186
19.0		
	192	876 36
19.4		
	196	885 44
19.8		
	2	894 43
20.2		
	204	903 33
20.6		
	208	912 15
21.0		
	212	920 87
21.4		
	216	929 52
21.8		
	22	938 09
22.2		
	224	946 58
22.6		
	228	954 99
23.0		
	232	963 33
23.4		
	236	971 6
23.8		
	24	979 8
24.2		
	244	987 93
24.6		
	248	996
25.0		

Group 3

A	B	C
25.0		
	252	100 4
25.4		
	256	101 193
25.8		
	26	101 981
26.2		
	264	102 762
26.6		
	268	103 538
27.0		
	272	104 308
27.4		
	276	105 072
27.8		
	28	105 831
28.3		
	286	106 9587
28.9		
	292	108 075
29.5		
	298	109 1795
30.1		
	304	110 273
30.7		
	31	111 356
31.3		
	316	112 4284
31.9		
	322	113 491
32.5		
	328	114 543
33.1		
	334	115 586
33.7		
	34	116 62
34.3		
	346	117 644
34.9		
	352	118 66
35.5		
	358	119 667
36.1		
	364	120 665
36.7		
	37	121 656
37.3		
	376	122 638
37.9		

Group 4

A	B	C
37.9		
	382	123 613
38.5		
	388	124 58
39.1		
	394	125 539
39.7		
	4	126 492
40.4		
	408	127 7505
41.2		
	416	128 997
42.0		
	424	130 2313
42.8		
	432	131 454
43.6		
	44	132 666
44.4		
	448	133 866
45.2		
	456	135 056
46.0		
	464	136 236
46.8		
	472	137 405
47.6		
	48	138 565
48.4		
	488	139 7146
49.2		
	490	140 855
50.0		
	504	141 9865
50.8		
	512	143 109
51.6		
	52	144 223
52.4		
	528	145 328
53.2		
	536	146 425
54.0		
	544	147 513
54.8		
	552	148 594
55.6		
	56	149 667
56.5		

A	B	C	A	B	C	A	B	C	A	B	C
56.5			70.5			84.5			98.7		
	57	150 9974		71	168 5235		85	184 391		994	199 4
57.5			71.5			85.5			100.0		
	58	152 316		72	169 706		86	185 473	(not inclusive)		
58.5			72.5			86.5					
	59	153 6236		73	170 881		87	186 548			
59.5			73.5			87.5					
	6	154 92		74	172 047		88	187 617			
60.5			74.5			88.5					
	61	156 2056		75	173 206		89	188 68			
61.5			75.5			89.5					
	62	157 481		76	174 356		9	189 737			
62.5			76.5			90.5					
	63	158 746		77	175 5		91	190 788			
63.5			77.5			91.5					
	64	160 001		78	176 636		92	191 834			
64.5			78.5			92.5					
	65	161 246		79	177 764		93	192 873			
65.5			79.5			93.5					
	66	162 481		8	178 886		94	193 908			
66.5			80.5			94.5					
	67	163 708		81	180 000		95	194 936			
67.5			81.5			95.5					
	68	164 925		82	181 108		96	195 96			
68.5			82.5			96.5					
	69	166 133		83	182 209		97	196 977			
69.5			83.5			97.5					
	7	167 333		84	183 303		98	197 9905			
70.5			84.5			98.7					

SOURCE: Copyright 1952 Marchant Calculators, Inc., reprinted with permission of SCM Corporation.

APPENDIX TABLE 3 Scribner Decimal C Log Rule for Logs 6 to 32 Ft in Length

Diameter, in.	Length, ft													
	6	8	10	12	14	16	18	20	22	24	26	28	30	32
	Contents, bd ft in tens													
6	0.5	0.5	1	1	1	2	2	2	3	3	3	4	4	5
7	0.5	1	1	2	2	3	3	3	4	4	4	5	5	6
8	1	1	2	2	2	3	3	3	4	4	5	6	6	7
9	1	2	3	3	3	4	4	4	5	6	6	7	8	9
10	2	3	3	3	4	6	6	7	8	9	9	10	11	12
11	2	3	4	4	5	7	8	8	9	10	11	12	13	14
12	3	4	5	6	7	8	9	10	11	12	13	14	15	16
13	4	5	6	7	8	10	11	12	13	15	16	17	18	19
14	4	6	7	9	10	11	13	14	16	17	19	20	21	23
15	5	7	9	11	12	14	16	18	20	21	23	25	27	28
16	6	8	10	12	14	16	18	20	22	24	26	28	30	32
17	7	9	12	14	16	18	21	23	25	28	30	32	35	37
18	8	11	13	16	19	21	24	27	29	32	35	37	40	43
19	9	12	15	18	21	24	27	30	33	36	39	42	45	48
20	11	14	17	21	24	28	31	35	38	42	45	49	52	56
21	12	15	19	23	27	30	34	38	42	46	49	53	57	61
22	13	17	21	25	29	33	38	42	46	50	54	58	63	67
23	14	19	23	28	33	38	42	47	52	57	61	66	71	75
24	15	21	25	30	35	40	45	50	55	61	66	71	76	81
25	17	23	29	34	40	46	52	57	63	69	75	80	86	92
26	19	25	31	37	44	50	56	62	69	75	82	88	94	100
27	21	27	34	41	48	55	62	68	75	82	89	96	103	110
28	22	29	36	44	51	58	65	73	80	87	95	102	109	116
29	23	31	38	46	53	61	68	76	84	91	99	107	114	122
30	25	33	41	49	57	66	74	82	90	99	107	115	123	131
31	27	36	44	53	62	71	80	89	98	106	115	124	133	142
32	28	37	46	55	64	74	83	92	101	110	120	129	138	147
33	29	39	49	59	69	78	88	98	108	118	127	137	147	157
34	30	40	50	60	70	80	90	100	110	120	130	140	150	160
35	33	44	55	66	77	88	98	109	120	131	142	153	164	175
36	35	46	58	69	81	92	104	115	127	138	150	161	173	185
37	39	51	64	77	90	103	116	129	142	154	167	180	193	206
38	40	54	67	80	93	107	120	133	147	160	174	187	200	214
39	42	56	70	84	98	112	126	140	154	168	182	196	210	224
40	45	60	75	90	105	120	135	150	166	181	196	211	226	241
41	48	64	79	95	111	127	143	159	175	191	207	223	238	254
42	50	67	84	101	117	134	151	168	185	201	218	235	252	269
43	52	70	87	105	122	140	157	174	192	209	227	244	262	279
44	56	74	93	111	129	148	166	185	204	222	241	259	278	296
45	57	76	95	114	133	152	171	190	209	228	247	266	286	304
46	59	79	99	119	139	159	178	198	218	238	258	278	297	317
47	62	83	104	124	145	166	186	207	228	248	269	290	310	331
48	65	86	108	130	151	173	194	216	238	260	281	302	324	346
49	67	90	112	135	157	180	202	225	247	270	292	314	337	359
50	70	94	117	140	164	187	211	234	257	281	304	328	351	374
51	73	97	122	146	170	195	219	243	268	292	315	341	365	389
52	76	101	127	152	177	202	228	253	278	304	329	354	380	405
53	79	105	132	158	184	210	237	263	289	316	341	368	395	421
54	82	109	137	164	191	218	246	273	300	328	355	382	410	437
55	85	113	142	170	198	227	255	283	312	340	368	397	425	453
56	88	118	147	176	206	235	264	294	323	353	382	411	441	470
57	91	122	152	183	213	244	274	304	335	365	396	426	457	487
58	95	126	158	189	221	252	284	315	347	379	410	442	473	505
59	98	131	163	196	229	261	294	327	359	392	425	457	490	523
60	101	135	169	203	237	270	304	338	372	406	439	473	507	541

SOURCE: U.S. Forest Service.

(Continued)

Diameter, in.	Length, ft													
	6	8	10	12	14	16	18	20	22	24	26	28	30	32
	Contents, bd ft in tens													
61	105	140	175	210	245	280	315	350	385	420	455	490	525	560
62	108	145	181	217	253	289	325	362	398	434	470	506	542	579
63	112	149	187	224	261	299	336	373	411	448	485	523	560	597
64	116	154	193	232	270	309	348	387	425	464	503	541	580	619
65	119	159	199	239	279	319	358	398	438	478	518	558	597	637
66	123	164	206	247	288	329	370	412	453	494	535	576	617	659
67	127	170	212	254	297	339	381	423	466	508	550	593	635	677
68	131	175	219	262	306	350	393	437	480	524	568	611	655	699
69	135	180	226	271	316	361	406	452	497	542	587	632	677	723
70	139	186	232	279	325	372	419	465	512	558	605	651	698	744
71	144	192	240	287	335	383	430	478	526	574	622	670	717	765
72	148	197	247	296	345	395	444	493	543	592	641	691	740	789
73	152	203	254	305	356	406	457	508	559	610	661	712	762	813
74	157	209	261	314	366	418	471	523	576	628	680	733	785	837
75	161	215	269	323	377	430	484	538	592	646	700	754	807	861
76	166	221	277	332	387	443	498	553	609	664	719	775	830	885
77	171	228	285	341	398	455	511	568	625	682	739	796	852	909
78	176	234	293	351	410	468	527	585	644	702	761	819	878	936
79	180	240	301	361	421	481	541	602	662	722	782	842	902	963
80	185	247	309	371	432	494	556	618	680	742	804	866	927	989
81	190	254	317	381	444	508	572	635	699	762	826	889	953	1016
82	196	261	326	391	456	521	586	652	717	782	847	912	977	1043
83	201	268	335	401	468	535	601	668	735	802	869	936	1002	1069
84	206	275	343	412	481	549	618	687	755	824	893	961	1030	1099
85	210	281	351	421	491	561	631	702	772	842	912	982	1052	1123
86	215	287	359	431	503	575	646	718	790	862	934	1006	1077	1149
87	221	295	368	442	516	589	663	737	810	884	958	1031	1105	1179
88	226	301	377	452	527	603	678	753	829	904	979	1055	1130	1205
89	231	308	385	462	539	616	693	770	847	924	1001	1078	1155	1232
90	236	315	393	472	551	629	708	787	865	944	1023	1101	1180	1259
91	241	322	402	483	563	644	725	805	886	966	1047	1127	1208	1288
92	246	329	411	493	575	657	739	822	904	986	1068	1150	1232	1315
93	251	335	419	503	587	671	754	838	922	1006	1090	1174	1257	1341
94	257	343	428	514	600	685	771	857	942	1028	1114	1199	1285	1371
95	262	350	437	525	612	700	788	875	963	1050	1138	1225	1313	1400
96	268	357	446	536	625	715	804	893	983	1072	1161	1251	1340	1429
97	273	364	455	546	637	728	819	910	1001	1092	1183	1274	1365	1456
98	278	371	464	557	650	743	835	928	1021	1114	1207	1300	1392	1485
99	284	379	473	568	663	757	852	947	1041	1136	1231	1325	1420	1515
100	289	386	482	579	675	772	869	965	1062	1158	1255	1351	1448	1544
101	295	393	492	590	688	787	885	983	1082	1180	1278	1377	1475	1573
102	301	401	502	602	702	803	903	1003	1104	1204	1304	1405	1505	1605
103	307	409	512	614	716	819	921	1023	1126	1228	1330	1433	1535	1637
104	313	417	522	626	730	835	939	1043	1148	1252	1356	1461	1565	1669
105	319	425	532	638	744	851	957	1063	1170	1276	1382	1489	1595	1701
106	325	433	542	650	758	867	975	1083	1192	1300	1408	1517	1625	1733
107	331	442	553	663	773	884	995	1105	1216	1326	1437	1547	1658	1768
108	337	450	563	675	788	900	1013	1125	1238	1350	1463	1575	1688	1800
109	344	459	573	688	803	917	1032	1147	1261	1376	1491	1605	1720	1835
110	350	467	583	700	817	933	1050	1167	1283	1400	1517	1633	1750	1867
111	356	475	594	713	832	951	1069	1188	1307	1426	1545	1664	1782	1901
112	362	483	604	725	846	967	1087	1208	1329	1450	1571	1692	1812	1933
113	369	492	615	738	861	984	1107	1230	1353	1476	1599	1722	1845	1968
114	375	501	626	751	876	1001	1126	1252	1377	1502	1627	1752	1877	2003
115	382	509	637	764	891	1019	1146	1273	1401	1528	1655	1783	1910	2037
116	389	519	648	778	908	1037	1167	1297	1426	1556	1686	1815	1945	2075
117	396	528	660	792	924	1056	1188	1320	1452	1584	1716	1848	1980	2112
118	403	537	672	806	940	1075	1209	1343	1478	1612	1746	1881	2015	2149
119	410	547	683	820	957	1093	1230	1367	1503	1640	1777	1913	2050	2187
120	417	556	695	834	973	1112	1251	1390	1529	1668	1807	1946	2085	2224

APPENDIX TABLE 4 International Log Rule, ¼-in. Saw Kerf, for Logs 8 to 20 Ft in Length

Diameter (small end of log inside bark), inches	Length of log, feet							Diameter, inches
	8	10	12	14	16	18	20	
	Volume, board feet							
4	.....	5	5	5	5	5	10	4
5	5	5	10	10	10	15	15	5
6	10	10	15	15	20	25	25	6
7	10	15	20	25	30	35	40	7
8	15	20	25	35	40	45	50	8
9	20	30	35	45	50	60	70	9
10	30	35	45	55	65	75	85	10
11	35	45	55	70	80	95	105	11
12	45	55	70	85	95	110	125	12
13	55	70	85	100	115	135	150	13
14	65	80	100	115	135	155	175	14
15	75	95	115	135	160	180	205	15
16	85	110	130	155	180	205	235	16
17	95	125	150	180	205	235	265	17
18	110	140	170	200	230	265	300	18
19	125	155	190	225	260	300	335	19
20	135	175	210	250	290	330	370	20
21	155	195	235	280	320	365	410	21
22	170	215	260	305	355	405	455	22
23	185	235	285	335	390	445	495	23
24	205	255	310	370	425	485	545	24
25	220	280	340	400	460	525	590	25
26	240	305	370	435	500	570	640	26
27	260	330	400	470	540	615	690	27
28	280	355	430	510	585	665	745	28
29	305	385	465	545	630	715	800	29
30	325	410	495	585	675	765	860	30
31	350	440	530	625	720	820	915	31
32	375	470	570	670	770	875	980	32
33	400	500	605	715	820	930	1,045	33
34	425	535	645	700	875	990	1,110	34
35	450	565	685	805	925	1,050	1,175	35
36	475	600	725	855	980	1,115	1,245	36
37	505	635	770	905	1,040	1,175	1,315	37
38	535	670	810	955	1,095	1,245	1,390	38
39	565	710	855	1,005	1,155	1,310	1,465	39
40	595	750	900	1,060	1,220	1,380	1,540	40
41	625	785	950	1,115	1,280	1,450	1,620	41
42	655	825	995	1,170	1,345	1,525	1,705	42
43	690	870	1,045	1,230	1,410	1,600	1,785	43
44	725	910	1,095	1,290	1,480	1,675	1,870	44
45	755	955	1,150	1,350	1,550	1,755	1,960	45
46	795	995	1,200	1,410	1,620	1,835	2,050	46
47	830	1,040	1,255	1,475	1,695	1,915	2,140	47
48	865	1,090	1,310	1,540	1,770	2,000	2,235	48
49	905	1,135	1,370	1,605	1,845	2,085	2,330	49
50	940	1,185	1,425	1,675	1,920	2,175	2,425	50
51	980	1,235	1,485	1,745	2,000	2,265	2,525	51
52	1,020	1,285	1,545	1,815	2,080	2,355	2,625	52
53	1,060	1,335	1,605	1,885	2,165	2,445	2,730	53
54	1,100	1,385	1,670	1,960	2,245	2,540	2,835	54
55	1,145	1,440	1,735	2,035	2,330	2,640	2,945	55
56	1,190	1,495	1,800	2,110	2,420	2,735	3,050	56
57	1,230	1,550	1,865	2,185	2,510	2,835	3,165	57
58	1,275	1,605	1,930	2,265	2,600	2,935	3,275	58
59	1,320	1,660	2,000	2,345	2,690	3,040	3,390	59
60	1,370	1,720	2,070	2,425	2,785	3,145	3,510	60

SOURCE: U.S. Forest Service.

APPENDIX TABLE 5 Doyle Log Rule for Logs 6 to 20 Ft in Length

Diameter (small end of log inside bark), inches	Length of log, feet							
	6	8	10	12	14	16	18	20
	Volume, board feet							
8	6	8	10	12	14	16	18	20
9	9	13	16	19	22	25	28	31
10	14	18	23	27	32	36	41	45
11	18	25	31	37	43	49	55	61
12	24	32	40	48	56	64	72	80
13	30	41	51	61	71	81	91	101
14	38	50	63	75	88	100	113	125
15	45	61	76	91	106	121	136	151
16	54	72	90	108	126	144	162	180
17	63	85	106	127	148	169	190	211
18	74	98	123	147	172	196	221	245
19	84	113	141	169	197	225	253	281
20	96	128	160	192	224	256	288	320
21	108	145	181	217	253	289	325	361
22	122	162	203	243	284	324	365	405
23	135	181	226	271	316	361	406	451
24	150	200	250	300	350	400	450	500
25	165	221	276	331	386	441	496	551
26	182	242	303	363	424	484	545	605
27	198	265	331	397	463	529	595	661
28	216	288	360	432	504	576	648	720
29	234	313	391	469	547	625	703	781
30	254	338	423	507	592	676	761	845
31	273	365	456	547	638	729	820	911
32	294	392	490	588	686	784	882	980
33	315	421	526	631	736	841	946	1,051
34	338	450	563	675	788	900	1,013	1,125
35	360	481	601	721	841	961	1,081	1,201
36	384	512	640	768	896	1,024	1,152	1,280
37	408	545	681	817	953	1,089	1,225	1,361
38	434	578	723	867	1,012	1,156	1,301	1,445
39	459	613	766	919	1,072	1,225	1,378	1,531
40	486	648	810	972	1,134	1,296	1,458	1,620

SOURCE: U.S. Forest Service.

APPENDIX TABLE 6   The Distribution of t

df	Probability								
	0.5	0.4	0.3	0.2	0.1	0.05	0.02	0.01	0.001
1	1.000	1.376	1.963	3.078	6.314	12.706	31.821	63.657	636.619
2	0.816	1.061	1.386	1.886	2.920	4.303	6.965	9.925	31.598
3	0.765	0.978	1.250	1.638	2.353	3.182	4.541	5.841	12.941
4	0.741	0.941	1.190	1.533	2.132	2.776	3.747	4.604	8.610
5	0.727	0.920	1.156	1.476	2.015	2.571	3.365	4.032	6.859
6	0.718	0.906	1.134	1.440	1.943	2.447	3.143	3.707	5.959
7	0.711	0.896	1.119	1.415	1.895	2.365	2.998	3.499	5.405
8	0.706	0.889	1.108	1.397	1.860	2.306	2.896	3.355	5.041
9	0.703	0.883	1.100	1.383	1.833	2.262	2.821	3.250	4.781
10	0.700	0.879	1.093	1.372	1.812	2.228	2.764	3.169	4.587
11	0.697	0.876	1.088	1.363	1.796	2.201	2.718	3.106	4.437
12	0.695	0.873	1.083	1.356	1.782	2.179	2.681	3.055	4.318
13	0.694	0.870	1.079	1.350	1.771	2.160	2.650	3.012	4.221
14	0.692	0.868	1.076	1.345	1.761	2.145	2.624	2.977	4.140
15	0.691	0.866	1.074	1.341	1.753	2.131	2.602	2.947	4.073
16	0.690	0.865	1.071	1.337	1.746	2.120	2.583	2.921	4.015
17	0.689	0.863	1.069	1.333	1.740	2.110	2.567	2.898	3.965
18	0.688	0.862	1.067	1.330	1.734	2.101	2.552	2.878	3.922
19	0.688	0.861	1.066	1.328	1.729	2.093	2.539	2.861	3.883
20	0.687	0.860	1.064	1.325	1.725	2.086	2.528	2.845	3.850
21	0.686	0.859	1.063	1.323	1.721	2.080	2.518	2.831	3.819
22	0.686	0.858	1.061	1.321	1.717	2.074	2.508	2.819	3.792
23	0.685	0.858	1.060	1.319	1.714	2.069	2.500	2.807	3.767
24	0.685	0.857	1.059	1.318	1.711	2.064	2.492	2.797	3.745
25	0.684	0.856	1.058	1.316	1.708	2.060	2.485	2.787	3.725
26	0.684	0.856	1.058	1.315	1.706	2.056	2.479	2.779	3.707
27	0.684	0.855	1.057	1.314	1.703	2.052	2.473	2.771	3.690
28	0.683	0.855	1.056	1.313	1.701	2.048	2.467	2.763	3.674
29	0.683	0.854	1.055	1.311	1.699	2.045	2.462	2.756	3.659
30	0.683	0.854	1.055	1.310	1.697	2.042	2.457	2.750	3.646
40	0.681	0.851	1.050	1.303	1.684	2.021	2.423	2.704	3.551
60	0.679	0.848	1.046	1.296	1.671	2.000	2.390	2.660	3.460
120	0.677	0.845	1.041	1.289	1.658	1.980	2.358	2.617	3.373
∞	0.674	0.842	1.036	1.282	1.645	1.960	2.326	2.576	3.291

SOURCE: This table is abridged from Table III of Fisher and Yates, "Statistical Tables for Biological, Agricultural, and Medical Research," published by Oliver & Boyd Ltd., Edinburgh, and by permission of the authors and publishers.

APPENDIX TABLE 7   Five Thousand Randomly Assorted Digits

	00–04	05–09	10–14	15–19	20–24	25–29	30–34	35–39	40–44	45–49	50–54	55–59	60–64	65–69	70–74	75–79	80–84	85–89	90–94	95–99
00	54463	22662	65905	70639	79365	67382	29085	69831	47058	08186	59391	58080	52098	82718	87024	82848	04190	96574	90464	29065
01	15389	85205	18850	39226	42249	90669	96325	23243	60933	26927	99567	76364	77204	04615	27062	96621	43918	01896	83991	51141
02	85941	40756	82414	02015	13858	78030	16269	65978	01385	15345	10363	97518	51400	25670	98342	61891	27101	37855	06235	33316
03	61149	69440	11286	88218	58925	03638	52862	62733	33451	77455	86859	19558	64432	16706	99612	59798	32803	67708	15297	28612
04	05219	81619	10651	67079	92511	59888	84502	72095	83463	75577	11258	24591	36863	55368	31721	94335	34936	02566	80972	08188
05	41417	98326	87719	92294	46614	50948	64886	20002	97365	30976	95068	88628	35911	14530	33020	80428	39936	31855	34334	64865
06	28357	94070	20652	35774	16249	75019	21145	05217	47286	76305	54463	47237	73800	91017	36239	71824	83671	39892	60518	37092
07	17783	00015	10806	83091	91530	36466	39981	62481	49177	75779	16874	62677	57412	13215	81389	62233	80827	73917	82802	84420
08	40950	84820	29881	85966	62800	70326	84740	62660	77379	90279	92494	63157	76593	91816	03505	72389	96363	52887	01087	66091
09	82995	64157	66164	41180	10089	41757	78258	96488	88629	37231	15669	56689	35682	40844	53256	81872	35213	05810	34471	74441
10	96754	17676	55659	44105	47361	34833	86679	23930	58249	27083	99116	75486	84989	23476	52967	67104	39495	39100	17217	74073
11	34357	88040	53364	71726	45690	66334	60332	22554	90600	71113	15696	10703	65178	90637	63110	17622	53988	71087	84148	11670
12	06318	37403	49927	57715	50423	67372	63116	48888	21505	80182	97720	15369	51269	69620	03388	13699	33423	67453	43269	56720
13	62111	52820	07243	79931	89292	84767	85693	73947	22278	11551	11666	13841	71681	98000	35979	39719	81899	07449	47985	46967
14	47534	09243	67879	00544	23410	12740	03540	54440	32949	13491	71628	73180	78783	75691	41632	09847	61547	18707	85489	69944
15	98614	75993	84460	62846	59844	14922	48730	73443	48167	84770	40501	51089	99943	91843	41995	88931	73631	69361	05375	15417
16	24856	03648	44898	09351	98795	18644	39765	71058	90368	44104	22518	55576	98215	82068	10798	86211	36584	67466	69373	40054
17	96887	12479	80621	66223	86085	78285	02432	53842	42346	94771	75112	30485	62173	02132	14878	92879	22281	16783	86352	00077
18	90801	21472	42815	77408	37390	76766	52615	32141	30268	18106	80327	02671	98191	84342	90813	49268	95441	15496	20168	09271
19	55165	77812	83666	86028	28420	70219	81869	41948	47366	41067	60251	45548	02146	05597	48228	81366	34598	72856	66762	17002
20	75884	12952	84818	95108	72305	64620	91318	89872	45375	85436	57430	82270	10421	05540	43648	75888	66049	21511	47676	33444
21	16777	37116	58550	42958	21460	43910	01175	87894	81878	16620	73528	39559	84434	88596	54086	71693	43182	14414	79949	85193
22	46230	43877	80207	88877	89380	32992	91380	03164	98656	59337	25991	65959	70769	64721	86413	33475	42740	06175	82758	66248
23	42902	66892	46134	01432	94710	23474	20423	60137	60609	13119	78388	16638	09134	59880	63806	48472	39318	35434	24057	74739
24	81007	00333	39693	28039	10154	95425	39220	19774	31782	49087	12477	09965	96657	57994	59439	76330	24596	77515	09577	91871

	00-04	05-09	10-14	15-19	20-24	25-29	30-34	35-39	40-44	45-49	50-54	55-59	60-64	65-69	70-74	75-79	80-84	85-89	90-94	95-99
25	68089	01122	51111	72373	06902	74373	96199	97017	41273	21546	83265	32883	42451	15579	38155	29793	40914	65990	16255	17777
26	20411	67081	89950	16944	93054	87687	96693	87236	77054	33848	76970	80876	10237	39515	79152	74798	39357	09054	73579	92359
27	58212	13160	06468	15718	82627	76999	05999	88680	96739	63700	37074	65198	44785	68624	98336	84481	97610	78735	46703	98265
28	70577	42866	24969	61210	76046	67699	42054	12696	93758	03283	88712	06514	30101	78295	54656	85417	43189	60048	72781	72606
29	94522	74358	71659	62038	79643	79169	44741	05437	39038	13163	20287	56862	69727	94443	64936	08366	27227	06158	50326	59566
30	42626	86819	85651	88678	17401	03252	99547	32404	17918	62880	74261	32592	86538	27041	65172	85532	07571	80609	39285	65340
31	16051	33763	57194	16752	54450	19031	58580	47629	54132	60631	64081	49863	08478	96001	18888	14810	70545	89755	59064	07210
32	08244	27647	33851	44705	94211	46716	11738	55784	95374	72655	05617	75818	47750	67814	29575	10526	66192	44464	27058	40467
33	59497	04392	09419	89964	51211	04894	72882	17805	21896	88864	26793	74951	95466	74307	13330	42664	85515	20632	05497	33625
34	97155	13428	40293	09985	58434	01412	69124	82171	59058	82859	65988	72850	48737	54719	52056	01596	08845	35067	03134	70322
35	98409	66162	95763	47420	20792	61527	20441	39435	11859	41567	27366	42271	44300	43899	21105	03280	73457	43093	05192	48657
36	45476	84882	65109	96597	25930	66790	65706	61203	53634	22557	56760	10909	98147	34786	33863	95256	12731	66598	50771	38665
37	89300	69700	50741	30329	11658	23166	05400	66669	48708	03887	72880	43338	93643	58904	59543	23943	11231	83268	65938	81581
38	50051	95187	91681	66315	91428	12275	24816	68091	71710	33258	77888	38100	03062	58103	47961	83841	25878	23746	55903	44115
39	31753	85178	31310	89642	98364	02306	24617	09609	83942	22716	28440	07819	21580	51459	47971	29882	13990	29226	23608	15873
40	79152	53829	77250	20190	56535	18760	69942	77448	33278	48805	63525	94441	77033	12147	51054	49955	58312	76923	96071	05813
41	44560	38750	83635	56540	64900	42912	13953	79149	18710	68618	47606	93410	16359	89033	89696	47231	64498	31776	05383	39902
42	68828	83378	68369	71381	39564	05615	42451	64559	97501	65747	52669	45030	96279	14709	52372	87832	02735	50803	72744	88208
43	46939	38689	58625	08342	30459	85863	20781	09284	26333	91777	16738	60159	07425	62369	07515	82721	37875	71153	21315	00132
44	83544	86141	15707	96256	23068	13782	08467	89469	93842	55349	59348	11695	45751	15865	74739	05672	32688	20271	65128	14551
45	91621	00881	04900	54224	46177	55309	17852	27491	89415	23466	12900	71775	29845	60774	94924	21810	38636	33717	67598	82521
46	91896	67126	04151	03795	59077	11848	12630	98875	52068	60142	75086	23537	49939	33595	13484	97588	28617	17979	70749	35234
47	55751	62515	21108	80830	02263	29303	37204	96926	30506	09808	99495	51434	29181	09993	38190	42553	68922	52125	91077	40197
48	85156	87689	95493	88842	00664	53017	55539	17771	69448	87580	28075	31671	45386	36583	93459	48599	52022	41330	60651	91821
49	07521	56898	12236	60277	39102	62315	12239	07105	11844	01117	13636	93596	23377	51183	95126	61496	42474	45141	46660	42338

SOURCE: This table is reproduced by permission from "Statistical Methods," by George W. Snedecor, 5th ed., c. 1965 by The Iowa State University Press.

INDEX

INDEX

Units of measure, English and metric, 3, 4
Upper log taper, 83–85
Upper stem diameters, 75–77

Variability, effect of plot size on, 137, 138
Variables, continuous and discrete, 126
Variance, 130, 203
Variation, coefficient of, 130, 131
Veneer yields from logs, 109, 110
Vertical photographs, 185
Vertical sketchmaster, 197
Volume, board-foot, 46, 47
  cord, 30
  cubic-foot, 39–42
  point sample, 177–179
  stacked wood, 30–36
  standing tree, 92, 93

Volume tables, aerial, 198–201
  form-class, 93–96
  local, 97–101, 161, 162
  standard, 93–97
  weight/, 104, 105

Weight scaling, of cordwood, 36–39
  of sawlogs, 63–67, 104, 105
Weight-volume relationships, 36–39, 65–67, 104, 105
Wheeled pentaprism tree caliper, 76, 77
Witness trees, 27
Wood naval stores, 115, 116

Xylometer, 36

Yield tables, empirical, 215, 216, 230–233
  normal, 214, 215